Trail of the Jaguar

A Clayton T. Porter Adventure

BOOKS BY JONATHAN HANSON

Tales of the Southwest

Essential Sea Kayaking

Complete Sea Kayak Touring

Outside's Great Destinations of the World: Sea Kayaking

Vehicle-dependent Expedition Guide, version 4.1

(with Tom Sheppard)

Trail of the Jaguar

A Clayton T. Porter Adventure

Jonathan Hanson

For R.B.H, E.R.B.,
and R. and M.

CONTENTS

CHAPTER 1

The diamondback rattlesnake inched down the slope, its four-foot-long body molding to the contours of the rocks and detritus that littered the desert hillside. It was just before dawn on a late July day that promised 110 degrees in the shade by noon, but the temperature in the murky half-light was a tepid 85—perfect for the metabolic needs of the snake. It had been coiled next to a faint rodent trail all night, head resting on the outer circle of its body, ready to snap forward in less than a tenth of a second had a pocket mouse or pack rat come within its twenty-inch strike range. But nothing had passed, and now it needed to reach the shelter of a familiar rock crevice to avoid the rising ground heat. Its failure to capture anything on this particular night was inconsequential to an animal that could survive months without food, so it continued on its patient reptilian way, knowing—as much as rattlesnakes are aware of such things—that the next night, or perhaps the next, a meal would wander within reach. And there was always a chance of successfully ambushing something even while on the move.

There. The snake stopped as an infrared source somewhere ahead tickled the heat-sensitive orifices between its eyes and nostrils, which give members of the subfamily *Crotalinae* their nickname: pit vipers. It remained motionless for a time, sampling the air with its forked tongue. There was nothing recognizable, so it began to ease forward to home in on the heat source.

But no—this emission was too big to be prey. Synapses in the snake's primitive brain clicked over from *food* to *danger*, and it stopped, tested the air again, then began to sidle sideways to avoid the hazard.

The lateral movement caught my peripheral vision, and I turned my head to the right to see the snake, alerted by my own movement, withdraw its head into a defensive S-shape and emit a short warning rattle from the loosely jointed appendage on its black-and-white striped tail: *cht cht*—like that. I was sitting in a sling chair in a depression in the hillside. The snake was about four feet uphill from me—out of striking range, but the slope was steep and loose, and any sudden movement could well send it sliding into my lap. Rattlesnakes can be surprisingly clumsy.

I nodded and said, "Well, good morning."

The nod elicited another *cht cht*.

"My, you're a bit grumpy. No luck last night?" I pursed my lips and squeaked what I thought was a creditable impression of a frightened *Perognathus baileyi*. Talent wasted—rattlesnakes have no external ears.

The snake regarded me warily, in a pose I knew it might hold for the next ten minutes. I also knew it would avoid me now, so I turned my attention (*cht cht*) back to the task at hand, which was looking through a tripod-mounted pair of Swarovski 15x56 SLC binoculars at an overhanging rock formation across a steep ravine. Under the formation was a seep—a minuscule trickle of water brought up through the rocks by some quirk of geology. The pool fed by the seep never exceeded twenty gallons or so before it was sucked off by the fierce heat or the local wildlife. In the million-plus acres of southern Arizona's Cabeza Prieta National Wildlife Refuge and surrounding public lands, it was one of perhaps three reliable natural sources of water. What made this one unique was that, as far as I knew, I was the only human aware of it.

Water had been an issue here—for wildlife and humans—for thousands of years. The Sonoran Desert, which stretches across 100,000 square miles of Arizona and northwestern Mexico, rarely receives more than ten inches of rain each year, so reliable surface water is precious. Early Native Americans knew where to find it, and when their ancient trails were co-opted during the westward European expansion, the main east-to-west route became littered with graves of those who didn't. This track, meandering between Caborca and the flowing oasis of the Colorado River at Yuma, became known as *El Camino del Diablo*—the Road of the Devil. In places crude crosses and stone mounds stood ten to the mile.

Once the railroad reached Yuma in 1870, the need to risk the crossing on foot or horseback diminished, and the region was largely abandoned except for a few hardy prospectors digging exploratory mine tunnels and shafts, looking for copper or more rare minerals. Finally, in 1985, the Cabeza Prieta gained formal protection as a wildlife refuge.

Wildlife refuge? Don't let the lack of rainfall fool you —the Sonoran Desert is an astonishingly diverse ecosystem. The Cabeza Prieta boasts almost 400 plant species and 275 animal species, from desert bighorn sheep and coyotes down to my friend the rattlesnake, to kangaroo rats so adapted to the conditions that they can metabolize their own water from the dry seeds they eat.

That diversity was what brought me here.

It had been a rough few decades for the refuge. Before the 1990s, you could spend a week exploring without seeing another human, except for occasional A-10 overflights from the adjacent Barry Goldwater Air Force Gunnery Range. But when illegal immigration and the drug trade spiked—along with the huge U.S. Border Patrol buildup to fight it—the area suffered devastating abuse thanks to its proximity to the international border and the broad paved ribbon of Mexico 2 just to the south, the jumping-off point for thousands of migrants and smugglers. Tracks from vehicles blowing through the wire border fences damaged the fragile cryptobiotic soil, and the suspension of environmental laws resulted in plenty of abuse from our side as well. The Border Patrol sent out 24-hour patrols to drag existing roads and chase migrants and smugglers—whether or not they were on those existing roads. Migrants on foot who evaded the patrols faced the same fate that gave the Camino del Diablo its name: In just one year—2010—the bodies of 223 people were found across southern Arizona. And that's just the ones who were found.

No one was sure of the effects on the wildlife, from the common species to rare residents like cougars, and critically endangered animals such as the Sonoran pronghorn. When a massive steel barrier was blasted and hammered into the landscape along the border, across desert flats and over pristine desert mountains, what had been a single functioning ecosystem was cut violently in two. Cross-border human traffic was reduced, as was Border Patrol activity—but the natural movement of large mammals was completely blocked.

With a new and more environmentally sympathetic administration in place, questions arose as to what was left, wildlife-wise, and how it was fairing.

And why me? Good question.

You could call me a biologist. I have the necessary diplomas. But I failed at the academic genuflecting necessary to get on the tenured gravy train. Faculty at liberal colleges were scandalized when they discovered that I hunt for food, have a concealed-carry permit, and retain friends still serving in the military. On the other hand, an interview for employment as staff biologist at one extractive corporation fell flat when their background check uncovered lobbying efforts in Washington, in which I'd participated, to demand mandatory felony sentences for CEOs whose companies were convicted of violating environmental laws.

"Oh, heh . . . *that* lobbying?"

Instead I assembled a free-form career that combined wildlife photography with contract biological surveys. If you know anything about either of those vocations, you'll know that the typical practitioner of either lives a life to which the word "penurious" would lend glamour. However, I had a secret weapon that allowed me to obtain steady contract work, sell a lot of photos, and maintain a decent income: I'm really, really good at finding animals.

I know what you're thinking, but don't worry, I'm not going to go all mystic on you. I could try to elevate the talent to the level of a sixth sense, as some colleagues have. But I think it's simply the result of living outside for most of my four-plus decades, starting with backpacking solo at eight years of age into the mountains outside Tucson to escape a stepfather who would have been happy had I never made it back.

(While most kids my age were playing ball with dad, I was trying to figure out how to slip something venomous into one of his slippers.) I distracted myself with single-minded curiosity about how the natural world worked, and how the animals in it lived. After years and years of this I apparently developed a subconscious talent for figuring out where the individuals of any particular species might be found, and what they might be doing at any time of the day— or year.

It wasn't until much later that I realized this wasn't a mundane skill. The first time anyone noticed it was during a herpetology field trip in college. The professor remarked casually that he was interested in a tiny, mostly subterranean reptile called a variable sandsnake, but that it was highly doubtful we'd see any. That night I went out and brought him three, after marking where I had found each one for later release. At the start of the spring semester a woman doing doctoral work on Harris's hawks asked for help finding nest sites; I doubled her sample size. By the time I graduated I'd contributed to twenty research papers—normally a red carpet ride toward professorship. But by then I'd also pissed off the faculty with my "right-wing" views— which eventually led me to a hillside in the Arizona desert with a rattlesnake just up the . . .

Right: Where did that thing go? Ah, there it was— ten feet downslope, disappearing into a clump of prickly pear cactus. As a kid I played a game that involved following one until the head disappeared into the undergrowth, then grabbing the tail and giving it a yank before jumping out of strike range as the front part came boiling back out at me. But I'd grown out of teasing rattlesnakes, which after all really just want to be left alone to control the rodent population and are usually polite enough to give fair warning before they bite. More useful and more considerate than most humans I've known.

Eyes back at the binoculars, I reviewed what I'd seen through the night, when instead of the Swarovskis I'd used a set of ATN PS15-4 night-vision goggles. These are the type of device featured and misrepresented in action novels and a hundred Hollywood movies, typically when a bad guy wearing them is excruciatingly blinded by a sudden bright light shined at him by a good guy—pure BS, because internal circuitry shuts down the optics when that happens. In real-world use, a Gen 4 device such as the ATNs magnifies existing light by a factor of 30,000 or more, enabling bright, green-tinted views of scenes lit only by starlight. In fact, looking upward at those stars one sees thousands more than are visible with the naked eye, while meteors otherwise invisible streak across the firmament every few seconds. It's a mesmerizing sensation, and even though I've been using night-vision devices for years, I frequently find myself gazing slack-jawed starward when I should be looking for wildlife. Or combatants.

(Regarding the latter: It turned out I was really good at finding them too, which led to me postponing my college experience for eight years. But that's another story.)

Where was I? Let's see: three gray foxes—ten-pound, semi-arboreal canids found in a huge variety of habitat across the U.S.; two bobcats, the lanky, twenty-pound desert version of the animal that grows to twice that in colder climates; a family group of coyotes, like the bobcats much smaller than their northern cousins; and an assortment of smaller animals: ringtails, pack rats, jackrabbits. No deer tonight, which was unusual. Just before the rattlesnake showed up a group of four bighorn sheep visited, nearly draining the seep dry as they leaned in under the ledge and sucked loudly enough that I could hear it clearly across the ravine. Desert bighorns can take in nearly five gallons at a go, then not drink for several days, even in 110-degree-plus weather that can fatally dehydrate a human in hours.

The bighorn is the most famous large mammal on the refuge, but I'd been hoping to spot one that is much more rare.

The Sonoran pronghorn is a smaller and endangered subspecies of the *Antilocapra americana* common farther north. Male Sonoran pronghorns rarely weigh over a hundred pounds; females are twenty pounds lighter. The population has fluctuated alarmingly over the last few decades, bottoming out in the U.S. at just nineteen animals after the severe 2002 drought. Since then it had rebounded thanks to a captive breeding program and the construction of rain-catchment basins here and there on the refuge. But the fate of these creatures was now in serious doubt with a wall blocking off a large portion of their habitat.

The thing about the pronghorn is, it is a creature of the plains and the flats, capable of sprinting at sixty mph. It wasn't made for rugged terrain, so, on the face of it, hoping to record them high in a jagged canyon was nuts. But some morphological anomalies I'd seen in skeletons of the subspecies made me wonder if the animal didn't have an adaptive trick or two up its sleeve. I knew they'd not discovered the seep as yet, because enough of the Cabeza Prieta population is radio-collared that any regular foray into the canyon would have been recorded via GPS trace and investigated, and my secret water hole would have been blown. So my strategy for now was to continue monitoring through the summer, get as many marketable photographs as I could, and keep my fingers crossed that a curious pronghorn or two might catch the scent of water from the mouth of the canyon. In September I planned to turn in my material to the refuge biologists, who would be *extremely* interested in hearing about an entirely unknown water source on the refuge.

It was fully light now, and the sun fired the tops of the peaks to my north. The temperature was rising quickly; soon most animals would retreat to the shade of crevices, burrows, and overhanging ledges to wait out the fierce, dehydrating heat. Through the Swarovskis the last morning flight of white-wing doves clattered in and landed, and once they'd settled down to drinking I heard the engine noise.

CHAPTER 2

It *was* an engine, that was for sure; not a steady aircraft drone but rising and falling in tempo—a vehicle. The direction was impossible to determine given the acoustic jumble of the canyon, but I shouldn't have been able to hear an engine at all—ninety-three percent of the refuge is designated wilderness, and I was far off the main Camino del Diablo track. Plus, even though the Camino was now easily traversed by almost any vehicle due to the blading done when the wall was put in, traffic in July was usually about zero. My old Land Cruiser pickup was parked three miles away at Thule Well, and no road came closer to me than that.

The sound—so faint that when any cicada lit off within fifty yards it disappeared entirely—ricocheted softly from the rocks, waxing and waning at the limit of perception. Nevertheless, it was annoying. Had some redneck in a jacked-up truck decided to see how far up the canyon he could get? I'd seen it happen in too damn many other places, too damn many times.

Finally I remembered an old track that led to an abandoned mine tunnel in the west face of the Cabeza

Prieta Mountains, as a raven flies a little over a mile or so from my position. The trail had long been closed off; even the Border Patrol didn't use it as it accessed only a dead-end canyon and thus was on no smuggling or migrant routes.

Curiosity mingled with high dudgeon, and I decided I needed to see for myself. I packed up my camera and its massive 800mm lens, the tripod for it and the other one for the binos, folded the seat, and stuffed it all with the ATNs back in the big pack attached to my ancient Camp Trails frame. The lot went under the ledge where I'd intended to sleep for the day. I put the Swarovskis in my field bag along with a two-liter water bottle, slung it over my shoulder, and jogged/rock-hopped up the canyon toward its head.

The sun hit me with that southwestern Arizona summer intensity that makes you fully comprehend you're being warmed by nuclear fusion. The cicadas were going full blast now, as Paul Bowles wrote, ". . . like the sound of heat itself," so I couldn't hear the engine noise over the insects and my own footfalls. At the head of the canyon there was a short scramble to gain the ridge, then I headed west on a side slope, dodging saguaros, prickly pear, and cholla cactus, second by second gauging each footfall to land on a rock that wouldn't roll, grateful for the all-leather boots I wore even at this time of the year, with stiff Vibram soles.

After traversing two more small canyons, I angled up toward the ridge overlooking the larger canyon where I thought the mine was. There was a massive outcropping near the top, broken into several spires. I squeezed between two of them into the welcome shade, then moved forward until I could look down a hundred feet or so into the cul-de-sac that formed the upper end of the canyon.

It was surprisingly bigger, and flatter, than I expected —a good hundred yards across. The mine, too, was more extensive than I expected. The rectangular black hole of the tunnel entrance sat atop a flattened tailings pile that indicated substantial work, unusual in the area. Below me the two-track trail—clearly well-used—that led into the canyon ended in a turnaround just below the tailings pile. In the other direction it disappeared around a ridgeline—and now I could clearly hear the sounds of an engine laboring in four-wheel drive.

Then, an anticlimax: The white and green of a Border Patrol Chevy Tahoe lumbered around the corner, rocking side to side on the rocks and ruts of the track.

Slightly disappointed that my redneck theory had been wrong, but still annoyed that this trail had been opened again for no apparent reason, I had just about decided to back out of the slot and find a way down to say hello, since I knew a few of the agents still stationed on the refuge and thought I would find out what was up. But something—and much subsequent mental searching has failed to tell me what—made me sit instead, concealed in the shade of the rocks, my head barely above a boulder and most of me out of sight.

The Tahoe rolled up to the turnaround and parked, about seventy-five meters away from my elevated position (in situations such as this I always instinctively revert to military/metric ranging). The driver's door opened and a tall agent I didn't recognize stepped out. He was wearing the standard OD uniform and looked fit. Basic tactical belt, billed box cap. Rather amusing mirrored aviator shades. He closed the door and walked up toward the tailing slope, then stood in the edge of the detritus and looked slowly around the perimeter of the cul-de-sac. By this time I had fished out the

Swarovskis, and now he filled a good part of my field of view. He looked to be fortyish; dark hair, well-tanned. I noticed he was carrying a full-size Glock—unusual because the current issue sidearm for the Border Patrol was the HK P2000 in .40. I was pretty sure he would have needed clearance to carry a non-issue model.

Then he stopped, facing in my direction, and drew the pistol from its holster.

Whoa there, pal. I was virtually certain I couldn't be seen, that there was no reflection flash from the binos, but "virtually certain" has gotten people killed, so I froze but poised to duck if he actually aimed the Glock anywhere toward my corner of the planet. However, he just gave it a quick once-over, and then did something odd: He pointed the pistol skyward and racked the slide. A round that had been in the chamber spun out, twinkling in the sunlight, and tumbled into the rubble while the round below it in the magazine snicked home. The agent looked down for the ejected cartridge, but it had apparently bounced out of sight between the chunks of tailing. From across the clearing I heard him curse, and lean down to peer into the rocks. I was thinking, *Well what did you expect, you stupid* . . . but then he and I both heard the sound of another engine.

This one was different: an even snarl that sounded like a two-stroke at steady rpm, coming from the south. It grew slowly in volume, then jumped abruptly as the source cleared the local horizon: a powered paraglider—essentially a double-layer fabric wing equipped with a motorized backpack driving a shielded propellor. I'd used them in Africa on game surveys. They are a blast to fly, a lot safer than they look since you're flying a parachute, and the entire contraption including the fabric wing weighs less than fifty pounds.

But what was this one doing here? The pilot had skimmed the far ridge by a fathom (stylishly cutting between two saguaros no more than thirty feet apart); it appeared he'd been flying a drastic ground-hugging course. I glanced down at the BP agent, who was watching with arms akimbo, and the Glock reholstered.

The pilot banked gracefully toward the Tahoe, throttled back and descended, slipped out of the sling seat so he was hanging from the leg harnesses, then braked the wing and landed as perfectly as if he'd merely stepped off a curb, despite the weight of the paramotor behind him and the small duffel strapped to his chest. (My first landing with one of these things climaxed with me tipping backwards into a fresh pile of elephant dung—with the prop still spinning. But that's another story.) He popped a couple of Fastex buckles and lowered the duffel to the ground, then extracted himself from the PPG and set the mechanism on the ground.

He removed his helmet and goggles, revealing himself to be a Hispanic of thirty or so, of the slim and compact build suited to powered paragliding. Except for the flight headgear he could have come straight from a well-to-do *estancia*—Wrangler jeans, western shirt with snap buttons, cowboy boots with showy heels. I half expected him to pull a straw Resistol out of the duffel.

He began to bundle the fabric of the wing—but the BP agent, who had by then walked up, stopped him, said something I couldn't catch, and began toeing the canopy open again with one boot. The pilot reacted with a disbelieving look, then anger. The two began to argue in words I could catch only now and then, a heated back and forth of " . . . situation's changed," "not . . . arrangement," " . . . maybe later but not now." The pilot grew so agitated he clenched both fists and assumed a belligerent foot-forward stance—at which point the agent suddenly backed off, palms forward, and began talking in conciliatory tones. The two talked in lower voices for some time, then the agent walked to his vehicle, leaned inside, and came back with a thick letter-sized envelope. The pilot took it, folded back the flap, and seemed satisfied with the contents. He stuffed the envelope in the back of his jeans, and again began folding up the canopy, while the agent picked up the duffel and cradled it carefully in both arms. With the paraglider bundled, the pilot picked up the whole craft, and the two trudged up the shallower slope of the tailings pile. At the rectangular entrance, the agent pulled an issue flashlight from his belt and the two disappeared into the blackness.

Well, well, well.

This had turned out far more interesting than I'd thought, but also more confusing. The facile conclusion was that I'd stumbled onto a drug-smuggling ring involving a crooked Border Patrol agent. There was an obvious logic there: The agent would be able to determine when the route over the border wall was clear, and inside smuggling operations had been uncovered time and time again among the Border Patrol and U.S. Customs personnel. It was a powerful lure to think of multiplying one's government salary by an order of magnitude or more, and the main reason agents tended to be rotated in and out frequently.

But the scale made no sense. Given the increasing number of U.S. states that were legalizing marijuana, pot-smuggling had become passé. The enduring hot tickets were opioids, especially Fentanyl, and methamphetamines. But even the high profit margins of Chinese-sourced Fentanyl wouldn't justify the risk of such a small operation. Bringing stuff across one duffel at a time—and a small one at that—seemed stupid, even with inside knowledge of patrol schedules. There were just too many variables for the economics to work for me. Typical smuggling operations involved either a group of mules (as human couriers were termed) carrying collectively a couple hundred kilos, or a semi truck loaded with a couple thousand. Either was a crapshoot the cartels were happy to take; the loss of a load or two per year was pocket change compared to the amount that got through, and mules or drivers were easy to replace. The big cartels were building their own submarines with the help of Russian engineers, for God's sake. So I couldn't imagine that a Border Patrol agent, no matter how greedy, would risk the consequences for so low a per-trip profit.

Muffled by distance and the depths of the mine tunnel, the sound of a pistol shot was nevertheless unmistakable.

CHAPTER 3

In the time it took for the echoes to ripple around the head of the valley, my head shifted into an entirely new dimension of situational awareness.

The average citizen is a notoriously poor witness to violent events. The atavistic portion of the brain shuts down everything it thinks isn't directly involved with the self, so that even when such witnesses are convinced they remember a scene accurately, the recollections of different people will be almost comically at odds. A group watching the same convenience-store robbery will describe a perp as short, tall, dressed in wildly different clothing, with an age span of decades, even conflicting race. Forget capturing a consistent description of the weapon or getaway vehicle.

Part of what I learned during my eight-year gap-year, as I liked to call it, involved conditioning one's brain to do exactly the opposite. Thus, by the time those echoes faded away I had noted through the Swarovskis and committed to memory both the number on the white government license plate of the Tahoe and the vehicle number; I spotted and filed away a vertical crease in the left rear fender and another on the right of the rear bumper, as well as an arc-shaped scratch in the rear window where something had caught in the rear wiper and marred the glass. I confirmed that the tires on the vehicle were the standard Goodyears. I also checked the time on my Sinn chronograph. Meanwhile I was subconsciously recording even seemingly irrelevant details—the air temperature, wind speed (zero), clouds (zero), even the smells of the rock and plants. Better to have too much information than too little.

The entrance to the mine tunnel seemed somehow blacker now. I waited. The Border Patrol agent walked out into the light, shading his eyes with the envelope he'd handed to the pilot until he fished the mirror shades from a pocket and put them on. The Glock was holstered, but he was not carrying the duffel (*Huh?*). He walked back down the tailing slope, climbed into the Tahoe, started the engine, turned it around, and drove back down the track.

And just like that, the little valley resumed its outwardly peaceful and torpid Sonoran Desert morning.

I stood as the sound of the Tahoe receded. I had two thoughts—first, to see if by some miracle the pilot was still alive and could be saved; second, to get out of there and get help. I stuffed the binoculars in the field bag, made my way around the back of the rock outcropping I'd been concealed in, and slid down a steep rubble slope to the floor of the valley. I stopped and listened, but the sound of the Tahoe was still receding, so I ran up the trail to the turnaround, then headed up toward the tailing pile. As I started up the slope a glint of something caught my eye, and I looked down to see the cartridge the agent had ejected, peaking out from a crevice.

I stopped, reached down, and picked it up by the rim with my fingernails to avoid smearing any prints. It was a decidedly odd one: a .400 Cor-Bon, a semi-custom cartridge formed from .45 ACP brass necked down to take a .40-caliber bullet. The designer's goal was to achieve the velocity of the potent 10mm Auto round with less pressure. A nominal load gave a solid 1300 feet per second with a 150-grain bullet. It never really caught on, and frankly I thought it was a solution to a problem that didn't exist. I doubted one pistol in a million was chambered for it, but it was definitely a giveaway for someone who was seriously geeked out on terminal ballistics in his sidearm. It also probably identified the agent's Glock as a model 21, which was chambered in .45 from the factory but could be rebarreled for the .400.

I seemed to be fresh out of evidence bags, so I dropped it in my shirt pocket and buttoned the flap, then climbed the tailing pile and crossed to the tunnel entrance.

The opening sported the standard skull-and-crossbones sign warning about rockfall and vertical shafts, and was guarded against casual trespass by vertical bars welded to a framework that spanned the tunnel and was securely bolted to the rock walls. The bars were spaced far enough apart so that bats could fly through to use the tunnel for shelter, and in the center was a padlocked gate.

Except the gate was standing open, the padlock hanging from the bolt with its hasp free.

Whoever he was, this agent was either incredibly stupid or incredibly arrogant. The latter possibility was far more worrisome.

I stepped inside, the reflected light offering no more illumination than a candle after the blazing sun outside. Ideally I would have waited ten or twenty minutes to give my eyes time to switch from cone-dominated photopic vision to rod-dominated scotopic vision. (*Well, ideally*, I muttered to myself, *it would have been nice to have, like, a flashlight?*) But I didn't want to wait that long, so as soon as my pupils had dilated enough for me to see shapes, I started down the passage. It was a good fifteen degrees cooler than the outside temperature, and would have been pleasant in other circumstances. The floor was powdery dust mixed with small ore fragments; the walls were jackhammer- and dynamite-rough. There was enough overhead clearance for me to be able to walk upright, but I stooped anyway, anticipating low-hanging outcroppings. Soon I came across the paraglider and its engine and prop, simply tucked against the side with the wing bundled on top of the propellor cage.

My eyes were adjusting, but the farther I got from the entrance the less ambient light there was. Net effect? It was getting darker, quickly. About twenty meters in the tunnel bent to the right, and once around the kink I could see virtually nothing. I kept moving, using my hands on the walls to guide me, crouching for overhead clearance while stepping high to avoid tripping.

Nevertheless, trip I almost did, when one boot hit something soft on the floor.

I've been near corpses before, okay? But somehow tripping over one in the dark was significantly more creepy. I leaned down and felt around, and it was not a corpse at all, but the duffel the pilot had delivered. In fact further groping revealed there to be several of them. I moved back to heft the most recent one, still sun-warmed, debating whether to take it with me—and the goddamn thing moved.

It was a small squirming movement, small enough that I could have convinced myself I was imagining it, but combined with the warmth radiating from it the effect raised the hair on the back of my neck.

More than a little spooked, at that point a smell hit me—one of those things thrillers do get right: When you die—especially suddenly—all the muscles in your body that normally hold in waste products relax, with predictable results. It was unmistakable, and convinced me that it would be futile to go any farther in the dark and futile to hope the pilot was alive. It was time to get out and get help in the form of some law enforcement agency that was *not* the U.S. Border Patrol—I had no idea if this was a conspiracy of one or dozens.

I turned around and began shuffling back, able to see more clearly now with the light in front of me. I have to admit to allowing what I'd felt and smelled to, let's say, accelerate my progress, so that by the time I reached the entrance I was moving at a good clip. I burst into the blinding sunlight, had a split second to wish I owned some of those mirrored shades, and then tripped over an inconsequential piece of rubble and sprawled face first into the dirt. In hindsight it was probably good that I did, because as I lifted my head I saw the Tahoe coming back around the corner a couple hundred meters away, followed closely by an unmarked white Ford Excursion.

I had no idea if they'd seen my ignominious exit from the tunnel. I ducked flat and scrambled backward to get more of the lip of the tailing pile between me and them, trying not to raise more dust than I already had. They were now below me enough that I couldn't be seen, but looking around for an escape route, it was clear that I'd be completely exposed if I tried to sneak in either direction around the mine and back into the desert.

There was really only one place to go.

It didn't sound like the vehicles had accelerated, so I cautiously decided they hadn't spotted me. I stayed low until I was well inside the tunnel, my night vision completely destroyed again. At least I now knew the route as far as the cache, which I assumed was why they were returning. However, I knew the agent had a flashlight, so I had to get far beyond that point and, if possible, beyond the pilot's corpse as well. I shuffled past the eerie pile of duffels, in complete blackness now, and continued as quickly as I could while feeling for the walls and overhead clearance. I also expected to run into the pilot (that smell was getting stronger), so I kept kicking ahead with each foot, continuing in this cartoonish fashion for another ten yards or so until I kicked into thin air and plunged straight down.

I fell for about a second—a good fifteen feet if I remembered my physics correctly. That would have meant a pair of broken ankles at best except—I suppose through the same geologic quirk that produced the seep—I plunged into water, glancing off something solid but yielding as I went under. I spluttered to the surface, which was oily and slick with a foul film, as the waves from my entry rebounded off the walls and gently propelled the pilot's corpse back into me.

Did I mention being creeped out before? That was nothing. I shoved hard on his head and my middle finger found a pulpy exit wound on the back of the skull. The push did no good as his legs buckled against the side of the shaft and propelled him right back into me.

For a moment I more or less lost it. I scrabbled for the side of the shaft and groped my way upward for about three feet before slipping off and splashing back in, then did it again. Finally it hit me that if I did make it back to the floor of the tunnel I'd likely find myself pinned in the beam of a 600-lumen Surefire flashlight with some extremely awkward explaining to do. So I got a grip on myself, found a couple of solid handholds near the waterline, and waited.

It seemed like hours but was probably a couple of minutes before I heard faint sounds of conversation, and saw the faint flicker of reflected light above me. The light stabilized, then diminished, and the sounds receded for several minutes. I was hoping they'd gone for good when the same process was repeated—they were ferrying out the duffels. After the third trip something different happened: The light started getting brighter and the sounds louder. They were coming toward the shaft.

Remember when I was outside the tunnel and mentioned there was really only one way to go? My choice now was even less attractive. I waited until the light was partially shining over the edge of the shaft, then ducked under the surface, tucked, and dove straight down. I had no idea how deep the shaft was, nor any feel for how transparent the water was—until suddenly it was pierced by a lancing dagger of nice bright 5000° Kelvin LED light. Particulates swirled in the beam but I couldn't tell if they concealed me. The shadow from the corpse was a wavering column of darkness and I ducked into it, continuing downward—why, I had no idea, as below was only murk and, as you might be aware, humans cannot actually breathe water, so I was going to have a problem soon. Then there was the darker murk of the bottom—and a side tunnel. I frog-crawled into it, at least now completely out of sight. And inside, improbably, as I felt along the rock above me with my

23

hand, it splashed. There was a void. I stuck my face into the three-inch space and found air—heavy, dank, stale, but life-saving air.

I gasped and recharged my lungs, and then heard three measured, flat thuds, dulled by the twenty feet of water. Had they seen me and were putting random rounds into the water? I thought they would have started shooting earlier if so. I held my breath and turned to watch the shaft, still lit by the flashlight's coruscating beam. Nothing . . . and then a pair of legs came into view, and the pilot's corpse settled slowly into the mud, three trails of bubbles spiraling up from his back. In a few seconds the light winked out and I was plunged into pitch blackness again.

I put my face back in the air space and took even breaths, trying to slow my pulse and make the oxygen last as long as possible. When I started to feel the tingling of hypoxia, I ducked out of the shaft and kicked slowly to the surface, exhaling on the way because I figured the air pocket in the shaft was compressed and I didn't want to risk pulmonary embolism, even from a mere twenty feet down. I lifted my head out of the water as quietly as I could, and boy was my scalp tingling waiting for the light to flash on again and one of those 150-grain slugs to vertically transit my brain pan at 1300 feet per second. But there was nothing, and no sound I could make out. By now I was feeling mildly hypothermic and thoroughly fouled by the scum on the surface, so I started climbing—first orienting myself to make damn sure I climbed out on the exit side.

Feeling my way slowly, it really wasn't that difficult; I would have called it a 5.7 in my rock-climbing days. After one false start I made it to the tunnel floor and sat on the edge for a minute to collect myself, which I thought understandable under the circumstances. Then I headed for the entrance, dripping, stinking, boots squelching, past the empty space where the cache had been, around the bend past the paraglider—*still there*— and back toward the white-hot rectangle of sunlight, thinking as I reached it that I really hate it when the gate is locked on a mine tunnel I'm trying to get out of.

How much of a drama this was going to be all depended on what I found when I reached around to the back of my belt . . . and with relief I found the Leatherman Wave that had managed to stay with me in its case through my Greg Louganis/Jacques Cousteau routine. And it happens that I habitually replace the file attachment on my Waves with a hacksaw blade, which I find more useful—rather an understatement at the moment. But what use, you might ask, is a hacksaw blade against a hardened padlock shackle? Not much. However, typically on these gates the padlock secures a hasp made out of perfectly ordinary mild steel. And that was the case here.

The hacksaw cut through the hasp in under a minute, and I was free. The Tahoe and Ford, of course, were long gone, so my plan was to get back to my Land Cruiser and head northwest out of the refuge to Yuma to report the incident. Thinking of the Toyota made me realize, for the first time, that my field bag was gone, no doubt embedded in the ooze at the bottom of the mineshaft—along with the Toyota's keys in a zippered pocket. That wasn't a problem, as I had a spare key soldered to the passenger's seat frame of the vehicle, but losing a pair of three-thousand-dollar Swarovskis and a nice Chapman bag was annoying. I made a mental note to see if the divers who would be recovering the body could check for it. There was a better than even chance nitrogen-purged Austrian binoculars would survive a few days under twenty feet of water.

I took a short-cut back to the truck, pretty sure that my pack stashed at the seep would be safe for a few days. It took me twelve minutes to cover the two miles to the Land Cruiser, engaging in some serious mountain goat boulder hopping and then flat out sprinting across the gentler *bajada* to make it an as-the-crow-flies line.

The Land Cruiser was a non-U.S.-spec 70-series pickup model I'd imported from the Middle East under the twenty-five-year exemption for such vehicles, obtained through a contact who also supplied "technicals" to various buyers both legitimate and otherwise.

The term "technical" came about when NGOs in Africa, needing armed security backup, hired local militia, who mostly drove Toyota pickups equipped with pedestal-mounted, Russian-made 12.7mm DShK ("Dushka") machine guns in the bed. The payments for the trucks and personnel were described in budget reports as "technical support," and a legend was born. Mine, sadly, lacked the machine gun; instead a canvas canopy covered the bed to provide a modicum of dust protection for my equipment. The truck was powered by Toyota's 1HZ diesel—not the most sophisticated of powerplants, or the most powerful, but dead reliable. I'd had a mechanic friend who lived in a backwater town in New Mexico rebuild the engine and transmission. I had installed Recaro seats for comfort (a relative term in a leaf-sprung Land Cruiser) and a 1/8th-inch-thick steel lock box behind the driver's seat, which held my tools, air compressor, and tire-repair kit, and which I kept stocked with a couple of liters of extra water, a few tins of food, an HK P2000 9mm pistol, and an extra pair of loaded magazines. I'd also bolted on an ARB front winch bumper equipped with a Warn 8,000-pound winch.

First I crawled into the bed, where my main water supply was ratchet-strapped up against the cab: two twenty-liter Scepter jerry cans. I unbuckled one, pulled it out into the open, unscrewed the cap, and emptied the contents over my head to at least minimally wash away the blood and shit caked into my hair and clothes. I drank the last liter or so and tossed the empty can in the bed.

I opened the driver's door and leaned across the seat to feel for the hidden spare key. As I did I felt a lump in my shirt pocket: the .400 Cor-Bon cartridge. I pulled it out and set it on top of the instrument binnacle so I could figure out a more secure place for it, then leaned back down, found the key, and twisted it free. It only fit the ignition, not the tubular cylinder on the lock box, and I made a mental note to affix keys to both there next time.

The Land Cruiser's diesel rattled to life after five seconds of glow-plug, and when it did the cartridge vibrated off the instrument binnacle and into the slot under the windshield where the defrost vent exited. I couldn't get a grip on it and didn't have time to waste, so I left it—it wasn't going anywhere. I put the truck in gear and headed west away from the little Thule Well cabin, on the quickest route to Yuma. I knew the road would wind through desert flats and hills for a few miles, then straight across the desert to where I could turn northwest toward Interstate 8 and then west to Yuma.

The 70-series Land Cruiser is not a desert racer, but it's damn near unbreakable, so I built up a good head of steam and let the Australian OME suspension soak up the washboard on the flats and the sudden plunges into

27

narrow washes lined with palo verde and ironwood trees. I passed the blocked-off road to the mine, and noted obvious signs where someone had swept the new tire prints to conceal them. That trick looks all tactical in movies but it's patently obvious to anyone who's done any tracking.

The furnace blast of air through the open window dried me in minutes, and as I was coming out of a wash and around a bend past some trees I locked up the brakes, slewing sideways to a stop about twenty feet behind a white and green Chevrolet Tahoe. A Tahoe with a vertical crease in the rear bumper and an arc-shaped scratch where the rear window wiper had caught some bit of debris.

No surprise that it also had the license and vehicle numbers I'd memorized.

Ahead of the Tahoe, the Ford Excursion was off the side of the track, canted like a lame elephant, left rear wheel off and the brake disk and hub embedded in the dirt. Two men were struggling to get a Hi-Lift jack back under the rear end. It was instantly apparent what had happened: They'd had a flat, jacked up the truck with the Hi-Lift on their nice solid aftermarket bumper, then, after the wheel was off, the truck had tipped off the jack. I'd seen it happen before. Hi-Lifts aren't the greatest tool for changing tires. It fully explained how I had been able to overtake them.

Leaning casually against the Tahoe, arms crossed and looking at me through his mirrored shades, was the Border Patrol agent.

CHAPTER 4

I debated reversing at speed and trying to get away via the other exit to the refuge east of Tacna, probably fifty miles away. But fleeing would be beyond suspicious, and the Land Cruiser had zero hope of outrunning a V8-powered Tahoe. My only hope was to bluff it out—after all, at this point all the agent knew was that I'd been driving way too fast. He didn't know why.

The agent shrugged upright and strolled to my window, waving away the dust. Miller. The name tag on his shirt read Miller. He leaned both elbows on the sill, violating my space. An amateurish psychological trick.

"What's the rush?"

I've always been a horrible liar, so:

"I, uh, got some wildlife photos for an article and I need to get them uploaded tonight."

He pulled off the shades, tucked them into his cap, and looked past me around the cab.

"Where's your camera gear?"

Right. *That would be back in a ravine in the desert about a mile from where I saw you kill someone.* See what I mean about my skills at lying? *Try to infuse as much truth as possible*, I thought.

"I left it stashed where I was taking photos at a water hole."

Actually true, but he was looking at me like I was an idiot. He also seemed to be wrinkling his nose at some disagreeable odor.

"Well let's see the memory card."

This was so not working.

At that point I decided to try the aggrieved-citizen-who's-having-his-civil-rights-violated act.

"Look, is there a reason you're . . ."

But right then his gaze and entire demeanor changed. He looked toward the windshield, reached in with his left hand, plucked something off the dash, and looked at it with open-mouthed astonishment. The mischievous Cor-Bon cartridge had popped free of the defrost vent and had been sitting there twinkling at him.

He looked back at me, still disbelieving but coming around to it, dropped his right hand to the Glock and index-fingered the anti-snatch lever of the Kydex holster, half-drawing the weapon.

"Get out of the truck."

Options swirled in my head, all of them bad, some of them *really* bad. With my own weapon locked in a box behind me, and outnumbered three to one, the tactical situation was, as one of my instructors would have said, " . . . not indicative of a satisfactory *denouement*."

Miller palmed the cartridge, reached over and pulled up on the door handle, unlatching it. Instinctively I grabbed the bottom of the window opening and held the door against his tug. Which thoroughly pissed him off. He drew the Glock and pointed it down at low ready, and pulled harder.

"I said get the *fuck* out."

The cartridge was condemnation. If I got out I was going to wind up as dead as the . . .

An inspiration hit me—one with a thin chance of success, but better than none.

I looked Miller in the eye, cocked my head toward the bed of the Toyota, smiled, and said,

"Your pilot's in the back of my truck."

It worked. His face went slack with shock, and he looked toward the canvas cover over the bed.

The instant he broke eye contact, I shoved on the door with all my strength. The window frame caught him in the face, hard. He stumbled backward, losing the Glock, windmilling his arms before plopping comically to the ground in a sitting position. By then I'd floored the throttle and dumped the clutch. The Land Cruiser leaped forward with the torque of the diesel. The men working on the Ford had realized something was up and were looking my way. When they saw Miller in the dirt they bellowed at me and one of them stupidly tried to stand in my way, waving his arms and leaping aside at the last second when he realized I was not going to meekly stop again. The other one, quicker-thinking, picked up a lug wrench from the ground and heaved it at my open window. I slammed my head back against the headrest as the tool skimmed my nose, banged into the passenger door, and clattered to the floor. Second gear by then and around the Ford back on the track, third gear and forty miles per hour when *BAM!* . . . *BAM!* . . . *BAM!*—measured fire from Miller's Glock first shattered my left-hand side mirror, showering me with shards of glass, then opaqued the entire rear

31

window as a round came through past my right shoulder and continued on to hole the windshield as well. More shots—a Glock 21 still held 11 rounds even after you'd stupidly lost one and put another through someone's face—but then I was around a bend and out of sight, still accelerating until the Land Cruiser was doing a suicidal sixty miles per hour.

My reprieve was temporary. It was at least forty miles to the interstate, and Miller would be on me with the Tahoe before I covered a tenth of it. Indeed even as I had the thought the road bent and through the passenger side rear-view mirror I could see a dust cloud rising behind me. In another half mile around another bend the cloud was much closer. I leaned back with an elbow and punched out enough shattered glass so I could monitor things through the center rear-view mirror. Now when a stretch of road threw up less dust I could see the white dot of the Chevy gaining steadily.

I'd come around a range of rugged hills on the left, and the track stretched arrow-straight across the desert. To my left was an undulating landscape thickly vegetated with creosote shrubs, the plant that survives where nothing else can in the Sonoran Desert. I knew Miller would overtake me in minutes on the straight, so my only option was to use the strength of the Land Cruiser in broken country to get away. The front hubs were already locked, so I reached down and yanked the transfer case lever into high-range four-wheel-drive. The gears howled in protest at being engaged at a speed they were never intended to see. Then I did what I'd never done in my life: I pulled hard-left on the wheel and headed off the track into the desert.

The change in ride was jarring as the suspension bounced across bare desert rubble, slammed over undulations in the ground, and crashed through the small dry drainage channels that fed summer rainstorms into the larger washes. The dust cloud behind me was now massive since I was plowing through undisturbed soil, and completely obscured my view. The Land Cruiser fishtailed from side to side as I dodged creosote bushes and cholla cactus, the latter of which would fling viciously spined segments through my open window if I clipped one. Jackrabbits bolted from resting spots in the shade and zig-zagged off at warp speed, ears flat. I curved back southeast toward the hills without any real plan except to hope the Tahoe broke before the Land Cruiser did.

Then something did break, or come loose—the ratchet strap holding the remaining Scepter can of water in the bed. The plastic can started bouncing wildly, appearing sporadically in the rear-view mirror, before the cap let go and spilled its contents. The water began cascading out between the bed and the tailgate, and for a few seconds dampened the dust billowing behind me, clearing my view.

And, like an apparition, the Tahoe emerged no more than fifty yards behind me.

I was pretty sure that if I could keep this up for, say, another 20,000 miles, the Land Cruiser would win the durability contest. But I didn't have that leeway. I needed an immediate solution. I had turned almost directly east to parallel a wide sandy wash that appeared to be bordered by a vertical embankment about two feet high. Still doing a good forty miles per hour, I waited for a break in the dense ironwood trees lining it, then turned hard right and aimed straight at the lip.

The Land Cruiser cleared the edge and there was a second of almost peaceful quiet as all four wheels arced through air, then an almighty crash as the front end impacted, sending up a curtain of sand. The truck instantly lost half its speed and threatened to stall, but I slammed the gear lever into second and pulled through, accelerating through a wide left-hand arc to continue heading east as I looked in the mirror to see what would happen to the Tahoe.

What happened was, Miller didn't take the bait. He continued paralleling the wash, now directly to my left. The sand was sucking at the Land Cruiser's narrow BFG tires, and I had to keep the engine screaming to maintain speed, which Miller effortlessly matched even as he had to dodge vegetation I didn't. I was effectively trapped now, with vertical banks on both sides.

I know what you're thinking. *Nice move.* And you're right.

Still roaring along in third gear at forty miles per hour, I kept looking for a break in the bank on my right, but it, like the opposite one, was now a good three feet high. Then *BAM!BAM!BAM!*—I looked to see a break in the trees and Miller taking wild shots at me through his open passenger window. From fifty yards away and at our speed they were unlikely to make contact, but "unlikely" has gotten as many people killed as "virtually certain."

And then ahead of me I saw a chance. The wash split into two branches—or rather, since I was driving upstream as it were, two branches were coming together. To my left Miller was still blocked off by a bank now four feet high, and stuck paralleling the left-hand branch.

At the juncture the wash widened to at least seventy yards. I twisted the wheel to the right—not too abruptly so as not to scrub off speed or, worse, bury the tires—and aimed for the incoming watercourse. In the mirror I watched to see what Miller would do—and the bastard slid the Tahoe in a wild turn and accelerated straight at the head-high cut right between two ironwood trees. As the wheels left the bank and the vehicle arced gracefully through the air I had exactly enough time to think *Pal, I think you've been watching too many mov* . . . and then the Tahoe hit.

Nose first. With the satisfying finality of instantaneous cessation of forward movement, and a massive cloud of steam that blew out of the grille.

I whooped, and nearly plowed into the V of the wash confluence. Second gear, long, looping fishtail and accelerate, and I was around the bend and out of sight. I hoped but doubted Miller had been seriously injured, given multiple air bags in the Tahoe and the fractional give of the sand when he hit. I had to assume he'd be fully mobile and would either run after me (unlikely) or head back toward the main track. Which meant I had to find a way out of that wash and get to Yuma before he was able to contact someone and turn in a decidedly different story from the one I had to tell—such as making me the murderer.

I made it another two hundred meters at good speed —then hit a soft spot in the sand that instantly sucked the tires down. I downshifted to keep the revs up but they continued to bog and dig, and as soon as they were doing nothing but going straight down I stopped—to stay on the throttle would only bury the vehicle farther. I shifted the transfer case to low range and tried inching forward in first gear, the tires barely turning, tried reverse as well, but the truck was insistent on traveling vertically rather than my strongly preferred orientation of horizontally.

I knew exactly what the problem was. When I'd entered the refuge and hit the dirt road I'd aired down my tires from their street pressure of 40 psi to 26. That was fine for packed dirt to soften the ride somewhat and add traction, but in soft sand you need much lower pressure—right down around 14 or so to lengthen the footprint of the tires and allow them to float over the surface.

In my currently inaccessible strongbox I had a set of automatic deflators which you simply screw onto the valves and dial in a desired pressure. Now I had only the much slower option, so I left the truck running, got out, pulled out my Swiss Army knife and extracted its small blade. I unscrewed the cap on the left front tire valve and pushed in the plunger with the tip of the blade, letting air hiss slowly out of the tire. When it looked nearly flat I moved to the right front and had started the same process when something hit the tailgate of the truck with a metallic *pang*, there was the instantaneous sound of a shot, and I looked to see Miller standing at the bend of the confluence, a good 200 yards away, locked in a Weaver stance. *Nice shooting*, a distracted part of my brain thought.

And then there was nothing to do but run. I ducked around to the driver's side, which was partially shielded from Miller's line of fire, leaned in and turned off the engine and stuffed the key in my pocket, then turned and ran for the edge of the wash, keeping the Land Cruiser as much as possible between me and Miller. Sand spurted to my left—he was doing a fabulous job estimating bullet trajectory—but then I was up the bank and into the desert and had some vegetation for cover.

My Vibram-soled boots were not made for running. On the other hand they're excellent for ankle support and for protection against the kind of rubble I now found myself fleeing across. I'm also in excellent shape. Against that was the fact that I'd only drunk a liter of water since dawn, and the desert was now baking under its full daily ration of summer sun. That was going to be a problem soon. Despite the efforts of various armies over the centuries to prove otherwise, you can't train the human body to need less water. Losing just two percent of one's body fluid is enough to induce dizziness and fatigue, and 110 degrees in the desert while running from someone who is shooting at you will do that in a half hour. Five percent loss will spike your heart rate and core temperature and cause extreme nausea and muscle cramps, and at ten percent you're looking at seizures and unconsciousness. I needed to sort out my Miller situation, and quickly.

The plan that formed in my head was to lead him toward the hills east of us, testing his stamina and keeping in sight but out of pistol range. If I could wear him down I could lead him in a partial circle, then try to get beyond his sight and make a dash for the truck.

Except the three pistol shots I heard just then made me suspect Miller wouldn't care if I made it back to the truck. Shit. That engine rebuild had been expensive; if he'd holed the block rather than just shooting out the tires I was going to be really pissed.

I was climbing a slight slope toward the hills, so I looked back and sure enough, the small figure was coming my way just beyond the Land Cruiser. *Fine, let's do it your way then; I'll run you into the ground.*

And I did. Soon I had a half a mile on him, and had to be careful to keep him in sight. I wanted to know if he quit or tried to cut me off in whatever direction he thought I might try to circle—and given the proximity of the border wall, north was about my only choice for circling.

But a mile later I was flagging noticeably, feeling the first serious symptoms of dehydration. When I looked back to check on Miller, he was noticeably closer, and I realized why when he stopped, unslung something from around his shoulders and tipped it up to his face. Of course—he had a canteen. Not fair. I briefly fantasized what fun it would be to have my Steyr SSG and blow the canteen out of his hands from a third of a mile away, just to make things more sporting. But then if I'd had the SSG I would have been aiming for center mass, screw sporting.

The hills were getting steeper and I was fatiguing quickly. I decided I needed to lose Miller once and for all so I could slow down and conserve energy and fluids, and just hope we didn't run into each other later. To my left was a narrow canyon and I headed into it to get out of sight, then continued up the dry watercourse, the sun reflecting heat off the rock wall on the north and not helping. There was nowhere to walk where my footprints wouldn't show, so I tried to keep up speed until the canyon got steeper and rockier and I could slip out to one side undetected. Unfortunately as it got rockier the sides also got more precipitous until I was effectively walled in.

Didn't this just happen?

I scrambled over a couple of head-high ledges as the sides continued to narrow, and then I was boulder-hopping to continue, with nothing but rocks and brush choking the bottom. About a hundred meters ahead I saw something the looks of which I did not like, and as it drew closer my impressions were confirmed: A cliff about thirty feet high and fifty feet wide spanned the wash. A dark grey stain marked the fall line where infrequent flows spilled over, and a deep hole in the sand at the bottom showed that summer thunderstorms sometimes produced flash floods that created what would be an impressive temporary waterfall if you were there at the right time.

I was not there at the right time.

As I approached I started eyeing a line to the top. If it were difficult enough to be challenging to me, with rock-climbing experience, perhaps it would stop Miller —unless he also had experience. I marked a line up the right side of the water mark that looked disappointingly easy, and started up it. Indeed it was a doddle, as my British climbing companions would say. Solid handholds up to about twenty feet, where there was a large, shaded ledge about two feet wide and a foot deep that I could actually stand on. From there it was an easy seven feet to the top—but as I started to pull myself onto the ledge an idea hit me.

I looked behind me. Nothing in sight. But I was certain Miller would come this way. I downclimbed to the base, turned, and began scanning the brushy verges of the slot and the debris piles and boulders there. Not there; not there; not there. Then . . . *there*. I hopped over to a dense mound of detritus and started pulling debris and rocks out of the way. *Ah. Not perfect, but you'll do.*

In a minute I was climbing again, much more awkwardly. I got past the ledge, and was just a couple feet from the top when someone walloped me hard in the lower back with a baseball bat.

CHAPTER 5

No, wait, that couldn't be right, could it? Nope—the sound of the pistol shot reached me a fraction of a second later. I looked down to see a bloom of blood above my right hip, and a ragged exit hole in a nearly new Filson shirt. Churchill wrote that nothing is as exhilarating as being shot at without effect; being shot at *with* effect is, I can assure you, significantly less exhilarating. There was little pain yet, and I knew there wouldn't be for a bit, but only a bit. I looked back and spotted Miller, still a good hundred and thirty yards away, locked in that Weaver stance. *Nice shooting,* I thought. Again. The next round gouged rock a foot to my left, but then I was over the edge and out of his field of view.

I knew Miller would expect I might try to wait and ambush him with a boulder as he ascended the cliff, so I jogged breathlessly up the ravine, putting pressure on the exit wound. The sides of the ravine sloped gently here, so I began climbing up to the left to gain elevation. In a quarter mile or so I looked back, and could see Miller standing where he had fired from, watching for me to appear. I turned and kept going until it was clear I couldn't make it back in time to catch him if he started climbing. The wound was starting to sting by this point, and bleeding freely, so I stripped off my shirt and tied it around my waist with one sleeve balled up to partially block the exit wound, which was leaking the worst. Fortunately it was a through-and-through wound in the outer muscle tissue of my lower torso, thus not life-threatening on its own. The loss of blood, however, was not going to help my dehydration issues.

When I looked up again the tiny form of Miller had vanished. He was coming.

So I sat down in the mottled shade of a mesquite tree and started counting on the Sinn. Give it a minute for him to reach the base of the cliff—even though it was rough, he'd be in a hurry. Another minute to climb to the ledge, and . . .

A thin, high-pitched scream reached my ears, then was abruptly cut off.

I stood up (*ow!*) and hiked back down to the cliff. Even though I was pretty sure that scream and its sudden terminus couldn't have been faked, I was careful about looking over the edge. When I did, I saw Miller on his back in the rocks, a dark, spreading pool of blood under his head where it had impacted the sharp corner of a boulder. On his right cheek, just below his open and glazed eye, I could make out a superficial wound about an inch across. I looked straight down, where the six-foot-long coachwhip snake I had left on the ledge was now nosing around, trying to find a way to the ground to get back under cover.

Thanks, buddy.

It took me five minutes to gingerly and painfully downclimb the cliff, including the interesting bit when I had to hang on with one hand off to the side of the ledge and grab the snake again. It was thoroughly riled up by now and struck furiously at me; I had to feint and dodge so I could snatch it behind the head. I didn't want to leave the poor thing stuck twenty feet off the ground, even though coachwhips are good climbers. I three-pointed the rest of the way to the bottom, and put the snake back in the brush, where it zipped off at speed with a story to tell. Then I limped back to Miller.

Poor Miller. Had he been able to maintain his cool after the—admittedly startling—experience of lifting his head over a ledge and having a big-ass black snake bite him in the face, he would have been fine. Coachwhips have the worst temper of any snake I know—herpetologists jokingly change the genus name *Masticophis* to "*Nastycophis*"—but they are totally nonvenomous. Miller had flung himself backwards off the cliff for nothing more than a boo-boo.

I kneeled down and checked his body—first for any water in the canteen slung around his neck. Empty, the selfish jerk. The Glock was still secured in its Kydex holster; the anti-snatch lever had held it in. I considered for a moment, then reached down, fingered the release, and drew the pistol. There was a remote but real chance that Miller's accomplices would be waiting for him, or had even followed us, and I wasn't about to be caught weaponless again. I confirmed that a round remained in the chamber and four in the magazine, then stuffed the pistol in my belt on the opposite side from the wound.

The sweat stains on Miller's uniform, under his arms and in a V in front, were already dry, leaving a rime of white salt crust. There was nothing more for me to do —I didn't want to disturb the scene any further. I stood up—and the world spun crazily and my vision vignetted around the edges. I barely made it to a sitting position again without completely blacking out. I was approaching the dangerous phase of dehydration.

I faced a dilemma. The sooner I reached help, the better. However, the sun was still high and the temperature was above 100 degrees, and I had no shirt on. The alternative was to find solid shade and rest until nightfall, even though I would still be losing some moisture to evaporation and would thus be at more of a deficit when I started walking. I was pretty sure I'd find the Land Cruiser rendered inoperable in some suitably dramatic .40-caliber fashion, and the emergency water in the strong box was as inaccessible as if it were on Mars. Shooting the tubular lock wouldn't work like it did in the movies, and the hollow-point rounds would bounce off the thick steel of the box, so I couldn't aim where I knew the water bottle was and hope to penetrate everything and drink what dribbled out the bottom. I held a glimmer of hope there would be something in Miller's Tahoe—if there weren't, my options would be narrowing quickly given my deteriorating condition.

I know what you're thinking: What about all those famous SAS desert survival tricks? Digging in a wash for moisture? Cutting open a barrel cactus? Sorry to say, but they're mostly bullshit. Cut open a barrel cactus and you'll find a lovely juicy pulp—suck on it and you'll soon be puking, because it's full of oxalic acid. And except within a few days of a flow, you can dig to bedrock in a desert wash and not find water. I once produced drinkable water using a solar still, but not enough to make up for the sweat lost digging the thing, and besides, right now I was sorely lacking a shovel and several square yards of plastic sheeting. On a more realistic basis, certain kinds of cactus fruit are edible and juicy, but I was too late in the year for saguaro fruit and too early for prickly pear fruit.

Lamenting the fact would be fruitless.

I decided to split the difference, and wait until near sunset before setting off. The south side of the ravine boasted a narrow strip of shade, and the rock there was noticeably below body temperature. I stretched out on my back, trying to dump as much core heat as possible. The wound was stiffening and burning seriously now. It had clotted reasonably well, but I needed to leave the shirt on it.

In an hour the sound of the flies around Miller's corpse was driving me crazy, and I was beginning to feel the effects of hypovolemic shock from the gunshot wound and the blood and fluid loss. I needed to get moving. So I eased myself upright and started back down the canyon.

It took me two hours to get back to the Toyota, and ten seconds to find the two holes in the engine block and another through the radiator that told me it wasn't going anywhere. I trudged the 300 yards to the Tahoe. It was well-crumpled in the front. The driver's door was ajar, the steering-wheel air bag hanging flaccidly from the center. Leaning over to look inside precipitated a bout of dizziness and nausea. The M4 on a rack would do me no good—in my condition its seven pounds were literally too heavy to carry—and it was locked anyway. I eyed the radio. Should I chance using it to contact a sector headquarters? I was seriously concerned about a conspiracy, and if that was so, Miller's two accomplices might have contacted others involved to warn them that things hadn't gone so well with their last pickup. I vaguely remembered the BP frequencies being in the 160 MHz range; possibly the radio would allow me to get down into the two-meter bandwidth around 146 MHz to try to contact an amateur operator.

It became a moot point when I hit the power button and nothing happened. The radio should have worked without the ignition key. I looked up and saw the interior light wasn't on. Something had cut off the power from the battery. I pulled the hood release and tried prying open the hood, but it was jammed solid.

I walked to the bank of the wash and climbed up it, to the shade of the trees. My mouth was dry and my head was aching. Soon I would stop perspiring, and then my core temperature would quickly spike to unsurvivable levels. The closest accessible water was at the seep where my camera gear was stashed, probably five miles away. I was doubtful I could make it that far, but it seemed the only option.

In fleeing from Miller in the Land Cruiser I had curved back to the east, so the Cabeza Prieta range was now northeast of me. I figured the shortest route to the seep would be cross country to try to hit the junction of the road to the mine, then up to the mine and back over the mountain the way I had come what seemed like days ago.

I walked, and felt myself getting weaker with every hundred yards. The sun was finally angling down behind me and the peak heat of the day was past, but I wasn't going to live much longer in 100 degrees than I was in 110. Whenever I could, I ducked into the long shadows of saguaros and walked the meager length of respite they offered. By luck I came out on the Camino del Diablo just yards from the road to the mine, and staggered north until it turned eastward into the mountains and cut between rising bluffs. My tongue was now swollen, and I was starting to lose concentration every few minutes, wandering off the side of the track and stumbling over the rocks along the edge, jarring me back to awareness.

The track seemed to stretch forever. The map in my head told me it couldn't be more than a mile to the mine, but the twists and turns of the track went on and on. Miller's Glock seemed to weigh thirty pounds, so I stashed it under a flat rock next to a dead tree that looked distinctive. At last the path bent around a final outcropping, and before me was the little flat-floored valley and its cyclopian tunnel entrance.

It was a hundred yards to the northeast corner and the outcropping from which I had watched events unfold. I nearly didn't make it, and then I realized I was no longer perspiring. I had fully entered the life-threatening second stage of dehydration, and would soon collapse from hyperthermia. My body no longer had enough moisture in it to produce sweat, which meant it could no longer cool itself. My blood would actually be thickening in my arteries, and soon the cramps I'd been feeling would progress to seizures.

I looked at the mine entrance, and the desperate thought hit me to go back in, jump into the shaft, and fill my stomach with the foul water that waited there in tens of thousands of gallons. But I knew I'd never be able to climb back out. I'd wind up in the muck on the bottom, decomposing next to the pilot.

The pilot.

What was it about the pilot I felt like I should remember?

And then I did remember.

CHAPTER 6

Magdalena Ryan poured a glass of chardonnay and walked barefoot out to the red-brick patio of her adobe house, flipping on the outside light to check for rattlesnakes even though it was too early in the evening for them to be moving about. She knew she was still at risk of stepping on an unseen scorpion, but after wearing a U.S. Fish and Wildlife Service uniform and boots all day it just felt too good to divest herself of as much clothing as possible, especially since the air temperature was still sinking slowly through the nineties. But the evaporative cooler pushed a gentle breeze through the sliding screen door, so the patio was quite pleasant, and the wine was cold.

She plopped into a comfortable old Adirondack chair at the edge of the semicircle of light and crossed her feet safely on top of a tiled cocktail table. To the south, Scorpius was high in the sky, the red supergiant Antares fiery in the constellation's heart. Almost straight overhead, Jupiter shone brightly. Magdalena debated bringing out her little three-inch refractor to see what the Galilean moons were doing in their dance around the planet, but despite the pollution-free skies over Ajo, Arizona, viewing would be poor through the rising waves of heated air. So she contented herself with listening to the trilling of lesser nighthawks, the soothing hoot of great-horned owls, and the peeping of sparrow-sized elf owls calling from their nest holes in saguaros. The resident family pack of coyotes had their nightly meet-and-greet, yapping and yowling like ten animals instead of four before heading off to hunt.

As a biologist for the Cabeza Prieta National Wildlife Refuge, Magdalena's job revolved around animals and plants, but she never tired of pondering the miraculous strategies life found to flourish in the harsh terrain of the Sonoran Desert. The diversity here actually exceeded that on the summits of the 9,000-foot mountains outside Tucson, which enjoyed 30-degree-cooler temperatures and nearly two feet more rain each year. How that could be was an endless and intriguing puzzle. Less enjoyable, but just as critical, was her study of how the desert would adapt to continued global warming and the spread of invasive plant species.

A single moment had set her on her life's course. Her father, the descendant of an Irish immigrant to Mexico who married a Mexican woman, was born in Magdalena's namesake town in Sonora, emigrated to the U.S., and opened a hole-in-the-wall *cevicheria* in Los Angeles. A young Irish woman studying evolutionary biology at UCLA took a position as his sole employee, and the two fell in love, completing a convoluted ethnogeographic circle. She happily abandoned her academic track to make the little restaurant a success (with an eventual four locations), but made sure their daughter saw as much as possible of the wild lands in and outside the city. This indoctrination went more or less well until one day when Magdalena was eight, when, on a stroll near dawn in the Santa Monica Mountains, one of the range's near-mythical cougars stepped into the path twenty feet in front of them. Magdalena's mother gasped and stopped, stunned but unafraid, and the cat turned and looked directly into the little girl's eyes as she stared back, her breath caught in her throat. In that instant every potential future for her coalesced into one driving goal: Whatever she did must revolve around animals such as this one.

Now Magdalena sat and enjoyed the cooling air. It was bright enough that she could see the bats swooping overhead, and the white highlights of a skunk that waddled in to drink at the water trough she kept filled at the edge of what passed for her yard but was really just lightly trimmed desert. She watched the skunk's movements carefully—the dry period during summer, when animals collected around scarce water sources, was a prime time for the transmission of rabies, and skunks were common victims since they were so easy for other rabid animals, out of their minds with the fever, to catch and bite. But this one exhibited none of the staggering or other unnatural behavior of rabies, and it was abroad at the right time. It drank and waddled off again, and then Magdalena heard the noise.

It was a droning coming from the southwest, behind the house. She dismissed it as a random transiting aircraft, but it kept getting louder, and soon it sounded closer than any normal aircraft would. The noise reminded her of the two-stroke dirt bike one of her friends had when they were kids, except that it stayed steady rather than oscillating with speed. Soon it was close enough that she could sense directional movement; it seemed to drift to the south of the house, then resume getting closer. And now the sound changed

—it began to sputter and cough, like whatever it was was running out of fuel.

Magdalena jumped up, ran into the house, slipped on her boots without tying them, and grabbed a flashlight. She headed to the south side of the house, where an abbreviated concrete driveway led from the carport to the dirt road that accessed the highway. She began shining the light around in the air in the direction of the noise.

Like a scene from some war movie, the light pinned a human hanging from a parachute-like canopy, heading directly toward her and descending rapidly. The engine stopped abruptly, the person—a man, she was now sure, as he was shirtless—worked the control lines, slowing the craft until he overcorrected, landing on his feet but immediately tipping back until the cage of the propellor crashed into the concrete. The man struggled with the harness while Magdalena stood transfixed, wanting to help but wary of the surreal situation. At last the man freed himself and struggled to his feet, lurching toward her. Now she saw the bloody shirt tied around his waist, and the bloodstain soaking the right side of his trousers. He was filthy, haggard, wild-haired—but with a jolt she recognized him.

"My God! Clayton! What happened?"

I managed to croak, "Hi Mags. I ran into a little trouble."

And then the strangest thing happened. Magdalena tilted ninety degrees sideways, and at the exact same instant her driveway rose up and smacked into the side of my face.

CHAPTER 7

I threw the book across the hospital room, rattling the IV tube against the bracket from which dangled my third liter of saline solution.

For God's sake, does every other trash-action-novel hero *have* to be a "troubled ex-Navy SEAL?" I've worked with a half-dozen SEALs on various odd jobs, and overwhelmingly they came across as the most well-adjusted humans on the planet, ready to change a diaper or swim ten miles at night to cut someone's throat, as the situation demanded. This modern propensity for assuming that everyone who's been within a hundred miles of hostile fire must have PTSD and be in desperate need of therapy is absurd. The last straw in this "grippingly realistic" so-called thriller came when the author described a slug from the hero's .45 auto as "lifting the bad guy off his feet." Simple Newtonian physics will tell you no pistol can deliver that kind of energy, or the recoil would be . . .

Oh. Where was I? Right—hospital.

A transfusion package of PRBCs, FFP, platelets, and plasma plus the saline had me feeling half-normal again. My circulation was fine and there were no signs of metabolic acidosis. However, I still hadn't had the slightest desire to pee. They'd cleaned up and stitched the through-and-through flesh wound from Miller's Glock—fortunately he'd been shooting controlled-expansion hollow points, so the bullet hadn't opened too much on its three-inch path through the flesh above my hip. Still hurt like the dickens, though.

I'd given a statement to a Pima County Sheriff's Department detective whose eyes and mouth both got wider as I progressed. Then I'd slept for thirteen hours. Then a seemingly teenaged doctor—Wharton, I think was his name—had come in once, given me a caring smile that would go far when he was making $300 an hour as a specialist, flipped some pages on my chart, and left me in the clutches of the afternoon-shift "health-care professional," a 170-pound nurse whose scrubs and not-found-in-nature titanium hair were redolent of cigarette smoke, and who insisted on grilling me incessantly about the state of my bladder and bowels. I refused to believe her name could really be "Dawn." She had to have exchanged badges with some unseen, 110-pound non-smoking brunette Dawn just to make me imagine what I was missing.

I was going through a list of potential real names for my inquisitor (Bertha? Igor?) when three people walked in. First was Magdalena, looking concerned enough that my heart gave a pleasant little jump. Next was a mildly annoyed-looking guy with a flat-top in an olive-green Border Patrol uniform bearing the silver star of a Deputy Chief Patrol Agent. Third was a cheerful-looking six-foot-two bloke with an outrageous, OK-Corral handlebar mustache, in the same brown and tan of the U.S. Fish and Wildlife Service as Mag, except he also sported a law enforcement badge and the silver eagle collar tabs of a GS12 inspector. I couldn't remember running over any ocelots or bald eagles while I was trying to get away from Miller, so I wasn't sure why he was there. I sincerely hoped he wasn't planning to issue me a citation for driving off a marked road . . .

"How are you feeling?" asked Mag.

I allowed as to how I was feeling a lot better with a gallon of fluids in me.

She got right to it. "Clayton, this is Jeff Hinwood with the U.S. Border Patrol, and Dexter Bowie with the U.S. Fish and Wildlife Service."

Dexter Bowie? Seriously? But it fit the mustache perfectly.

"Gentlemen," I said.

Hinwood took the lead.

"Mr. Porter, I want to take the opportunity to apologize on behalf of the United States Border Patrol for the ordeal you suffered."

Fascinating. No questions. No denial of responsibility. Not even any prevaricating. Straight to an apology from an official representative of a government agency. If I'd been the lawsuit type my eyeballs would have been replaced with spinning dollar signs.

I said, "You already knew about this guy."

Hinwood paused, debated silently, then said, "Agent Miller was the subject of a multi-departmental investigation. Unfortunately, we're now at an impasse with that investigation. It's unlikely we'll be able to identify his accomplices and, more importantly, superiors."

Unfortunately, I thought? What, unfortunate that I hadn't let Miller kill me so the investigation could proceed unhindered?

At that point Wyatt Earp took over.

"Do you have any idea what was in the packages you discovered in the mine?" said Bowie.

"I really didn't stop to . . . wait," I said. "You *caught* the guys in the Ford?"

"That's correct. After Ms. Ryan here called 911 and then informed her superiors, we contacted DPS and State Troopers. The suspects were found alongside eastbound Interstate 8, near Gila Bend. The left rear hub on their vehicle was destroyed. Apparently they'd changed to the spare tire at some point but had somehow lost the lug wrench, and tried tightening the wheel nuts with a pair of pliers. That didn't last long."

I smiled, then said, "So I assumed it was drugs, maybe opioids? Although one duffel at a time in a paraglider seemed like a peculiar strategy. Not the case?"

Hinwood broke in, as if grasping at any straw to show this wasn't your run-of-the-mill crooked Border Patrol agent activity. He said, "Jaguar skins."

Bowie nodded solemnly, and added, "And skulls."

Now I knew why he was here.

Bowie held up a list, although it was clear he didn't need it.

"Sixteen jaguar skins, fourteen jaguar skulls."

I said, "You're tracking an on-call hunt operation." On-call hunts are a vile perversion of sport hunting in which a captive animal is released to be shot by a paying client. If jaguars were the prey that would add a threatened species to the perversion. And a lot to the profits.

Bowie and Hinwood looked at each other. Bowie said, "Partly."

I said, "What's the other part?" then remembered. "Hold on—I swear one of the . . ."

Bowie filled in, " . . . and a jaguar cub."

I said, "A live cub."

"Yes. Heavily sedated. It's at a wildlife rehabilitation center in Tucson now. Doing okay, surprisingly."

"So you're tracking an on-call hunt operation with a side of exotic pet trafficking."

Bowie and Hinwood looked at each other. This time it was Hinwood who said, "Partly."

This was getting ridiculous.

They looked at each other again.

Hinwood: "I'm sure you've read of some of the ways the drug cartels take revenge or send warnings. Beheadings, mutilations; showy messages like that. Bodies left in conspicuous places or hung from bridges."

Of course I had.

Hinwood again: "Over the past year there's been a new kind of message. Some of the corpses left in those conspicuous places had clearly been killed and partially consumed by a large predator, probably feline.

"We suspect this is all related."

CHAPTER 8

I digested that information for a moment. Perhaps a poor choice of verbs.

"So, the guys you caught," I said. "Will they be any help?"

Hinwood: "Hard to say right now. They've already lawyered up—in fact some high-powered asshole from Phoenix just appeared like magic before they even made their phone call. We don't know if they're partners with the principals or just hired drivers. They can be charged with first-degree homicide under Arizona's Felony Murder Law, in addition to the Lacey Act violations. So they have some inspiration to cooperate. We've asked the judge to deny them bail as flight risks; that would help too. But it's still going to be difficult without Miller."

Yeah, I got that the first time, thanks. I changed the subject.

"So about the jaguars. They don't tend to be man-eaters or even man-killers." This was an understatement; in fact the sole human death from a jaguar of which I was aware was a young fisherman in Brazil in 2008. There were a few more anecdotal tales and several records of non-fatal attacks, but statistically the odds were near zero that a jaguar or jaguars would suddenly start killing and feeding off humans, unless . . .

"We're assuming these attacks are from jaguars that have been captured and partially starved," Bowie said. "And the victims were forced into some sort of enclosure with them."

"Very sporting," I said. "Any idea where this is originating?" The closest habitat that supported a solid breeding population of jaguars was about sixty miles south of the U.S. Border with Mexico, in the state of Sonora.

Back to Hinwood: "Almost certainly in the Sierra Madre, we think somewhere southeast of Moctezuma. But we don't know more than that, and the Mexican Army has not been much of a help. They seem to be seriously spooked by this shit, and some of those guys are hard to spook."

I put up a map in my head. Moctezuma was about a hundred miles directly south of Douglas, Arizona, so that would be in the right area. Jaguars exploit a wide range of habitat, but in Sonora they preferred mountainous terrain, the more remote the better, and the Sierra Madre still encompassed a whole bunch of remote country. There was a growing environmental movement in Mexico, and a few ranchers had adopted a live-and-let-live attitude toward jaguars as well as the even rarer Mexican wolves, but a depressing majority still adhered to a shoot-on-sight policy. Biologists working on jaguars relied on bait stations and leg-hold snares when they needed to radio-collar a study animal; otherwise, autonomous camera traps were the easiest way to confirm a resident population.

"So help me with the connection," I said. "On one hand you've got a cartel using captive jaguars to eliminate competitors or informants in spectacular fashion, and spread terror among the general populace. But then you've got trophies from—apparently—some kind of on-call hunts smuggled across the border, to . . . whom? Not to mention a live cub?"

By this point Hinwood was looking as though he was about to say something like, "That's on a need-to-know basis," or some such tripe, but Bowie took over.

"Doctors."

I looked a question at him.

"Doctors who are obsessed with high-end trophy hunting, and who also happen to prescribe an awful lot of opioids."

Suddenly I began to see the connections.

As someone who hunted strictly for food I felt no attraction to trophy hunting; however, I had good friends, ethical hunters, who would always shoot a buck with a bigger rack over one with a smaller one, and I didn't condemn them for it. Some trophy hunters take this urge to extremes, and are happy to spend thousands or tens of thousands of dollars to be guided to a record-class bighorn sheep, grizzly bear, or Cape buffalo. I don't understand the drive, but the money realized from the death of one animal can be used to save habitat for dozens. No species has ever gone extinct from properly regulated trophy hunting.

For some extremely wealthy men, however (and it is virtually always men), the drive becomes a sickness, one that subsumes any lingering notions of conservation, fair chase, or even concern for the survival of a species —in fact, the rarer the quarry, the better. To shoot as many as possible—or all—of the fifty-odd worldwide

58

species of "trophy" wild sheep, for example, they will ignore international laws, legal seasons, or outright bans. And of course where there is a market, there is always the means to satisfy it, in this case through crooked guides and corrupt officials. Big cats have always been high on the list of trophy animals, legitimate or not, and a jaguar—the third largest cat in the world and listed as near-threatened on the IUCN Red List—would be a prime target for such degenerates.

The drug connection fit right in. Who would be better positioned to launder Mexico-sourced opioids than private-practicing MDs, who could offer patients direct access to the pills to which they were addicted, rather than potentially raising alarms with too many drugstore prescriptions? You might think it would be uneconomical for a cartel to bother moving product through individual doctors, unless you knew, for example, that in 2017 a single GP in Pennsylvania had been indicted for prescribing three *million* doses of opioids in a nineteen-month period, and causing the overdose deaths of five patients. Cutting out the necessity for the drugstore and the associated risks of paperwork and records was a natural move. Direct marketing at its best.

"So," I said. "Do the high-grossing doctors get perks in the way of a Mexican vacation and a jaguar hunt?"

Hinwood: "Well, it's going to be hard to prove a . . ."

"You know," I interrupted. "I'm getting tired of hearing about how I fucked up your investigation by staying alive."

To my surprise, Hinwood blinked, stood quietly for a few seconds looking at me, then nodded and said, "You're right. Sorry." And that was just about the last time he and I had a problem.

He sighed, then said, "Our investigation into Miller's involvement in all this was in its initial stages, which was why we weren't monitoring his movements two days ago. We'd only recently connected his name to what at first seemed like an improbable story about on-call hunts and a direct opioid supply chain to doctors in the U.S. from a cartel in Sonora. You can imagine why we were skeptical at first."

"Where did the original information come from?"

He sighed again.

"Last December two Mexican nationals blew through the Agua Prieta/Douglas border checkpoint in a brand-new Toyota Hilux, then immediately pulled over and gave themselves up. They begged for asylum, and then gave the investigating agent a wild spiel about man-eating jaguars and cages and a *"muy grande"* hunting lodge with guests from the U.S. whom everyone was supposed to refer to as Doctor this or Doctor that. Also, supposedly, some very high-powered Mexican government officials—and no one was supposed to acknowledge recognizing them. The two claimed they'd been working for this group and had escaped. But at that time we had zero prior or corroborating evidence."

I would have thought the fact that they were driving a new Hilux would have been unusual enough to raise eyebrows, but . . .

"So what happened next?"

"They were deported. The U.S. only approves something like two percent of asylum claims from Mexico."

"That usually takes weeks, doesn't it?"

"Not this time. They were shipped back over the next day."

I sensed there was more. Indeed, after a pause:

"A week later they showed up again in Agua Prieta. Or most of them. Each had been killed with a crushing bite through the occipital bone and cervical vertebrae, then partially consumed."

The bite location was textbook jaguar hunting technique, the ideal way to quickly put down large and potentially dangerous prey. Google "jaguar and caiman video" and you'll see what I mean. The poor guys had clearly been trying to flee, but to paraphrase my more smart-assed sniper acquaintances, if you run from a jaguar you'll only die tired.

"Then we started hearing about more such incidents. Officials down there had been working harder than they normally do to keep it out of the news."

I said, "Okay, I get the connections right up to the live cub. What was that about?"

Hinwood—finally—cracked a wry smile, shrugged, and said, "Maybe a drug-pushing MD who belongs to PETA and wants to save the jaguars?"

I smiled back and said, "Well he'd need one hell of a securely fenced back yard in his country club. If poodles and labs started disappearing there'd be an uproar in the neighborhood association."

"Much less elementary schoolchildren," said Hinwood.

Bowie piped up. "Do you know there are more tigers kept as 'pets' in the U.S. than there are left in the wild? Five thousand of them."

Hinwood and I gaped at him.

Bowie smiled then, too, and said, "Imagine how many of those little pop-top cans of Fancy Feast it would take to satisfy a 500-pound Bengal tiger. You're spooning out seafood medley like crazy into a little monogramed bowl while the tiger is eyeing you and licking his lips."

We were on a roll. But then Magdalena, who'd been following the conversation and its devolvement silently, rolled her eyes and said, "Uh, *boys* . . ."

We all stood—or sat—to attention.

She said, "Can we not lose sight of the fact that we're dealing with an extremely vicious group of people? Just on this side of the border we've had one cold-blooded murder and a highly energetic attempt at a second. Brutal killings on the other side. And apparently the Mexican Army is reluctant to mess with them? If Miller was as important a principal in this as it seems, he's going to have some pissed-off associates . . . or employers . . . who might want retribution." She looked at me.

I said, "I don't think it would make much sense for them to risk attracting further attention up here by sending a hit squad after me."

She said, "Does it make much sense to capture jaguars and train them to kill and eat people when you could just behead them? They clearly have their own sense of what makes sense."

She had a point. But it still wasn't worrying me much. It's not like I'd been investigating Miller; I was just a random passer-by.

I turned back to Hinwood and Bowie. "So what happens now?"

Bowie said, "The skins and skulls are on their way to the Fish and Wildlife Service's forensics lab in Oregon to be analyzed. They'll try to determine exactly how the animals died, see if any of the skulls match the skins, age them, look for, uh, DNA evidence under the claws —any information they can get."

I knew about the forensics lab in Ashland. It's the only science center in the world devoted exclusively to wildlife-related crime. I'd heard it described as "Scotland Yard for wildlife" and "CSI meets Doctor Doolittle." Flippant nicknames, but the lab is on the front lines of the national and international fight against trafficking in wildlife, wildlife parts, and products—which happens to be the fourth largest illegal industry globally, after narcotics, counterfeiting, and human trafficking.

I said, "Are you assuming the animals being hunted as trophies are the same ones that had been used for these executions?"

"That makes the most sense, although we can't assume that every single one of the animals brought across had been in the . . . system, if you want to call it that. They could also be hunting wild jaguars. And there's no way to know if the, uh, guests doing the hunting are aware of anything except that they're hunting illegally."

I looked at Hinwood, and he took over, changing the subject. "Divers from the Yuma County Sheriff's Department are on their way to the mine right now to recover the body of the pilot."

The Yuma County Sheriff's Department had divers? Who would have thought?

I said, "Remind them to look for my binoculars."

Magdalena rolled her eyes again, and asked, "Do you have any leads on where the skins and skulls—and the cub—were headed?"

Bowie: "Not yet. We don't even know if this was the first lot of stuff to come across, or if they'd been ferrying loads regularly. As Agent Hinwood mentioned, the investigation was in a very early stage. But cases like this don't stir up the usual interdepartmental jealousies, so we'll get a lot of cooperation: DOJ, FBI, etcetera. They'll be checking border crossing records, flights, things like that."

The two men made shuffling motions toward the door. Hinwood said, "Sorry we got off on the wrong foot." He turned, but then turned back and said, "By the way, we need Miller's Glock. That's critical evidence."

I said, quite truthfully, "I was pretty out of it when I stashed it. But I'll try to remember."

He nodded and left. Magdalena came over and sat on the edge of the bed. She put a hand on my non-tubed arm and said, "How are you feeling, really?"

In truth I was feeling pretty good, and her attention was making me feel even better, when . . .

Dawn walked in with a clipboard, looking officious.

"Mr. Porter, when you filled out your paperwork you only listed an initial for your middle name. I really need your whole name for the records. What does the "T" stand for?"

Mag looked amused. I snarled, "It stands for "T.""

Dawn adopted a doubtful *moue*, opened her mouth to protest, but then *hmmphed*, and left. I'd probably made her late for her cigarette break.

"What was that all about? Is your middle name really just T?"

Sigh. "No."

"Then why the obfuscation?"

"Because I don't *like* my middle name, okay?"

Mag just smiled and said, "Okaaaay."

But I could tell she was filing it away to circle back and ambush me with later. *Sigh.*

CHAPTER 9

I lived in a house I couldn't possibly afford.

Not that it was much of a house, at least as most Americans think of one. Built in the 1920s of mud adobe nearly three feet thick, it comprised a single rectangular room, about twenty by thirty feet, with a concrete floor, a ten-foot-tall ceiling of round pine rafters and pine planks, with a kitchen—added by me—at one end and a fireplace at the other. Out front was a full-width wood porch with a tin roof. The bathroom—toilet, sink, shower, also added by me—was in a separate six-by-eight foot building out back. In the main living area was a sofa bed and a sparse collection of quarter-sawn oak furniture as old as the house, including a massive banker's desk under a window that looked out over the porch.

The unaffordable part was largely due to the view out that window: The building nestled in the upper corner of a 2,000-deeded-acre ranch accessed by taking Interstate 10 east from Tucson, turning north on Mescal Road, and driving along the backside flank of the Rincon Mountains to a turnoff and locked gate signed

Oso Negro Ranch. The property extended from high desert up to nearly where the pines started, bordering the Coronado National Forest. "My" house looked out on juniper and oak trees, and the sycamores that lined a stream that flowed half the year in good years. Coyotes wandered up from the desert; cougars wandered down from the 8,000-foot peaks, as did the occasional black bear, giving the ranch its name. The local canyon wrens came down the chimney and foraged through the house, hopping unafraid across my desk and keyboard while I sat writing or editing images. Five or six species of hummingbirds battled over the sugar-water feeders I hung from the porch beams.

As the nearest powerline was five miles away, a solar array and a small wind turbine supplied electricity via a 2,500-watt inverter drawing from a bank of batteries. It provided plenty of power for lights, a small fridge and large chest freezer, a modem connected to a satellite dish, and my computer and camera-recharging needs. An ancient but well-oiled Aermotor windmill drew pure water from a 300-foot-deep well and pumped it into a galvanized tank on a tower that provided pressure-water to the house and bathroom. I cooked venison from the freezer off propane in the house or over juniper in the barbecue, and kept mostly alive a small garden enclosed in a very tall fence to keep out the non-venison white-tailed deer. There was an unspoken treaty between me and the resident deer—I wasn't going to shoot animals that barely deigned to step aside as I walked around the yard; in return, they did their best to get into the garden but left untouched the geraniums in the window boxes and the potted gardenias on the porch. Or maybe deer just don't care for geraniums or gardenias.

(And I know what you're thinking. *Window boxes? Really?* I just like flowers, okay?)

No such treaty existed between me and the coyotes, foxes, bobcats, skunks, badgers, and ringtails (am I forgetting anything?) that would have happily devoured the chickens or their eggs inside the coop. Not that I would ever employ lethal means against them—when someone asked me why I would kill a deer for food yet not kill a predator that was trying to get *at* my food, my response was, "Professional courtesy." Nevertheless I had no intention of professionally sharing either the hens or their eggs. As a result, the quaint barn-red clapboard coop itself was surrounded by a stalag-like enclosure of welded steel rod and wire, the walls of which extended two feet underground. A tall strip of quarter-inch hardware cloth ran around the bottom to prevent snakes getting partway through the chicken wire and getting stuck. The enclosure was big enough to give the half-dozen inhabitants space; when I was home I'd let them out during the day to forage in the yard while I worked on the porch.

Downhill about a mile, along a winding two-track, was the main ranch house, a much larger, sprawling affair with an adobe core from around the same time period as the upper house, and four or five additions, built as needed and out of whatever materials worked or were cheapest at the time—stone, red brick, plastered concrete block. An Aermotor twice the diameter of the one at the uphill house drew enough water for the stables and corrals out back, which housed a half dozen well-bred working quarter horses, several from famous Hashknife lineage. The solar array was four times the size of mine and fed a massive bank of Rolls-Surrette batteries, backed up by a ten-kilowatt diesel generator.

I pulled up to the big house and parked the brand-new rental 4Runner which, astoundingly, Hinwood had somehow arranged through official channels while my

Land Cruiser was recovered and trucked over to New Mexico to have its engine replaced by my long-suffering mechanic friend. I wasn't sure if they were buttering me up to keep me from thinking about a lawsuit, but if so they were wasting their money—I'm just not the opportunistic litigious type. Nevertheless, I was enjoying the air-conditioned 4Runner, which rode a lot better than the Land Cruiser and was thus much gentler on that .40-caliber hole through my hip.

A black-and-white border collie that had been dozing in the shade on the porch stood and watched the strange vehicle warily. When I shut down the engine he barked several times until I opened the door and shouted, "Kit! What's up with the barking?" At the sound of my voice the barks changed to high-pitched yips, and the dog leaped off the porch and raced toward me at top border-collie speed, which is alarmingly fast when you're in the way. At the last second he skidded and turned sideways so the body-slam collision-velocity with my legs was reduced to twenty miles an hour or so —at least that's what it felt like to the bullet hole. I kneeled down gingerly and accepted a flurry of licks, then the dog bounded off to lead me to the porch. As I mounted the steps I braced myself for the next greeting, and sure enough as I passed under the massive beam supporting the outer edge of the roof a huge black cat leaped from it onto my shoulder, secured himself with what felt like about sixty claws, and began purring loudly enough to rattle the screen door I was approaching. I reached up to scratch behind his ears and said, "How're you doing, Pounce?" Which elevated the purring another notch.

Through the door came a baritone voice, "'Bout damn time you were back. Gettin' tired of watering your damn flowers and feeding your damn chickens."

He wasn't at all, of course, but had to say so.

I opened the door and stepped into the cool, dim great-room that was the original core of the house. The wood plank floor creaked under my boots. Across the room a large window revealed a U-shaped courtyard partially shaded with a porch that edged the perimeter. Emory oaks in several red-brick tree-wells shaded the rest. Beyond was the blue shoulder of the Rincon Mountains.

Inside, the first thing one noticed—if one was aware of such things—was that most of that wood floor was hidden under exceptionally large Navajo rugs of exceptional quality—Two Grey Hills, Ganado, Chinle, Burntwater. Smaller and even finer examples graced the walls, in between pieces of western art hung so casually they could only have been originals—a sketch by Remington, a landscape study from Moran, a Catlin portrait, and, more contemporary but by far the most visually arresting, a Grand Canyon landscape by Peter Nisbet the size of a sheet of plywood, in which the Colorado glinted beneath rain-slicked rock ramparts, and evening-lit golden storm clouds seemed to billow out of the canvas.

The furnishings were a farrago of outrageously hokey mid-fifties cowboy furniture and outrageously expensive English antiques. A wagon wheel chandelier with fake kerosene-lamp globes hung over an Arts and Crafts dining table. A brace of pine and orange-vinyl reading chairs repeated the Westward Ho motif and were lit by a cholla-skeleton lamp with rodeo scenes and a jackalope silkscreened on the shade, while across yet another Two Grey Hills rug a Chesterfield sofa sat regally aloof, its tufted leather a deep burgundy under the glow of a black-shaded Bestlite, Winston Churchill's favorite desk lamp.

At a beat-up workbench under the Nisbet, Jedediah Carson sat winding silk on the stripping guide of a bamboo fly rod he was finishing for a customer who had ponied up something north of $5,000 in advance for it. He was wearing a headband magnifier and was working by the light of a modern chromatically corrected LED lamp—the cholla lamp and Bestlite were reserved for atmosphere.

Jed pushed back the magnifier, looked up at me, and said, "Damn, son, you look like something pulled half your stuffing out through the back zipper."

"Damn," for as far back as I could remember, was the only cuss word Jedediah Carson ever used, but he used it frequently.

I walked over to the bar cart—which rode on miniature wagon wheels and employed a cow horn as a towel rack—poured three fingers of Black Maple Hill 16 into a couple of tumblers, and carried them over to the desk.

"Tell you a story?"

He pushed back his chair, set the magnifiers on the desk, and switched off the lamp.

Thirty minutes later he got up and walked around the desk to stand in front of me. So I stood up too, and he enveloped me in a bear hug—which, since Jedediah is a head taller than my five-ten and outweighs me by sixty pounds, actually *felt* like a bear hug despite his eighty-ish years. Ouch. Hadn't I mentioned I'd recently been shot? In my ear he said, "Dammit, boy, if I lose you, too, I'll never forgive you." To my shock his voice choked up.

That was the thing about Jedediah: Just like his furniture, you could never, ever predict him.

CHAPTER 10

Jedediah Carson was the great-great grand-nephew of the famous mountain man and scout, claiming descent from Kit's oldest brother, who had stayed behind in Missouri while his sibling ran off to become legendary, and instead had married Daniel Boone's grand-niece. Jed's parents, immersed in the family aura, had given him the first name of another legendary mountain man and explorer. (Kit the border collie was a new thing, though—although Jedediah had had a succession of cattle dogs, Kit was the first one he thought exceptional enough to bear his relative's name.)

As a young man Jed started out fully embracing his ancestry as well, running a trap line in Michigan's Upper Peninsula before he was ten. He was at home in the woods and brought in a fine income for several years, presciently saving enough for college while still in high school. But he became more and more uneasy with the use of foot-hold traps, finally could no longer stand the looks and struggles of the doomed animals in them when he walked up with the club, and consigned that part of his heritage to history. He remained a hunter, but honed his proficiency with the Winchester Model 94 he'd bought with fur money to the point where he only ever took instantly fatal cervical spine shots on the deer he hunted for food—a skill that required not only an exact anatomical awareness from any angle, but a superhuman ability to estimate range and correlate it perfectly with the lazy trajectory of the 30-30 cartridge.

It was a gift from his father, however, that would fire Jedediah's passion and have a profound influence on his life—both directly and indirectly: an H.L. Leonard bamboo fly rod, one actually made by Hiram Lewis himself in the years before his death in 1907. The fourteen-year-old Jed was entranced that something made of six tapered strips of Tonkin cane glued together could feel like a living thing in his hands, and respond like thought itself when used skillfully. Within two years he was guiding clients on brook-trout streams in the U.P., including Hemingway's Two Hearted River and the Fox, and putting away yet more toward college. But on the advice of one client who hired him several times and took a paternal interest in the hardworking young man, in 1957 he invested fully half of his savings in the stock of three companies: Commonwealth Bank, Western Insurance, and a hardware wholesaler called Marshall Wells. Coincidentally these happened to be three of the companies a very savvy investor ten years Jedediah's senior—a Nebraska native named Warren Buffett—had targeted as promising.

College, however, never happened. The Cold War was at its height, as was the fear of communism. Jedediah had no political leanings, but he did have a strong sense of duty and a father who'd fought at Monte Cassino, a grandfather who'd flown a Spad S.XIII under Rickenbacker, and of course that great-great-grand-uncle . . .

Jedediah joined the Army with no particular goal except to serve his time and do what he was told. But his intelligence, natural fitness, and uncanny marksmanship soon attracted attention. The result was that in 1962 he found himself in the mountains of a southeast Asian country few Americans had yet heard of, a member of a small group of airborne-qualified soldiers highly trained in unconventional warfare, reconnaissance, and psychological operations—a group that had just then been authorized by President Kennedy to wear a green beret as the exclusive mark of their command.

The mission of the 1st Special Forces Group was to liaise with the Montagnards, a diverse group comprising thirty or so tribes, ethnically distinct from the lowland Vietnamese, many of whom considered them savages (some were convinced the Montagnards had tails). But the self-sufficient, fierce mountain people were kindred spirits to the self-sufficient, fierce Special Forces men, and together they formed an unconventional but effective army. The 1st Group men lived among the villagers in units of twelve, known as an A detachment, advising and fighting with ten times or more their number of what were called civilian irregular defense groups, or CIDGs (pronounced "*sidgee*"). Roaming the mountains along the western border with Cambodia and Laos, they harassed the North Vietnamese forces trying to move men and weapons southward. With the help of the Navy SeaBees, the Special Forces men also built schools, roads, dams, and bridges for the Montagnards.

Sergeant 1st class Jedediah Carson killed his first human. Then another. And another. He didn't enjoy it, but it was his job so he did it as well as he could, which was very well indeed given his background with the Winchester. Because of his well-known marksmanship (and his size), Jedediah had secured a 7.62-caliber M14, a much heavier but more accurate and powerful rifle than the WWII-era M2 carbines his companions favored for jungle warfare. In engagement after engagement the other U.S. soldiers and the Montagnards went through multiple magazines in their M2s, frequently on full auto. When the fighting stopped Jedediah would have four or five rounds left in his first 20-round mag—and fifteen or sixteen dead North Vietnamese scattered along his field of fire. Not once in his military career did he use the full-auto function of either the M14 or, later, the newfangled M16 "Mattel rifle" when the Army switched to the 5.56mm cartridge. Jedediah took one of the new weapons and a bunch of C-ration cans out on a landing strip to familiarize himself with the flat trajectory of the cartridge, in case he needed to use one, and then went right on carrying the M14.

Jedediah was happy living with the Montagnards. Along with almost all the SF soldiers, he admired their toughness and their bravery under fire. As the light weapons specialist of the team he found them quick studies with whatever he trained them on—the M2, the Madsen submachine gun, even the 40mm M79 "Thumper" grenade launcher. And their commitment to fighting the NVA subsumed any moral quandaries he might have had about killing people he did not know and with whom he had no quarrel except duty.

For a while. As time went on he began to wonder why the Montagnards remained committed. After the 1963 coup against South Vietnamese President Diêm, which was at best winked at and at worst partially funded by the U.S., Diêm's military successors instituted restrictive policies against the Montagnards. Meanwhile Jed had been reading and thinking a great deal about the causes of the war, which began with the Vietnamese demanding independence from France through the international community as early as the Versailles Peace Talks in 1919—demands that were ignored. Wanting freedom from colonial overlords, Jed reasoned, was pretty much what had happened in 1776. While he remained diametrically opposed to communism, he couldn't blame those who had experienced subjugation under a democratic colonial power for trying a different path. Nevertheless he re-upped after his first TDY (temporary duty) period was finished, and then for a second time.

In July of 1964 any philosophizing was temporarily put on hold. On the night of the 6th, Jed was at Camp Nam Dong with a dozen 7th Special Forces Group soldiers commanded by Captain Roger Donlon when, with 370 irregular troops, they fought off an attack by over 900 NVA regulars in a battle that lasted five hours. Donlon was wounded four times but continued to direct the battle, and would receive the first Congressional Medal of Honor awarded during the Vietnam conflict. Jedediah made it unscathed to nearly the end of the fighting when a slug from an AKM punched through his upper left chest, nicking a lung. He continued firing one-armed although, as he said later during the only instance I ever got the full story, "My aim suffered somewhat."

Medevacked to the 8th Field Hospital in Nha Trang, awarded a Silver Star, Jedediah did what every wounded soldier has done since the siege of Troy: He fell in love with his nurse.

Except this time, the nurse fell for him, too.

Her name was Sally. Petite, with short blond hair and green eyes, she joshingly fended off the brash flirtations of the rest of the men in her ward, but was drawn to the big, quiet man in the corner, who answered her questions with *yes ma'ams* and *no ma'ams* and shrugged dismissively when she asked him about the Silver Star. Finally she drew him out enough to get him talking about fly fishing and the clear streams of the Upper Peninsula, and was hypnotized by the faraway look in his eyes when he spoke of, just once, lying in his sleeping bag under the stars and hearing a wolf howl. In return, she told him stories about the ranch in Arizona where she'd grown up, riding horses from the age of four, wrangling from the age of eight, and at twelve helping her father reluctantly but resolutely hunt down a cougar that had taken a liking to calves. The skin had become a rug in her bedroom—not as a trophy, but as a way to keep tangible the memory of a magnificent animal toward which neither she nor her father harbored any enmity. She would sometimes lie on it at night before going to bed, with her head on its head, remembering the chase, glad that they'd been successful, but gladder still that there remained cougars in the mountains who were allowed the odd calf.

Sally watched Jedediah's eyes closely as she told him this, to see if he would object or, worse, humor her. Instead he just nodded solemnly, and something told her right then this was a man she could marry.

They did not, however, marry right away, or even soon.

Jed was back on active duty in two months, with Sally's P.O. address in Arizona tucked in his pocket. The two corresponded regularly and at length in the following years, each filling pages with increasingly intimate thoughts and dreams.

One of those increasingly intimate lines of thought was Jedediah's growing certainty that the war was a doomed effort as it was being waged by Washington. The continued fecklessness of rapidly rotating South

Vietnamese military governments, and the lack of commitment of its troops, stymied U.S. strategy, and attempts to transfer leadership of the CIDG forces to ARVN officers were disastrous, as the prejudice of the lowland Vietnamese officers was all too apparent. The Montagnards became so enraged at their treatment that the irregulars in five SF camps revolted in late 1964, killing 80 ARVN troops before being talked down by SF officers.

Jedediah decided he'd had enough. He finished his tour and rotated out for home.

Sally's path to southeast Asia had begun in 1961, the day after John Kennedy's inaugural speech challenging his fellow citizens to ask what they could do for their country, when she left her parents' ranch to attend nursing school and join the Army Nurse Corps. She finished her own tour shortly before Jed left, but immediately volunteered for the Red Cross's Supplemental Recreational Activities Overseas program.

The women of the S.R.A.O. were tasked with keeping the morale of the troops high; some staffed recreation centers, others travelled to fire bases with games and snacks. Sally's front-line nursing experience, however, meant that she was quickly conscripted back into that role in any FOB to which the Red Cross sent her. By late 1965 she had returned to nursing full-time at the new 3rd Field Hospital in Saigon.

Jedediah, back home in Michigan, stood in his beloved streams casting with his beloved Leonard rod, with a hollow feeling subsuming his every waking moment.

He had done his duty—more than, in fact, given his multiple tours. He acknowledged without false modesty that he was a distinct cut above the average soldier. He'd killed more men than he could count, but was convinced that it had come to naught. Public support for the war was already eroding, and he knew it would erode more once the obfuscation regarding purported progress against the NVA was revealed. Soon soldiers returning from duty in Vietnam would be insulted by college students with draft deferrals, or those who had managed to dodge conscription with insignificant physical issues and connections.

Jedediah wanted above all for his military experience to count for something honorable besides honorably completing his duty. He began to wonder if there might be somewhere, some conflict zone, where a people were fighting for a just cause, perhaps for their very survival. Somewhere that could purge the hollow feeling.

It did not take him long to find the right place. He sat his parents down in the living room of his boyhood home in L'Anse, on the shore of Lake Superior, and explained his motivations and the long, agonizing thought process that had led to his decision. They were secretly terrified but did not show it and did not attempt to dissuade him. He wrote Sally and told her; she wrote back simply, "I understand and love you more for this," hiding her own terror. He left the rest of his savings in the care of his ex-fishing-client, with power of attorney to invest it as he saw fit. In March of 1966 he bought a plane ticket.

October 14, 1967

Dearest Sally,

It's over and I am safe and well. In six short days that felt like thirty I feel that I filled that empty space within me, and justified the commitment of the last year and a half. I believe I contributed in a small way to a cause that, though it may sound cliché, was worth fighting for.

Two weeks ago, Israel was surrounded by a half million hostile troops, 5,000 tanks, and a thousand fighter aircraft. Gamal Abdel Nasser had blockaded the Straits of Tiran, Israel's only outlet to the Red Sea. His radio broadcasts boasted that the annihilation of Israel was at hand. Not defeat, but "annihilation." Instead, we destroyed his air force on the ground and drove his army across Sinai and over the Nile. Hussein's foolish decision to exploit what Nasser told him was Egypt's rapid advance (when in fact they were in rapid retreat), and attack the Jewish side of Jerusalem, resulted in Jordan losing not just Jerusalem but all the West Bank. Syria suffered a similar fate. So three countries with the goal of wiping Israel off the map once again lost, just as they did in 1948, after the United Nations set aside one percent of Arab-controlled lands as a homeland for the Jews, and four Arab nations tried to drive them into the sea. I cannot say enough about the courage and will of the Israelis—the Jews—who like no other people in history have had their very right to exist questioned for so long and so repeatedly. My only regret is that my grandmother, whose Jewishness enabled my acceptance as a volunteer in the IDF, did not survive the Holocaust to witness this day.

I was with the paratroopers under Colonel Matt in Sinai. We were airlifted by helicopter behind the Egyptian lines, and destroyed artillery emplacements and ammunition dumps to blunt the defenses around Um-Katef. We succeeded, but the tank forces under Sharon still faced intense fighting; at times the Egyptian and Israeli tanks were firing at each other from fifty feet. But the Egyptian commanders were so disorganized that at one point they called in artillery strikes on their own positions. At last their forces turned and ran, those who did not surrendered. In fact so many surrendered that

Israel simply could not accommodate them, and resorted to accepting only officer surrenders, sending enlisted men on foot toward the Nile.

I am still in Sinai but will be back in Tel Aviv within the month. I am now desperate to come home and see you again. Has it really been three years?

> *Yours always,*
>
> *Jedediah*
>
> *P.S. (I wrote this three times, erased it three times in terror, then finally left it in):*
>
> *Will you marry me?*

Sally sent back an airmail letter that contained just one word.

Her response signaled the dawn of three decades of peace—if not entirely uninterrupted—and happiness for Sally and Jedediah, after the horrors of war for which they had both volunteered. At the end of his IDF enlistment Jedediah flew home. His parents seemed to have aged ten years in the time he had been away, but they greeted him joyously, even after he told them he would be leaving for Arizona in a few days. He took the Leonard fly rod out on the Fox and caught a single 13-inch brook trout, which he released reverently. The river was his again; no hollow feelings lingered.

Jedediah's fishing client had compounded his investments so spectacularly that Jed was sure he'd misplaced a decimal point. He let it ride except to take out enough to buy a brand-new British Racing Green Triumph TR250, with the six-cylinder engine. It was an odd choice for him, especially since he barely fit inside the thing, but—despite the fact that she had agreed to marry him—after three years of separation he was apprehensive about how Sally would feel about him, and wanted to impress her.

She was impressed, all right—not only that he made it the 2,000 miles from L'Anse to Tucson in under three days, but that he then managed to flog the poor low-slung car all the way up to the ranch. The next day they drove it back to town and traded it in on a Ford pickup.

They held the wedding under a huge old oak tree. Jedediah's parents flew in and bonded instantly with Sally's—despite the gulf between their lifestyles they had shared the Great Depression and WWII, and had fallen instantly for each other's child. Some of Jedediah's friends from Special Forces came, as did a few Army nurses—precipitating an additional marriage a few months later.

Jedediah took to ranching as quickly as he had to fly fishing—and in fact managed to combine the two by stocking the largest of the ranch tanks with panfish. It wasn't the Two Hearted River but it satisfied. And Jed was enthralled by the landscape sweeping up from the San Pedro River, through Sonoran Desert cactus and mesquites, and into the pine-clad Rincon Mountains. The couple lived in a new addition to the back of the main ranch house; Jed got his own horse, which he rode adequately but never with the same effortless grace as Sally; he impressed Sally's father, Jack, with his work ethic and strength, and had her mother wrapped around his little finger in no time with his politeness and insistence on doing household chores as well as ranch work.

Some years passed. Jack, who'd been nearly fifty when Sally was born, seemed happy to have Jedediah take over more of the physical work in the ranch, while

Sally took over more of the business. Soon Jack was content to just saddle his horse in the morning and check the fence lines. A fulfilling but hard life had taken its toll, and there came a day when Jack's horse appeared at the house one afternoon with no rider. Sally and Jed backtracked the horse and found Jack sitting peacefully against the smooth trunk of a sycamore tree next to the little stream that flowed down from the mountains. To their surprise, Sally's mother smiled when they told her, said, "He wouldn't have wanted anything else," and hugged them both fiercely. But the loss hit her hard, and she began to fade away before their eyes, until Jed thought he could almost see through her—not around her, but through her, as though her molecules were bleeding off into the ether. One evening when he checked on her in her bedroom, she grasped his hand and said, "We were so happy Sally found you." And the next morning she didn't wake up.

As if the timing were ordained by some higher power, two months after the funeral Sally told Jedediah she was expecting.

They named their daughter Jaqueline, of course— and it was through her that the arcs of our lives began to converge.

CHAPTER 11

I was in Kenya, in the South Rift Valley, volunteering for a conservation NGO training a group of Maasai *morani* in anti-insurgent tactics, which are easily modified into anti-poaching tactics. The Maasai were just beginning to assert their identity as a tribe again, after having been sidelined politically since independence by the dominant and far more populous Kikiyu—on whom the Maasai had historically preyed so there was some ironic rough justice involved. The near-extinction of their traditional nomadic herding lifestyle had been devastating for the Maasai, and they were still struggling to figure out how to cope with a sedentary existence.

One potential source of income was wildlife tourism, which the Maasai had long disdained. They had no clue how to run lodges or conduct game drives at the level demanded by wealthy tourists, so they contracted with European operators who frequently cheated them. Nevertheless they were persevering, and one community had put together its own informal band of game scouts to deal with the poaching that was just starting to rise again after the quiet period of the 1980s and early 90s.

One problem was that the Kenyan government refused to let them be equipped with firearms. Given a couple dozen Maasai warriors armed with FN-FALs we could have rid the entirety of southern Kenya of poachers; as it was they had to make do with their splendid *emperi*—a six-foot spear normally used to take down lions. Combined with the near-mythical reputation of the Maasai as fighters, it was not an altogether ineffective alternative, but the element of surprise would be critical when they were up against AK-armed poachers.

I'd been living in the field in a wall tent for two weeks, embedded with eleven *morani* from the Olkirimatian community who were keen as the edges of their spears. The Maasai were generally good at animal tracking, but had no comprehension of tactical man-tracking. So we practiced the standard V formation, with a single tracker at the apex following the spoor, while a flanker on each side and behind him watched ahead for visual sightings of the quarry—or signs of a possible ambush. The stick leader follows about five meters behind, with the rest of the stick flanking him with at least five meter separation between each man. I tasked several of the *morani* as poachers, and they had great fun trying to outwit their compatriots.

Late one afternoon, back at my camp, I was chatting with several of the men in my broken Swahili and their much better English (mastering Maa is a task that has proven beyond all but a handful of Europeans), when a cruelly battered Hilux came down the track. Several of the men began waving at it and shouting, "Jack! Jack!" When it stopped and a petite young blond woman got out I assumed they'd mistaken her for someone else. But no: They lined up and greeted her with the three-grip African handshake, while she replied to them in—shut my mouth—fluid Maa. Then she walked my way, stuck out her hand and smiled, and said, "Hi, I'm Jack. You must be Clayton."

I tend to stammer at the best of times when meeting women. This apparition, combined with the odd name and her knowledge of mine, shut me down completely. When this happens I always for some reason revert to extreme formality, so I responded with a small bow and, "Clayton Porter, at your service." Yeah, I really did.

She laughed delightedly and said, "Well, I'm going to have to examine my service needs immediately," which left me blushing to the roots of my hair. Then she took pity and asked how the training was going; clearly she'd been comprehensively briefed on me while I'd been left to be ambushed. Someone would hear about this. While I motormouthed about formations and track displacement and the two ways to use the box method of determining the number of insurg . . . I mean poachers in a group (Christ, did I really go on about that?), I was trying to casually examine her in my peripheral vision.

She was maybe five-five and a hundred and ten pounds. Really quite pretty although her face was smeared with dust, which made her green eyes even more emerald-like. Her greasy hair was brusquely pinned back in a loop with a beaded Maasai clip. She was wearing khaki shorts, cheap Hi-Tec boots that were coming apart, khaki socks that might have actually been white at some point. Tanned legs with a Franz Kline pattern of thorn scratches, some healed, some still freshly red. Grimy, torn fingernails. A short-sleeved khaki shirt with "Caracal Camp" embroidered over the right pocket. The top few buttons were open—and in the V I spotted a lion's claw that did not look like it had been separated from its previous owner for more than a few days, hanging from a leather cord. This captivated my attention until I realized that I was staring right between her . . .

Damn it. I looked up guiltily.

She took pity on me again, because it was obvious I'd been looking at the claw. Wait—would she be insulted that I *hadn't* been staring at her . . . I hate this stuff.

She said, "Got it on a hunt a couple days ago."

I looked at her with dawning disbelief.

"A lion hunt—with the Maasai?"

"Uh huh."

"With spears." A statement this time.

"Uh huh." She smiled, then winked at me.

Unbelievable.

The Maasai were historically famous for their lion hunts, in which a group of *morani* would run down and corner a lion, then kill it with spears. Brave enough, you might think, but their real accolades were reserved for the warrior insane enough to rush in on the cornered lion and grab it by the tail so his companions could close in with their weapons. It was a marvelously sustainable arrangement, because the lion had just as good a chance coming out ahead as the Maasai, and in general the big cats learned to stay away from the tall humans in red *shukas*, as well as their cattle. The Kenyan government had, stupidly I thought, banned the practice (after which some Maasai took to poisoning lions instead), but it was an open secret that the hunts still occasionally happened. I would have given a kidney to be asked on one, and here this blond chick casually dropped that she'd just got back from one and had the claw to prove it. It was annoying as hell, and furthermore she smelled rather like she had just come out of the bush from a lion hunt with a bunch of Maasai *morani*. Kind of . . . gamey.

I was entranced.

She said, "How about a beer?"

I said sure—then realized she was asking if I had one, since I hadn't offered first.

Clueless.

She followed me into the tent while my troops wandered off snickering. I was thinking a twenty-kilometer run with full packs would teach them, but then they're Maasai. I opened the wheezing old Engel 12V fridge and pulled out two Tuskers, so named because the founder of the company had been trampled to death by one. The beer itself is just okay but how can you beat an aura like that?

She clinked my bottle with hers and said, "Here's to the Maasai."

I said, "And hunting lions with spears."

Over that evening, and the course of several following, I got her story. She was working on a WWF grant to study the changing relationship of the Maasai and lions, especially the nasty turn toward the use of poison to get rid of those prone to killing cattle. The Maasai felt they had no legal alternative; the Kenya Wildlife Service paid scant attention to complaints from the tribe. Her obvious interest and sympathy—not to mention her supernaturally quick grasp of the language—had endeared her to the elders, and finally resulted in an invitation to accompany the clandestine hunt. She had run alongside six *morani* as they tracked and surrounded a cattle-killing male lying up in an acacia thicket, and helped throw stones in until it emerged in a rage, to be punctured by five spears before succumbing, twisting and roaring as each one hit.

"It was one of the most magnificent experiences I've ever had, but not pretty in the end," she said. Still, we agreed that letting the Maasai kill as many lions as they wanted as long as it was done the traditional way would probably bring back at least some of the equilibrium nomadic herders and predators had managed for centuries before Europeans arrived on the scene. The poison alternative was cheap, readily available, and massively indiscriminate.

I asked about the Caracal Camp shirt. It developed she made extra cash leading game drives out of a lodge on the Ewaso Ngiro River, south of the village where my camp was. It was another of the European-owned lodges on land leased from the Maasai community, but she thought the owner was treating the locals fairly. Most of the other guides were Maasai, as well as two managers in training, learning how to deal with tourists who arrived from Nairobi via Cessna 210 on a twenty-minute flight and expected to be greeted with an ice-cold mimosa balanced on a shield held by "a real Zulu warrior."

I laughed. I knew the attitude.

She drew me out about my own project with the Maasai, then coaxed me backward through my life, somehow effortlessly prying out of me information about my "gap years" I'd never told anyone. When we went back still further from that and I mentioned a childhood outside Tucson, she shrieked, "*What!?*" and we spent hours comparing notes growing up on opposite sides of the Rincon Mountains, under very different circumstances. Hers sounded like heaven to me, and even though I tried to be dismissive about mine, she summed up the stepfather situation by saying, "Some people stay alive only because it would be just barely illegal to kill them."

Did I mention being entranced?

One evening a couple of weeks later—after increasingly frequent and anticipated conversations that ranged from the cooperative hunting strategies of African wild dogs to the likely morphology of extra-terrestrial life to the Israeli/Palestinian problem to our shared fondness of a book called *Querencia* by an under-appreciated New Mexico author—she said the lodge was having a last-night celebration for a large group that had rented the entire place for two weeks. "Why don't you come?"

To say a party with a bunch of wealthy tourists was not my cup of tea would be an understatement, but I had a powerful incentive, so the next evening I put on my best khakis, drove my ancient Land Rover 88 down the river to the lodge, and parked the poor thing next to a row of gleaming white Defender 130s with fringed canopies and safari seating for twelve.

It was a beautiful presentation in a beautiful setting: cavernous wall tents with thatched secondary roofs, elevated on platforms above the river under the shade of massive fig and mango trees. The main lodge was cantilevered out over the water. Flow diverted upstream ran in little artificial creeklets throughout the camp. Kerosene lanterns provided atmosphere, while twinkling LED fairy lights suffused everything with a soft glow.

The bar was a spectacular affair of bamboo and African ironwood, manned by a crisply white-garbed, cheerful Maasai elder—meaning forty or so, as defined by their age-set social hierarchy. He asked what I wanted in perfect English, and when I decided to take a wild chance and go for a martini, mixed one that would have satisfied 007. When I said, "*Ashe oleng*," he shouted, "Ho!" and reached across to shake my hand, laughing delightedly.

I turned and there she was.

The shirt was the same, except clean and pressed. A skirt had replaced the shorts, and leather sandals had replaced the Hi-Tecs. The lion claw was nowhere to be seen, undoubtedly so as not to cause palpitations among the guests. Her hair, the gleaming color of Sahara dunes, was still held back by the beaded clip, but in a graceful swirl.

Also, her face was clean. And she didn't smell, except of shampoo and some mild herbal soap.

To my intense discomfiture and pleasure she stepped up and kissed me on the cheek, then took my hand and said, "C'mon, you might as well get this over with." She led me over to the boisterous group I'd been studiously avoiding looking at, and said, "Everyone, this is Clayton, the man I told you about who's fighting poachers with the Maasai." To my utter mortification, they cheered and several clapped. An older fellow in a *de rigueur* multi-pocketed vest and Ultimate hat pulled out a chair next to him and invited me to sit. Then Jack said, "I'll be right back," and left me in their clutches.

And it turned out they were a delightful group of people, all friends from an Audubon Society chapter in Denver, having the time of their lives and fully aware of the difference between the Maasai and the Zulu. I asked them what was their favorite bird on the trip, got lilac-breasted roller, malachite kingfisher, and fish eagle in response, and allowed as to how my own was the pennant-winged nightjar. This got a chorus of groans as it was one of the few species they hadn't seen.

Jack returned, the lodge cooks served a superb meal centered around roasted Guinea fowl, and I had a thoroughly enjoyable evening, sneaking glances at Jack across the table, and wondering if there was any way I could convince her to feel the same way about me as I was feeling about her. When I said my good-byes and headed for the Land Rover she followed me to the parking lot, put her hands on my shoulders, and kissed me lingeringly on the lips. "See you soon?" was all she said, but it was enough. I drove back to my camp so weightless that I didn't even feel the track's corrugations through the Rover's rigid leaf springs. I lay awake in my cot for a long time with my hands behind my head, smiling, and listening to hyenas laughing at me from across the river.

A week later I lost her.

I found out when the *morani* showed up one morning, weeping copiously, and crowded around me while their captain, Michael, broke the news. Maasai boys are raised to completely ignore physical pain, including the piercing agony that accompanies their circumcision ceremony in their early teens. But the men have no qualms about crying openly due to emotional angst. And they were obviously devastated.

A new group of guests had settled in at the lodge. They'd been extensively briefed on protocol, the unbreakable tenet of which was that no one was to leave the camp alone under any circumstances. And the next morning one of the women decided to go for a jog. A cook spotted her and ran to tell Jaqueline, who didn't wait for an armed askari but took off on foot in pursuit. She caught the woman a kilometer down river, just as a young bull elephant burst out of the trees, alarmed by the running figure. By this time two askaris had jumped in a Land Rover and set off in pursuit; they arrived in time to witness what happened next.

The bull charged just as Jack caught up with the client and pushed the woman behind her. At that point the elephant's rush was just an investigation and a warning—ears fanned out, trunk straight down, lots of trumpeting and dust and bluster. Jack stood her ground and raised one hand, shouting to let the animal know they were just humans—elephants have good smell and hearing but poor eyesight, and they recognize the human voice.

The elephant stopped twenty feet away, and raised its trunk to get their scent. Jack continued speaking calmly but loudly.

Then the jogger panicked. And bolted for a tree off to the side.

The elephant instantly turned and went after the woman, this time with ears back and trunk tucked, a bad sign. Jaqueline sprinted desperately and got between the woman and the elephant—which plucked Jack off the ground with his trunk and flung her aside with no real malice. The jogger, meanwhile, had made the partial cover of another tree, and the askaris managed to distract the elephant with the vehicle, until it lost interest and strode off.

Jaqueline was already quite dead when the men reached her. Her head had impacted the trunk of an acacia. One of the askaris was for pulling his sword-like *olelem* and hacking the guest to pieces right there, but the other one calmed him enough to radio the camp and get help from another Land Rover. They put Jaqueline in one and loaded the tourist, glassy-eyed with shock, into another. The lodge staff were universally bereft and enraged; the managers quickly packed up the tourist and sent her, unresisting, back to Nairobi in a Cessna. The owner of the lodge, a white Kenyan native I had met in the field and respected, shouldered the burden of calling Arizona, and the further burden of arranging to have Jaqueline's body transported home to be buried on the ranch. It broke my heart to hear that Jack's parents had made a point of insisting the elephant not be killed.

I called off training for the day, then the next, and the next. From before dawn to after twilight I did little but sit in front of my tent, starting in on the Tusker at sunrise (how much more poignant its history seemed now). Finally the Maasai themselves coaxed me into activity, which helped at least on a temporary basis. I backed off on the morning drinking but developed a new habit of sitting at the fire after dark and voicing aloud new conversations we might have had, while an empty chair and an open Tusker sat mutely across the flames.

Ten days or so later I reached a decision with which I'd been struggling mightily. That evening I climbed the hill next to my camp, where mobile service was surprisingly strong, and dialed a number the lodge owner had given me.

It would be morning in Arizona.

A baritone voice answered.

I said, "Mr. Carson, you don't know me but I was a . . . friend . . . of your daughter. I . . ."

He interrupted me. "Is this Clayton?"

I was taken aback. "Well, yes sir. But how . . ."

"She wrote to us about you every day. Sometimes twice. Why don't you come see us?"

I stood stunned, both at the revelation that Jack had shared so much of what we had talked about through all those evenings, and at the magnitude of the invitation from a man who had just lost his only daughter.

What could I do but say yes?

I finished the training in three weeks, postponed a related assignment in Samburu country in the north, drove to Nairobi and sold the Land Rover, flew to London, then on to Atlanta and then Tucson. As I walked down the stairs into the luggage area where people waited for arriving passengers, I spotted with heart-wrenching familiarity a petite blond—now mostly grey—woman standing next to a bear of a man. They somehow recognized me immediately, and Sally ran to me—*ran*—and hugged me fiercely. Jedediah followed at a more stately pace and did the same.

"Thank you for coming," Sally said, and that broke the tide of tears in the three of us and we stood in the midst of the exiting passengers, arms around each other.

I picked my duffel out of the carousel, we walked out into the cool Arizona fall evening to a crew-cab Ford F350. The drive to the ranch took an hour, and as we got out at the sprawling house I looked up to see the constellations put themselves back into their familiar northern hemisphere positions, as they did each time I returned home. As we opened the door into the main room of the ranch house, a yearling border collie that had been waiting immediately zeroed in on me and powerslid into my legs. I knelt down and got a face-full of licks. "That's Kit," said Jedediah, "And . . ." he paused long enough for a black kitten to leap from the Chesterfield sofa onto my back, "That's Pounce."

Jed and Sally put me up in a spare room. The next morning they took me up the hill to a row of gravestones, with a new one on the right. Sally's parents were there, and one of her grandparents. I had never understood interment as opposed to cremation. But standing here in what could rightly be called God's country, and seeing the continuity of history and, yes, life, that connected each tombstone, it seemed right. Just ineffably tragic that the stones skipped a generation.

We spent the next three days talking. Just talking and sitting in that marvelous room. Sally, it seemed, was not the interior decorating type and had let Jedediah have free rein as they replaced the worn-out original furniture. And Jed had gone through a good chunk of his still-healthy investments buying the rugs and art.

We talked about Jaqueline during the day, when they weren't prying out of me what parts of my life story they hadn't already read in her emails and phone calls. At night, after Sally went to bed, Jed and I stayed up and talked about our respective experiences on the front lines.

Finally, I determined to leave and head back to the house I was renting fifty miles away, in the desert on the other side of Tucson. I'd never bothered buying because I was so rarely home; it served as more of a storage unit. When I told Jed and Sally, they looked at each other as though they had some prior agreement for this moment.

Sally said, "You remember the old place we showed you up the road?"

I said sure; I'd remarked on how lovely the setting was.

She said, "How would you feel about moving in there?"

CHAPTER 12

And now it was just Jedediah and me, and Kit and Pounce.

For the first two years I lived on the ranch, I worked at fixing up the upper house and helping Jed and the hired hands, in between photo assignments, biological surveys, and several more volunteer contracts training game scouts in Kenya and Tanzania. Oso Negro Ranch only minimally qualified as a working concern any more; Jed and Sally kept enough cattle to qualify for the tax breaks and keep up the lease on the federal grazing land, and ran a cow-calf operation in years of good rains, but they were well enough off not to rely on it for their survival.

Their virtual adoption of me had had such a heartbreaking genesis that it was some time before I stopped feeling like an interloper, and could rid myself of the fear that their gesture was simply a desperate attempt to cling to the last connection with their daughter. But their intentions were obviously sincere, as was their gratitude at what Jack had written them describing feelings for me that miraculously mirrored my own. And the more time we spent working and talking together, the more I felt I'd found the family I'd never had.

Then Sally began forgetting things. It was subtle at first, then noticeable, then worrying, then frightening, especially for her. The worst phase of dementia is that period when the sufferer realizes what is happening. Within six months she had become completely unresponsive, and after that it was just a matter of waiting. Jedediah refused to have her committed to a hospice, and he and I took turns caring for her basic functions. Once she would no longer accept food it was over quickly.

I was bereft enough myself that I worried about Jed. He asked for some time alone, and that terrified me even as I respected it. But four days later he walked in the door of the upper house with two fly rods and said, "Let's catch something for dinner." While the fierce little sunfish attacked our gaudy rubber-whiskered poppers, we talked and Jedediah addressed the despair I felt, and the guilt that came with resenting that he seemed to have handled both Jaqueline's and Sally's death better than I.

"Grieving is all about yourself. Nothing wrong with that for a while—we wouldn't be human if we didn't grieve. But lots of animals grieve. What sets us apart is our ability to *remember*, to keep something of the person we're grieving alive. And to do that you have to get beyond grieving the death and remember the life instead.

"Jack's life was too short, yes, and that made it harder to accept. But the length of one's life is the worst possible way to measure the worth of it. How many people live long lives that are concerned with nothing but their own interest? Sally lived a long life that was anchored around serving others. Jack's life was shorter but no less anchored around serving others—in her case both other people, and the wildlife she loved."

"But don't you miss them?

"Of course. I miss both of them every damn minute of the day and night. But missing them means they're still there. If I stopped missing them, now that would break my heart. Missing is different than grieving."

I wasn't sure I understood, but it helped me realize that much of my own grief was, indeed, centered around myself.

Now, three years later, Jed and I had evolved a relationship that suited both of us. He had taken up rod building shortly after Sally's death, and had proven a "magician," as one of his several repeat customers put it, at making those six tapered strips of bamboo come alive. But that wasn't enough for Jed. Most rod makers were satisfied with cork for the grip; he added elegant wound rattan strips. Most rod makers bought commercial burl wood for the reel seat; Jed harvested and dried his own mesquite. And simple nickel-silver ferrules and seat hardware left his desk fully engraved with a rose-and-scroll pattern like that on a fine shotgun —that, or, whatever might suit the customer, such as the Presidential Seal carved into the butt of a rod destined for one fan. Jed had taught me to master the organic, unhurried feel of a bamboo rod on a cast—so different from the modern, snappy, carbon-fiber descendant. We took a road trip to the Upper Peninsula and he showed me the house he'd grown up in, which he still owned but rented out. We fished his boyhood waters.

Meanwhile—partly since Jed and Sally had adamantly refused to accept any rent for the upper house—I'd been both banking money from biological surveys and image sales, and volunteering with more game ranger units on anti-poaching tactics, working through the Thin Green Line Foundation, which supports rangers around the world. Life had settled into a comfortable routine.

Until a few days ago.

Jed walked back around the desk and sat down. He tipped the chair back and crossed his boots on the desk.

"So, what are you planning to do?"

I shrugged and said, "Nothing. I think that will be the end of it. I just don't see them coming after me here and riling up law enforcement in the U.S."

He said, "Hmmm. I'd listen to Magdalena; she's a smart woman. These sound like some seriously psychotic people. You keep a weapon handy up there?" He tilted his head toward the upper house.

I shrugged again. "Sure; the HK is always within reach. But if you're worried, what about you? You'd be on the front line line if someone came out here."

He nodded at the wall, where the venerable Winchester Model 94 hung on a hideous rack made from inverted deer hooves, which he'd bought at a junk shop in Bisbee. The rifle's two-piece stock was sun-bleached on the right side from decades riding in the back window of a succession of Ford pickups. The blueing was completely gone from the area on the barrel where its owner's forward grip fell naturally.

There's an old saying: *Beware the man with only one rifle —he probably knows how to use it.* Undoubtedly true in Jed's case; still, a lever-action 30-30 with seven rounds in the tube and one in the chamber was hardly a match for a (theoretical) hit squad of Mexican gangsters armed with ARs or AKs.

"You want me to bring you something with more firepower?" I asked. There were several much more tactically appropriate long arms in my gun safe.

"Not unless you can outshoot me with it."

What. Ever. I rolled my eyes. He grinned at me.

CHAPTER 13

The Yuma County Sheriff's Department divers, in addition to retrieving a well-ventilated and slightly macerated corpse, actually brought up my field bag and binoculars. Rather incredibly, they were handed back to me rather than being impounded as evidence; equally incredibly, the Swarovskis showed no fogging after their extended immersion. Awesome Austrian optics. The field bag, however, went in the trash—it was too permanently impregnated with a stew of unpleasant odors. A pity, as it would take years for a replacement to stop resembling something sported by a bearded Seattle hipster trying to look outdoorsy.

A YCSD detective named Reid and, impressively, an FBI agent named Farmer insisted on accompanying me back into the Cabeza Prieta to retrieve my camera gear and retrace my path between the seep and the mine. (The seep was now an open secret, of course, to the delight of other refuge biologists but the annoyance of Magdalena Ryan, who was pouting at me for not letting her in on it earlier.) We left Yuma at daybreak. Farmer was wearing a crisp new hiking outfit and virgin boots with—could it be, as he climbed into the sheriff department's quad-cab Ford Raptor and one trouser leg lifted—white socks? He also had one of those little backpack hydration bladders with the sucky tube. I hate using those things; they make me feel like I'm not yet weaned.

We headed east on I-8 at an even 100 miles per hour, light bar flashing, then turned south on the dirt road into the refuge east of Tacna. Reid then really put the pedal to the metal on the Raptor, and soon we were blasting along the flats at 60, 70 and worse. Miller never would have caught me if I'd had one of these things. Reid barely deigned to slow through the twisted pass into Thule Well, and slid to a sideways stop in front of the little cabin below the Boy Scouts' monument. I'm sure he wanted to beat the heat as much as possible, but he was clearly enjoying himself. Farmer looked decidedly green around the gills.

My equipment was right where I'd left it. I secured the camera gear in the pack, hoisted it to my shoulders, and led the two through each step of my route to the mine. Farmer was sweating profusely by the time we reached it, and going at it with the sucky tube. At least he was hydrating and not trying to tough it out.

The bolt on the mine's entrance gate had been repaired and was padlocked again, but Reid had the key, so I left the pack in the shade, and with flashlights we headed into the tunnel. It was interesting to see clearly what I'd only dimly or not at all been able to make out before. There were of course lots of fresh bootprints. We wound up at the lip of the shaft, three beams pointing downward at the still surface of the water. Both of the men were familiar with my account, but I went through it again. Afterward Farmer muttered under his breath, "Incredible."

Back in the shade at the entrance, gate locked behind us, I described my actions up to heading back to the Land Cruiser. I thought we'd retrace that route then, but Reid said, "We need to find that Glock." So I led the way down the entrance track.

Reid looked a question at me. I said, "It was somewhere along here. I remember hiding it under a flat rock." Which didn't narrow the possibilities much. The two of them began turning over likely suspects. I joined in for a few minutes, but then skipped ahead and worked my way down the road around a bend. When we met up Reid said, "Any luck?"

I shrugged. "Remember, I was near delirium from dehydration at that point." Reid looked annoyed, and insisted on continuing the search for another hundred yards. By then Farmer was clearly flagging in the heat, so Reid reluctantly agreed to send out a separate search team, and we hiked back to the vehicle along the same short cut I'd taken two weeks before. I noticed Farmer sucking on his now-empty bladder, and silently held out one of the pair of two-liter Nalgenes I'd brought. He hesitated, then said, "Thanks," and drank half of it.

We got back in the Raptor and drove west along the Camino del Diablo. The spot where I'd turned into the desert was now a goddam highway from the passage of numerous law enforcement vehicles (and tow trucks) that had retraced the route. Shit. There was no point in suggesting we hike it instead, so Reid followed the twisting trail through the shrubs and cactus. The spot where I'd jumped the Land Cruiser off the wash bank was now broken down into a ramp. Reid didn't stop where I'd gotten stuck, but kept right on going in the compacted tracks until we hit the boulder-choked section of the canyon and had to walk. We refilled Farmer's hydration bladder from an orange Home Depot water cooler in the back of the truck, then headed up the watercourse.

There was still a thick stain where Miller's head had impacted the rock. I'd heard his body had been taken out by helicopter. As we looked up at the cliff, Reid said, "I'm not sure I would have tried that even with someone chasing me with a gun."

Farmer was eying the surroundings nervously, and I realized why when he asked, "Um, where did you get the snake?"

I pointed. "Right over there. You want me to find it again?"

"No! I mean, that's not necessary."

"Plenty of others around," I said. "Kingsnakes, rattlesnakes. Even coral snakes—they have the same venom as a cobra, you know." Now I was just being mean. Western coral snakes average about 15 inches long and have a mouth that can barely fit around your pinky finger. They inject so little venom that those who've been persistent (i.e. stupid) enough to actually get bitten report little more than numbness and some dizziness. Ask me how I know sometime.

I decided to take pity on poor Farmer.

"No snakes out in heat like this. They'll be well hidden until it cools off after dark."

"Ah, okay." His relief was palpable. "Just curious."

It was late by the time we got back to Yuma, so I booked a room in the Holiday Inn Express, then enjoyed a jailbait blonde.

Actually that's a Jailbait Blonde, one of the offerings on tap at the Prison Hill Brewery. Yep, not only does Yuma have scuba divers in the sheriff's department, it has a brew pub, too. And the food was great. Yuma's come a long way.

The hotel room was anodyne but comfortable. The breakfast buffet the next morning was infested with germ vectors, which I believe are also known as "children," handling everything and sneezing on what they didn't handle. So I filled a take-away cup with anodyne coffee, carried my duffel and the pack out to the anodyne 4Runner, and headed east on I-8 at a considerably slower pace than I'd been driven the day before. I pulled off for a date shake in Dateland—the remodeled ice cream counter and cheesy gift shop have way less character than the old one, but the shakes are still good.

I stopped in Tucson to do some grocery shopping and check my mailbox at a commercial service, then headed west on I-10 and north on Mescal Road to the ranch. It was dark and the lower house had no lights on when I drove in, so I continued to the upper house and parked, shutting off the engine and just reveling in the welcome peace, broken only by the sound of crickets, the vehicle ticking as it cooled, and the occasional sleepy *chrrr* from a hen in the coop. In the dry air at 4,500 feet the temperature had plummeted into the low eighties, which felt like refrigeration after the furnace of the Cabeza Prieta.

I went in and lit two kerosene lamps. I have plenty of power to run the LED lights in the main room, but when I don't need to do anything like cooking I prefer the ambiance of the lanterns. I poured a Fuller's ESB into a pint glass, felt my way out to one of the porch chairs, and carried it into the yard.

Scorpius was still high in the south, its tail piercing the very center of the Milky Way. A waxing moon arced overhead.

There was a noise. A splashing sound coming from the pan of water I kept filled for wildlife. I smiled because I knew what it was, and clicked on my Surefire on low. Fixed in the beam was a great-horned owl, absurdly too big for the pan but determinedly bathing in it anyway, ducking its head and wings and flinging water in all directions. It was a nightly routine. The bird paid no attention to me or the light; once it was thoroughly soaked it lifted off so ponderously it barely cleared the shrubbery before landing in an oak tree and shaking thoroughly. Then it was off on those eerily silent wings to look for rodents.

More noise—this time fluttering from the end of the porch. Another familiar sound, that of nectar-feeding bats that frequented the hummingbird feeders at this time of year, before migrating back south into Mexico for the winter. The bats love the sugar water, but can't hover like hummingbirds, so their approach is a sort of rising swoop up to the feeder, a jive hover of a few wingbeats while their long tongue laps up food, then a swoop off to circle and do it again.

Another noise, sounding weirdly like a telephone buzzing. Wait—it *was* a telephone buzzing.

I get maybe a half dozen phone calls a month, and ignore them all. I refuse to enslave myself with the Pavlovian response most people have when their phone summons them. If it's important, the caller will leave a message and I'll call back; otherwise it's clearly not important. Another thing: For me a phone is for relaying important information, not blathering on for hours. I can't remember the last phone call I made that lasted more than three minutes. Answering a text? "Yes" or "no" works admirably. Furthermore . . .

Oh. Sorry, where was I? Right: With various law enforcement agencies still attempting to pry more details out of me, I was trying to be more responsive, so I got up and walked inside, hoping it would stop ringing before I got there. Nope.

I said hello with little enthusiasm.

"Hello . . . Mr. Porter?" a woman's voice responded. Not the businesslike tone of a detective or reporter, this voice was diffident, quiet—frightened, even?

"Yes?"

A pause, then: "Mr. Porter, this is Rachel Miller."

Okaaaay.

This was going to be interesting. I'd asked about Miller's family and had been told, "Wife, no children." I was curious how she'd found my number, which is about as unlisted as they come.

I started to say something, but she went on in a rush, obviously assuming I'd known or guessed who she was.

"I want you to know that I don't blame you for what happened. I always knew it would end like this for Jim."

It was odd to hear the bastard referred to by his first name.

She went on. "But you don't realize what you've done. These people, they're . . . look, I can't talk any more. I really think we should meet."

Meet? This was rapidly turning positively surreal.

"Mrs. Miller, I don't think . . ."

"*Please*," she said, her voice strained. "My husband was a . . . a very frightening man. And the people he worked for are worse. Look, this is going to sound crazy, but the fact that you were able to . . . to overcome him . . . was a release from prison for me." She went on again, rushing. "Please can we meet? You can name where."

I bet you're thinking I'm going to write something stupid now, like, "My curiosity got the better of my judgement."

My curiosity got the better of my judgement.

"Are you in Tucson?"

She said yes.

"Go somewhere tomorrow morning and buy a burner phone. Text me at this number."

"Okay," she said. "I can't thank you enough for this."

I rang off.

What was that I was saying about a comfortable routine?

CHAPTER 14

I left the ranch at 3:00 a.m. The moon had set, so it was pitch black. I had decided it would be stupid to be completely stupid, so I left the headlamps off and drove with the ATN goggles clipped on, so if there were any vehicles waiting for me I'd have a better chance of spotting them first. I passed no one all the way down Mescal Road, so I flipped up the goggles and lit the headlamps when I hit I-10, which was nearly empty itself at that hour on a Saturday, except for the odd semi.

I buried the pedal on the 4Runner and took it up to ninety for several miles, risking a deer strike that would have had drastic consequences. No lights behind me, so I pulled off to the side of the highway, cut my lights, and watched the rear view mirror. Nothing. Good; I began to relax a little.

I drove to Tucson International Airport, parked in the rental car lot, and paid for a Camry, the most ubiquitous car on the planet. My choices for coffee were severely limited at 5:00 a.m., but I figured Starbucks would be better than Denny's, so I stopped in and got whatever it is they call large, and loaded it up with cream and sugar. I know, you were thinking I'd make a big deal about being a black-coffee tough guy. You were wrong. I bought a doughnut, too, with frosting. There's no such thing as a sugar high; it should be thought of as a *plateau*, and maintained as such.

North on the freeway to downtown, then east on Speedway to a parking lot near Campbell Avenue to wait for a better coffee shop to open.

Not for long. At 6:27 my phone buzzed with a text. *Where are you?*

Seriously? She was not wasting time. I debated texting back, *Still in bed.*

But, not so fast, honey. I texted back, with one index finger.

What are you driving?

A Toyota Camry.

Like I said—ubiquitous.

Color? License?

Blue. Wait. Then: *JTK4001.*

Where are you?

Congress at the freeway.

Go to Speedway, east to Whole Foods and park.

Ok.

I waited. Five minutes later a blue Camry went past, with the right license number. In the driver's seat was a female silhouette with dark hair. I waited. Traffic was still light, and aside from a city bus and a landscape truck nothing was behind her for a good half mile, so I pulled out and followed at a pace that closed the distance, so I could see her turn into the grocery store lot. I turned north across the street into a Circle K and backed into a space.

Where are you? she texted.

Head west to the McDonald's west of Campbell and park there.

Ok.

Again I waited as she drove past me, then followed a half mile behind. A few more vehicles were headed west, but none looked out of place for the day and time. I watched the blue Camry pull into the McDonald's lot; none of the other cars did so or turned beyond it. I turned into the lot and pulled in beside her. We made eye contact and she got out of her car. I looked around, then got out and walked to meet her, surreptitiously checking the front and back seats of the Camry as I circled.

She was quite beautiful. Younger than her husband by a few years, I guessed. As tall as I was—not that that's saying much, but tall for a woman—maybe 125 pounds, with dark auburn hair in an inward-curving bob that touched her shoulders. She was wearing Wrangler jeans, a chambray shirt, and expensive-looking cowboy boots which looked comfortably worn-in. Rather unsettling eyes with almost black irises, and a long, aristocratic nose. Hispanic? Somewhat drawn-looking as one would expect. In fact she had a severe demeanor that seemed more permanent and which harshened her beauty—perhaps the result of the life she had implied living. She looked around nervously, and the first thing she said was, "I'm sure I wasn't followed."

I said, "I don't think you were either. Where is the phone?" She gestured at her purse, a black leather one which I recognized, surprisingly, as almost identical to one I had helped Magdalena pick out a few months before.

"And your regular phone?

"I left it at home."

Smart lady, if she was telling the truth. I wasn't taking chances.

"May I see your purse?"

She hesitated, then handed it over. I glanced inside the main compartment, which contained a cheap flip-phone, a wallet, and not a lot else, then opened the driver's door of her car and put it on the floor.

"Leave it and come with me."

She obeyed without a word, clicking the car lock on her key fob. We got in my rental, I drove out of the McDonald's lot, crossed Speedway to Bentley's Coffee Shop, and parked there. We went in, I ordered coffee for us, and chose a table from which I could keep an eye on her Camry across six lanes of traffic.

As soon as we sat she reached across the table and grabbed one of my hands in both of hers. She wore no wedding ring, but there was a clear paleness where it had been on her otherwise tan skin. Fascinating—how many widows ditch their wedding ring a week on? Was she trying to prove something to me, or had she divested herself of it out of relief?

Her eyes welled up and she said, "Look, I know this must seem crazy to you. I mean, given who I am and what you . . . what you did." She shook her head as if to clear it of conflicting and confounding emotions. "But I've been living in a nightmare for the last three years. I married what I thought was a good man, and he turned out to be a monster. At first I thought he had been trapped or blackmailed into doing what he was doing, but it became clear he *enjoyed* it. He bragged about it to me, and told me that if I left him or informed on him they would take me to Mexico and kill me there. I've had no one to turn to. *No one.* When . . . this happened, it was like I'd finally found an ally. That's why I'm here. I owed it to you to warn you in person."

I said, "Mrs. Miller . . ."

"*Please* call me Rachel? I don't want to use that name any more."

"Okay . . . Rachel . . . look, I was where I was by sheer chance. I was lucky to get out of it alive. That hardly fits the definition of an ally."

She looked at me speculatively, then shook her head. "That's not how Agent Hinwood made it sound. He was in awe of what you did. He seemed to think you'd been some sort of military operative before you were a biologist."

I changed the subject. "What do you know about the people your husband worked with, and what they were doing?"

She thought for a minute, then said, "It took me a long time to accept that something was wrong. For the first couple of years of our marriage things seemed . . . okay. Not great like they'd been when we were dating, but then," she shrugged, "how old is that story? But about a year ago he started changing in a more serious way. More secretive, more annoyed when I asked how work was going. He started traveling to Mexico with 'friends,' he said, who had interest in a hunting lodge. He had a bunch of hunting trophies when I met him, and I didn't really like them, but he hung them in his study so I didn't make an issue of it. It was just deer and antelope, things like that.

"Then one day he told me he wanted to show me something. He took me into the study, and there was a jaguar skin on the floor. I'd read about the ones that show up in the U.S. and I knew it was illegal to hunt them. When I said so he became furious and said it was a stupid law, that jaguars were vermin in Mexico. And that was the first time he threatened me if I told anyone. It was around then that he started flashing a lot of cash, even buying me things when he wasn't angry with me. But he just got worse and worse, and the threats got worse and worse. One day when I was pleading with him to give up the hunting, he laughed in a way that terrified me, and said, 'Oh, there's a lot more to it than just shooting big kitty cats.'

"That's when he started bragging that the clients of this lodge were rich doctors from the U.S., big-shot drug lords, and even Mexican government officials. He said that what I thought he'd do to me if I informed on him was nothing compared to what they'd do to me. He asked me if I knew how a jaguar would kill a human." She paused, then said, "He asked in a way that made it sound like he *did* know."

She continued, "He kept saying that if anything happened to him because of me, they would come after me. When I asked who 'they' were, he just smiled and said, 'Well, you'll find out, won't you?'"

She shuddered, shook her head so her hair fell over her face, used her middle fingers to scoop it back behind her ears—a surprisingly girlish gesture—and changed the subject. "What Agent Hinwood told me about your . . . escape . . . was incredible. The woman whose house you flew to; you found it in the dark?"

I shrugged.

She persisted, "Is she . . . "

"Just a friend," I replied, suddenly wary. I didn't want anyone but me implicated in this situation.

"I'm sorry. I don't mean to pry. I'm just trying to think of something else besides him."

A newish Land Rover Discovery pulled into the McDonald's lot and parked on the other side of the Camry. It got my full attention and I leaned sideways to watch; Rachel's eyes widened and she spun around to look as well. An overweight woman got out, then led two overweight children inside—not likely to be surveillance. I leaned back and managed to tip my empty coffee mug over the edge of the table. The heavy stoneware cracked in three pieces on the floor. Rachel turned back and said, "Oh, that scared me!" I apologized, picked up the pieces, and went to the counter to pay for it (refused), get another cup of coffee, and give myself time to think.

When I returned I asked, "What are you going to do now?"

"I don't know. I'm just trying to stay quiet and hope they don't think I'm a danger to them. I shouldn't even be here but I needed to do this."

"What about asking for protection?"

She laughed ruefully. "What actual evidence do I have that I'm in danger? I'm afraid if I ask for protection it would *really* anger them. I'll be getting a life insurance settlement, so I'm just going to stay where I am for now. But I want to move somewhere else soon. Anywhere else."

There was not much more to discuss, really. I said, "Well, I hope you can put this all behind you soon and start over. And I'm grateful to you for warning me. I promise I'll consider it seriously."

I led her outside to the rental and drove her across the street. She waited until I walked around and opened her door, and even then seemed to hesitate, as though she was reluctant to leave. Finally she got out, walked with me to the driver's side of her car, and disarmed it with the key fob. I opened the door for her, and when I turned she stepped so close I thought for a second she was going to put her arms around me. But then she stopped and held out her hand. I shook it, then she looked intently into my eyes and said, "I wish we could have met under different circumstances." She got in the car, started it, and drove off without another word.

On my way home I added it all up.

On many levels Rachel Miller was convincing as an unwitting bystander to her husband's descent into corruption and murder. Her story had the ring of truth as far as it went. It fit with what little I already knew for certain.

But, I decided, it still didn't add up to a clear and present danger to me.

As things turned out I was right, in the literal sense.

CHAPTER 15

I knew who I needed to talk with to find out the truth behind this so-called hunting lodge, its on-call "hunts," and the grisly sideshow that was apparently associated with it. First I needed to get rid of the 4Runner, which was beginning to annoy me with its multitude of nanny devices apparently designed to free the driver from any need to actually pay attention while on the road.

My master mechanic friend in New Mexico had performed a miracle. Not only was the Land Cruiser repaired, he had sourced and completely rebuilt a factory turbodiesel replacement engine, which would give me a significant increase in power and better fuel economy to boot. Several days after my meeting with Rachel Miller I turned in the 4Runner at the airport, got a one-way rental (a Camry, of course), drove the back way up eastern Arizona through Alpine and Springerville to I-40, east to Thoreau, New Mexico, then north to Farmington. Bill handed me the keys and said, deadpan, "Try to bring it back in one piece this time, 007."

I drove back to the ranch and spent a week catching up on photo and writing assignments. During that time I learned that the two courier/drivers had indeed been indicted on felony murder charges, and that the high-powered mystery lawyer had been able to arrange bail even at the steep $250,000 each the judge had set. I wondered if the pair now faced a dilemma: Stay mum and earn a lengthy prison sentence, or cooperate and tell whatever they knew, perhaps go free, and spend the rest of their days looking over their shoulders for whomever had actually posted that bail.

I packed clothes for a few days, drove the Land Cruiser to Tucson and picked up a bottle of Ron Zacapa XO rum from Plaza Liquors, then headed east on I-10, south on 90 through Sierra Vista to the Miracle Valley, then west again along the border past the Coronado National Memorial. The massive wall had been halted before it bisected this part of the line, and at the end of a nondescript two-track only used by the odd deer hunter, I pulled up to a green Powder River gate secured with nothing but a cheap combination padlock. I dialed in four numbers, swung the gate open, drove through, and relocked it. Just like that I was in Mexico, on a 10,000-acre ranch that had been in the same family since the 18th century.

At nearly 5,000 feet in elevation, the track wound through hills peppered with oak and juniper. About a quarter mile south of the border I came a round a corner and pulled up to a military-style guard-post, complete with a candy-striped boom across the dirt track. Two young Mexican men stood in front of it, alerted by the noise of the Land Cruiser, but as soon as they saw the vehicle they relaxed and smiled, waving me forward. They were dressed in olive-drab military style uniforms, sans insignia except for a brightly colored patch over the right chest pocket. Each had an HK 416 at port arms, which they slung over their shoulders as I pulled up.

The taller of the two stepped up to my window, held out his hand, and said, "*Señor Porter, como está?*"

We shook. I said, "*Bien, Tomás! Como están todos aquí?*"

"*Muy bien, gracias.*"

I shook hands with his companion leaning in the passenger window.

"*Hola, Fernando! Está Alberto en casa?*" He nodded.

"*Y como está tu nueva hija?*" He beamed, and said, "*Muy bonita, como mi esposa,*" and produced a phone with photo of mother and daughter. I whistled appreciatively.

Tomás raised the barrier, saluted, and I drove through. The track dipped into a riparian corridor shaded by cottonwood and sycamore trees, then back up into the hills. A Coues whitetail bolted across the track, sporting an impressive set of antlers for a 110-pound buck. Among the many income sources for the ranch were extremely pricey trophy hunts for the diminutive and elusive deer.

A mile farther I crested another hill and the ranch house came into view.

It was a massive, classic square-U-shaped Spanish hacienda structure—three-foot-thick adobe walls painted white, blue window and door trim, red clay tile pitched roof, shaded verandas, riotous profusion of bougainvillea hiding the patio walls. The only non-19th-century touch was a 30-foot steel tower encrusted with several types of antenna. On the west side was a large garage and an absurdly small dirt airstrip. At the near end of the strip sat a Just Aircraft SuperSTOL, a high-winged, fat-tired kit plane capable of taking off or landing in roughly the length of a tennis court.

As I pulled close to the wall that enclosed the patio, the gate opened and Alberto Maldonado stepped out and raised his hand in greeting. I had never seen him dressed less than impeccably, and today was no exception—white, mother-of-pearl-snapped western shirt, Wranglers showing a precise half-dozen washes worth of fade, and deceptively plain oxblood cowboy boots that I knew to be one of his dozen pairs from Paul Bond's when Paul was still making them himself. In his late sixties Alberto was still trim and fit, with stylish silver Stewart Granger wings in his otherwise raven hair.

Alberto could reel off the better part of a dozen middle names redolent of Spanish royalty, *conquistadores*, and Aztec princes, and had grown up on the same estancia as his great-great-great grandfather. Careful range management from the beginning—a rarity on Mexican ranches—had kept the operation solvent and intact through spasms of revolution and the socialist collectivism that had turned many large properties in the country into marginally productive *ejidos* in the 1930s. While still in his twenties, Alberto had had the inspiration to exploit the abundant wildlife on the ranch by publicizing it as a trophy-hunting destination for wealthy sportsmen. He presciently surmised that a gracious *hacienda* experience would do as much as the actual hunting to impress clients, and scandalized his parents by spending profligately remodeling the ranch house's west wing, adding a professional kitchen and a well-stocked wine cellar, and hiring a chef from Mexico City. It worked, as articles in international sporting magazines waxed eloquent over the experience, and Hollywood celebrities and Fortune 500 execs began patronizing the ranch. Somehow its reputation was only burnished after Alberto unceremoniously dumped several movie stars back across the international line when they indulged in tantrums over what they thought was a lack of suitable fawning by the staff and guides.

A chance meeting with Jedediah Carson at a ranching seminar resulted in Jed being hired to consult on stocking one of the ranch's largest cattle tanks with largemouth bass. Alberto and Jed forged an instantaneous and unbreakable friendship, and that led to consulting and research work for me as well, including an ongoing remote-camera survey of the small population of ocelots that seemed to be thriving on the property.

There was one more intriguing aspect to Alberto.

He was implacably and militantly against the drug and human smuggling that had gutted Mexico as a functioning democracy—thus the armed guard post I had passed through, which was duplicated on the southern entrance road and augmented by a roving patrol. As a result, there was zero drug trafficking across his property (the patrols also gently nudged migrants heading for the border on their own east or west to other sections of the line). Yet Alberto was immune to any kind of retribution from the drug industry because of an incident that had happened some years before.

He'd been in Agua Prieta to buy supplies when the wife and nine-year-old daughter of the number three man in the Sinaloa Cartel were caught in an ambush intended to kill them both. Alberto was climbing into his truck, and noticed the woman and girl getting into a Mercedes in front of him. He also noticed the men in the three cars across the street who were watching them. As the Mercedes began to pull into traffic, the three cars screeched across the street, blocking it in. Three men in the passenger seats jumped out with handguns. But by that time Alberto had retrieved the Colt Government Model .45 for which he had a permit wrangled for him by a government official who'd been a guest at the ranch. Alberto stepped out of the truck and calmly dropped all three assassins with three center-mass shots, somehow remaining unscathed by the panicked return fire. He then took out two of the drivers before the remaining one fled in a cloud of tire smoke.

Three weeks after the incident a courier showed up at the ranch and delivered a dozen roses and a note from the woman, a crayon-scribbled card with hearts on it from the nine-year-old, and a Zero Halliburton briefcase. Inside the briefcase was one million American dollars in crisp one-hundred-dollar notes.

Alberto dumped the flowers and note in the trash, put the card on his desk, and donated the cash to the astonished nuns at the mission in Bacadéhuachi. Yet despite what could have been taken as an insult, from then on the word was out, and the ranch and Alberto were off the map in terms of any trouble from the Sinaloa Cartel—and, by dint of their brutal hegemony in Sonora, from any others as well. All he had to watch for were the small-time marijuana movers and human traffickers who tried to operate under the radar of the big boys—those who were satisfied with a few hundred thousand dollars a year in revenue rather than a few hundred million.

I parked the Land Cruiser, got out, and received a warm hug. I handed over the bottle of Ron Zacapa, which Alberto accepted with gracious delight that belied the stratospheric value of the dozens of bottles of Bordeaux and single malt in the cellar. We walked through the patio past a large fountain that echoed musically off the walls, and stepped inside the cool, massive great room, ceilinged with rough-hewn pine planks and whole-log beams as big around as my torso, darkened with age. The walls were lined with life-sized, gilt-framed oils of various illustrious ancestors, and a modest one of Alberto's gently pretty wife, Elena, who had died of influenza when she was just 23 and they had been married for only seven months. Alberto had never really recovered, and had never remarried. He was content to spoil the children of several cousins, who considered the ranch a giant, magical playground.

Alberto raised the bottle and an eyebrow, and I nodded. He poured three fingers into a couple of glasses, and we sat in overstuffed leather chairs. Small talk occupied a few minutes—how Jed was doing, the upcoming season for Coues deer. We spoke in Spanish, as Alberto was always working to improve mine. But then he turned serious, and switched to his formal but flawless English.

"I think you are here for a very particular reason, yes?"

I nodded. "You heard?" I knew Alberto had a hundred sources of news and gossip and kept abreast of them all.

"Yes, the gist of it. But tell me your story."

That took the three fingers of rum and another two. At the end, Alberto's expression was grave.

I said, "So tell me what you know about this."

He replied, "Some. And nothing of it is good." He got up and, dear God, poured us each more rum. I was already feeling lightheaded and in serious need of something else in my stomach. And, just like that, Alberto's septuagenarian family cook, Gloria, appeared, bearing a tray of *ceviche*, *guacamole*, and just-fried tortilla chips almost too hot to handle. I jumped up and gave her a hug equal parts affection and thanks.

(Gloria had endeared herself to me forever a couple of years back when, as we chatted in the old kitchen at the opposite end of the house from the gleaming stainless version run by the Mexico City chef, I asked if she was ever jealous at being upstaged. She snorted and said in her heavily accented English, "I don' make that *pinche* juppie food.")

Gratefully, I began stuffing my face to dilute my blood alcohol below what felt like about .25.

Alberto took another sip of rum (he was still annoyingly rock-steady) and began, "I have been curious about this operation for some time, and have followed it as closely as I could. From what I have been able to gather—without making it obvious I was trying—your friends in law enforcement are on the right track about the connections between an opioid-smuggling operation, the corrupt doctors in the U.S., and these . . . incidents . . . involving jaguars. But it is not a cartel operation—at least not directly."

Now that surprised me. I wouldn't have guessed any such operation could exist independently.

Alberto continued, "The history of this seems to have begun with a rather visionary small-time dealer in the U.S. who was sophisticated enough to contract only with physicians, and prescient enough to supply them with only precise copies of prescription OxyContin— no dilution, no adulteration with fentanyl. As a result, word spread rapidly and widely, as did business, and eventually the dealer was able to forge a direct relationship with the Sinaloa cartel, who were happy to simply be handed a check every month, as it were. These drugs are now supplied to a nationwide network of the client doctors through a dedicated delivery service, with orders placed through a secure app. The doctors themselves are dealing with a very wealthy clientele with plenty of vested interest in keeping the scheme hidden. They don't operate at all in Appalachia. So it is not only intelligently run but very low-risk."

He added, smiling, "Don't forget that doctors are statistically more likely than the general public to be addicted to opioids."

I was shaking my head in admiration. "But surely they're not bringing the drugs in with powered paragliders? That would be crazy."

"Of course it would be. The drugs are coming in through the standard channels—that is, hidden in trucks driving through otherwise legal ports of entry, and straightforward shipments through standard courier companies such as FedEx, even the Postal Service. Just as with over 90 percent of all illegal drugs except marijuana."

I said, "Okay, I get the high-class drug network. Where do these canned hunts fit in? Not to mention the retribution-by-jaguar angle?"

Alberto took another sip of rum and leaned back. He hadn't touched Gloria's tray of deliciousness—just as well, as I hadn't left much.

"I'm uncertain about the exact genesis. It might have resulted from a comment or even a request by one of the doctors—or perhaps from Miller himself, since as you say he was apparently already a trophy hunter. You are aware how much some of these so-called hunters are willing to pay to kill endangered animals?"

Indeed I was. Worldwide, the illegal wildlife trade was worth ten billion dollars a year, and even though trophy hunting for protected species represented but a fraction of that, it was still a lucrative activity. A wealthy degenerate in Arizona had been convicted of paying $30,000 for a clandestine bighorn sheep hunt—not even a threatened species but one for which tags were issued yearly through a lottery system. He had simply not wanted to wait his turn. Something like an argali—a rare Asian sheep—could fetch three times that. There was no telling what the upper limit would be for a chance to shoot the third largest cat in the world (*especially*, I thought, *if you were making extra tax-free income furnishing opioids to your patients*). And, importantly, the penalties for the organizers, if the operation were to be uncovered even on the US. side, would be light slaps on the hand compared to the punishments for smuggling drugs. The bighorn sheep hunter in Arizona wasn't even jailed. The jaguar skins and skulls I had stumbled on in the mine tunnel could have easily represented millions of dollars worth of profits—and there was no way to tell how many times that tunnel had been filled and emptied.

Alberto continued, "Whatever the origin, the idea was clearly adopted with enthusiasm. I was told about a luxurious lodge built in the Sierra Madre to entertain the guests, who are flown in by helicopter. And that guest list quickly expanded beyond less-than-estimable doctors to include some government figures, as well as members of the cartel." Alberto smiled, "Presumably at different times, if only to keep up appearances for the government figures."

He paused, then said, "Most people think of Mexican cartels as a few huge criminal organizations, but there are many smaller, specialist groups. I know of one cartel in Guanajuato that specializes in the theft and black-market distribution of oil from refineries."

I nodded; that was news to me.

"Any idea where this lodge might be?"

Alberto smiled. "I thought you might ask."

He rose and motioned me to follow him. We went into his study, where an enormous iMac Pro stood, screen glowing, on a 200-year-old desk. Alberto sat and pointed to another chair, which I pulled close. He called up a Google Earth image of his ranch and the international border, then scrolled south about 120 miles, past Moctezuma and Tepache, and east over the remote forested range straddling the Sonora/Sinaloa border. He obviously knew where he was taking me, and indeed soon zoomed in on an obvious, extensive compound set into the slope of a forested hill and an adjacent cleared area. Google Earth didn't have the resolution here that it did in more populous areas, but I could still identify an enormous curved structure with an expansive deck looking out over the canyon below. Barely discernible round dots on the deck—tables?—hinted at this being a lodge or restaurant. To the east was an orderly, well-spaced arc of smaller buildings; guest cabins I presumed. Southeast was what looked to be a smaller version of the lodge. Farther downslope across an open field was a line of trees, behind which was a longer building with vehicles and what could have been a tractor or backhoe parked outside, which looked maintenance-oriented, and a nearby square of concrete emblazoned with a circle and a large H—a helipad. Farther north, behind a denser stand of trees and seemingly invisible from the lodge, was another, larger warehouse-looking structure with a loading dock.

The flyover must have taken place in fall or winter, since I could make out patches of snow on the north-facing slope, and obvious smoke streamed from chimneys in several cabins and from a big one in the main building.

It had all the appearance of an exclusive resort that would have looked right at home in the Colorado Rockies.

"It only took me about an hour of searching," Alberto said. "They are clearly not worried about concealing it."

I was impressed, but, "How can you be sure this is it?"

Alberto smiled again and said, "Look closer."

I looked. At first I couldn't see anything. Then I noticed a faint square patch of ground on the side of the long building, with lighter parallel strips within its borders. And, downhill, a much larger area, a good 50 by 100 meters, delineated ever so faintly by a narrow perimeter of cleared vegetation, and divided lengthwise into five sections. I pointed to both areas on the screen and looked a question at Alberto.

He nodded and said, "I'm willing to bet the smaller area is a dog run."

I looked again, and filled in the rest. "And the larger area is divided into enclosures for larger animals—say, 200-pound felids."

Alberto nodded again.

It made perfect sense. The easiest—in fact, the only really practical—way to hunt jaguars was to run them down with dogs trained for the task of tracking big cats. In fact, the first jaguar to be photographed alive in the U.S. was cornered accidentally in 1996 by a New Mexico rancher named Warner Glenn, who was out training dogs he occasionally used to hunt mountain lions, the much more common resident of the borderlands. Glenn had photographed the jaguar, left it alive, and become a powerful voice for conservation of the species—unlike another, virulently anti-conservation Arizona rancher, John Klump, who had chased down and shot a jaguar ten years earlier and had eventually been convicted of trying to sell its skin and that of an endangered ocelot to undercover officers. If this operation was running canned hunts for jaguars they had captured and were holding in the larger enclosures, using dogs would ensure the cats would be run down and cornered quickly after being released, saving their clients the exertion of a real hunt.

I zoomed out and looked at the area surrounding the compound with more focus. The entrance road came in from the west. Some distance down it was an obvious set of corrals and stables. About three kilometers farther on was a pair of buildings straddling the road, with clear sections of wall extending 50 meters or so to either side. It was obviously a guardhouse built to turn back anyone clueless enough to stumble upon the place. Yet the brevity of the wall showed they really weren't all that worried about security—not surprising given the reputation the place must have had in the region. From the guardhouse the road extended west another kilometer or so, where it teed into a larger dirt road that wound northwest through the hills and eventually reached Highway 17 north of Tepache. Panning around the compound showed the vast surrounding wilderness, yet the place was probably no more than four hour's drive from Alberto's ranch.

Zooming out still farther resulted in a stab of recognition. The lodge was no more than twenty miles as a raven flies from the edge of a 55,000-acre reserve co-managed by the Mexican conservation organization *Naturalia* and the U.S.-based Northern Jaguar Project—a reserve formed with the specific intent of preserving safe habitat for jaguars. I'd worked with the managers and biologists of the reserve over the years, as they slowly but diligently won the cooperation of adjacent cattle ranches to halt the historically accepted practice of shooting jaguars on sight. The NJP had initiated a program that involved placing trail cameras on the ranches and paying the owners for every photo of a jaguar—plus a lesser amount for each ocelot, mountain lion, or bobcat—even repeat photos of the same animal. Thus ranchers could make more money from live jaguars than from the odd cow they lost to them.

Now I couldn't help but wonder: Were the operators of the lodge exploiting the reserve as their own convenient "reserve" from which to source animals? It would be easy to conceal baited leg snares, even crate traps, within the eighty-six square miles of wilderness encompassed by the project.

The pieces of the puzzle were falling into place—or rather being fitted by Alberto. But there were still things to clear up. I wrote down the latitude and longitude of the compound in my field notebook, then we went back to the great room and sat.

"All right. I get all this. But it makes no sense to me, given the sophistication of the rest of this operation, that Miller would have been flying skins and skulls over the border rather than just bundling them in with a few cases of pills."

Alberto said, "I considered that, and I believe I understand the strategy: He wanted to avoid the detection dogs stationed at all border crossings these days. They're trained to react to the scent of many different types of contraband, and hiding or disguising the odor of hides and skulls is much more difficult than doing the same for manufactured pills. Also, however lucrative it may be, this on-call hunt operation is still a sideshow, or at most a subsidiary, of the main business. I suspect the principals would have been unwilling to take a chance, however slight, of having the whole scheme blown.

"Also, think about Miller's position in the Border Patrol. Given his familiarity with the area and his ability to, if not control, at least be aware of the location and status of other agents and other traffic, the parawing flights represented an extremely low-risk method of importing those 'trophies' to distribute to some exceedingly private trophy rooms. It was sheer bad luck for him that you happened to be in the area."

He smiled rather wickedly and said, "Really quite bad luck."

I said, "Okay. So, what about these ugly retribution killings using the animals?"

To my surprise Alberto shrugged, as though this were but a detail. "I suspect one of their cartel allies or clients simply had a flash of inspiration. Why not get extra use out of the jaguars before they are hunted down? It would not take more than a few days, perhaps a week, of starvation before they would overcome their natural fear of humans and attack someone thrown in with them, no?"

I agreed.

"To the cartel it was merely a fresh psychological trick to keep potential competitors or informants terrorized. Beheading people and hanging them from bridges was getting a bit passé. And it probably represented a lucrative bonus for the lodge."

As gruesome as this seemed, in the context of cartel violence it made perfect sense. For that matter, the lodge could probably charge more for their "hunts" if they told clients the cat they were after was a "man-eater." I was curious, though, how they got the jaguar off its victim once it had attacked and started feeding. That would have to be a lively scene.

"Right," I said, as I scooped up the last gram of Gloria's *guacamole* with the last centimeter-square fragment of chip, "So, last but not least. Who is running this operation?"

Alberto sighed. "*That* is a mystery I have not been able to penetrate. It certainly wasn't Miller. But whoever it is is flying very, very low under the radar, or instilling enough fear that no one is willing to risk leaking a name. Probably both. I'm not even certain the drug operation and lodge are run by the same people. I got zero information about the former, and only a few odd rumors about the latter."

He paused, as if debating whether to tell me more, then said, "In fact, the most persuasive rumor I heard is that it is run by Che Guevara."

I blurted a laugh. "Seriously?"

Alberto smiled, shrugged, and said, "I heard the same rumor from three different people."

I just shook my head.

Alberto turned serious, leaned toward me and placed a hand on my knee, and said, "I don't think you should dismiss the potential for retribution from this incident. Vengeance is all some of these people have for entertainment. They have been jaded by all other kinds of amusement, no matter how violent, and striking back against those who have—what is your American term, 'dissed' them?—can become an obsession all out of proportion to the actual offense or monetary loss."

Coming from Alberto, this hit home more than it had from Magdalena or even Jed, even though I still didn't think trouble was likely to follow me north of the border.

I said, "I promise I won't dismiss it. I'll stay alert for anything out of the ordinary."

Alberto said, "Along those lines, what do you make of your meeting with Miller's widow?"

I said, "That was decidedly out of the ordinary. But there's no doubt her husband was a very bad dude, so on the surface at least her story has the ring of truth. One can only expect whoever was above him would be at least as bad. So her concern for me would be justified in her eyes, although that doesn't seem like enough reason to take the risk she did if she's right."

Alberto *hmmmed* noncommittally, and said, "And these two drivers. One would think they were simply hired underlings unlikely to know much, if anything, about the operation. If so, why go to the trouble of arranging very expensive bail?"

"Perhaps they do know more than they should, and getting them out was a way to keep them quiet?"

Alberto looked thoughtful, then said, "Or a way to get them out in the open and away from protective custody."

He thought some more, then said, "I will be curious to see what happens to them."

We found out the next morning.

CHAPTER 16

Gloria fixed us a dinner of venison *posole* accompanied by the flour tortillas she made daily, stretched to the impossible, translucent thinness that no one not born to it can ever achieve. Afterwards Alberto and I sat outside on the patio, leaned back in chairs watching for meteors and satellites, sipping a smoky *bacanora* he got from a friend in Nacozari. Alberto also lit some absurdly expensive Cuban cigar; I was grateful for the whisper of air movement that kept the scent of the vile thing away from me. I often wonder what an advanced alien civilization would make of our habit of sucking in the smoke from burning dried vegetation. And paying money for it.

The temperature by 10:00 pm was perfect for sleeping with the patio door to my bedroom open, so I could listen to the rising liquid trill of buff-collared nightjars, and the deep hoots of great-horned owls, before drifting off.

Alberto kept pretty normal rancher's hours, which is to say that at 4:30 the next morning he woke me up with a cup of coffee. Had he simply stayed up all night or was he really that perfectly turned out already? I showered, dressed, and joined him in the kitchen with Gloria, who was cooking an enormous pan of eggs and *chorizo*. With more tortillas. I didn't know how Alberto stayed as slim as I was.

After sunrise I packed the truck to leave, and out of duty checked my phone, which at the ranch was incapable of a voice signal but still managed to receive texts.

There were twelve of them.

I hadn't received twelve texts in the last five years.

Ten of them were from Reid, the Yuma County Sheriff's detective, each one saying simply, "Call me!" The other two were from Magdalena, saying, "Call detective Reid."

I told Alberto, who led me to his office, where he had a Motorola 9505 satellite telephone hard-wired to an external antenna. I dialed and put it on speaker.

Reid answered immediately. I identified myself, and he said, "Porter! Where the fuck are you?" When I said, "Mexico," there was a moment of stunned silence palpable enough to bounce off the satellite and ooze through the speaker, as if he couldn't believe I'd be that stupid.

Then, "Well you might not want to stay in Mexico. The two guys who were out on bail are dead. Bound, gagged, shot through the back of the head. And there's more. Rachel Miller has disappeared."

At this my lingering ambivalence about her leaped into full-fledged suspicion.

"Was she behind it?" I asked.

Reid said, "Probably not. Her house was torn up, and there was blood everywhere."

"Hers?"

"Yep. Plenty of DNA in the house. We ran it through our RapidHIT system and it matched. But that's not all. We found a good-sized piece of an ear."

"Hers, too." A statement this time.

"Yes. She must have put up quite a fight."

Whatever my doubts—even one's own blood can be planted, after all—cutting off a piece of one's anatomy would be going pretty far to deflect suspicion. Particularly if you were a beautiful woman. It was hard to escape the conclusion that Rachel Miller's fear had been real, and that the people behind her husband's activities were determined not to leave anyone around who might provide information about either the hunts or the drug operation, however peripherally.

If they had somehow found out about her contact with me, the remark Alberto had made about retribution could be a factor in her disappearance as well. And, as much as I wanted to doubt it, I could no longer afford to discount the possibility that it could extend to me. Or people I knew.

"When did this happen?"

"Yesterday morning. I've been trying to reach you since."

That meant I was twenty-four hours behind.

As I put down the phone, Alberto turned and left the room. He came back a minute later carrying his Colt 1911, which he extended toward me butt first. He knew I wouldn't have crossed the border with a firearm.

I took it without a word. He handed me two spare loaded magazines as well.

In thirty minutes I was back at the fence. I decided to head to Tucson, and so took the dirt road leading up to Highway 83 past Parker Canyon Lake. Then through

Sonoita toward I-10. As I approached the on-ramp I checked my phone again.

There was another text from Reid.

This time it said, "Call me. It's about Magdalena Ryan."

CHAPTER 17

Magdalena Ryan rinsed out her coffee cup and set it in the dish drainer. She picked up her purse, keys, and sunglasses, walked outside and locked the front door, then climbed into her Nissan pickup. The morning was already warm, so she hit the AC switch as soon as she started the engine. She pulled out of the drive and down the dirt road toward State Highway 86—then remembered that she'd intended to bring her personal laptop to work that day. She pulled to the verge, did a U-turn and returned to the house, reversed course again and left the truck idling in front of the yard.

She reached above a porch beam and retrieved the spare house key, opened the front door and closed it behind her—an instinctive anti-snake precaution—while she retrieved the laptop. She walked back through the living room and was reaching for the knob when both front windows and the small glass security pane in the door exploded inward, and a blast wave deafened her and pummeled the breath from her lungs.

She staggered backwards as blood from a dozen glass cuts streamed down her face and began spattering her uniform and the floor. Her ears were overwhelmed with a metallic ringing that drowned out any other sounds. She couldn't see out of her left eye, and it seared with pain.

The room spun. She barely managed to get to a sitting position as everything went black.

CHAPTER 18

"Detective Reid."

I identified myself. He explained what had happened. Mag was in ICU, stable, but they still had to remove a piece of glass from her left eye. They were not yet sure if it would permanently affect her vision. I was damning myself, furiously and at length, but asked, "Why the delay in the explosion?"

Reid said, "Simple. More and more new cars are coming with remote-start buttons, so owners can get the heat or AC working before they take off. So the current strategy for car bombs is to build in a delay. It also makes for a better show if the car goes up in traffic."

I told Reid I'd be there as soon as possible and rang off.

The on-ramp was ahead of me. Tucson and the hospital lay to the west.

I turned east.

I no longer had any doubt that whoever was behind this was not just interested in silencing potential witnesses. This was also about retribution. As I flogged the poor Land Cruiser at speeds never intended for it, I wondered if Rachel Miller could have been . . . persuaded . . . to reveal what we talked about. She had brought up Magdalena and my background. What else had she learned from talking with Hinwood?

I dialed Jed's number. No answer.

The Land Cruiser's diesel howled at its redline.

I didn't have to stop to unlock the Oso Negro Ranch gate because it was hanging open, its chain dangling from a cut link. I went through it nearly sideways, and took the next half-mile at a desperate speed.

I slid the Land Cruiser to a stop in front of the main house. The cloud of dust raised by my approach rolled away on the light breeze.

The front door stood open, the interior inscrutable blackness beyond. Both front windows were dark squares rimmed with daggers of silver. Bullet pockmarks scarred the stucco and the adobe beneath it. Instinctively I noted the linear patterns of holes betraying the magazine-emptying full-auto bursts of a shooter or shooters with zero fire discipline.

Kit was in the front yard, lying on his side, unmoving, a dark bloodstain spread beneath him. I exited the vehicle at speed, Colt leveled at the house, staying on the move. Tactically I was completely exposed, but there was nothing I could do about it. There was more blood in the yard—much more. Three large stains, two with drag marks and blood trails and other footprints that ended back near where I'd parked. Another bloodstain there, adjacent to a set of tire prints that spun out in reverse, then spun out again back down the road. Dozens of shell casings littered the ground, a mixture of 5.56 and 7.62x39. AR and AK. Three empty magazines as well.

"*Jed!*" I bellowed at the house, although I knew there'd be no response.

I went straight for the door, up the porch and through the opening, completely sun-blind. I sidestepped to get my silhouette out of the light, and swept the room with the Colt's muzzle. Slowly my pupils dilated.

Jed lay on his back under a shattered window, Winchester leaning against his chest, coagulated blood caking the Two Grey Hills rug beneath him. Too much blood.

I ignored him. There was every chance his assailants had left someone behind to ambush me, and wherever Jed was now he would never forgive me if I took one in the back of the head while crying over his body.

Clearing a building bears no relation to what you see in the movies, with the hero peering through doorways one pie slice at a time. Clearing is tactically the most stupid thing you can do, since your enemy has had time to situate himself behind cover you know not where, almost completely hidden, while you have to expose yourself at every opening. Unless it's a hostage situation it's better to just stand back and toss in grenades. But I had no grenades, so I simply went through the house at full speed, hoping a first shot at me would miss and betray the location of the shooter.

Kitchen—clear. Bathroom—clear. Sally's sewing room—clear. Jaqueline's room and closet—clear.

I went through the main bedroom door and swept from the left side with the muzzle of the pistol.

Wrong direction. A flash of movement to my right. I spun and crouched, tucking the weapon tight so it couldn't be grabbed and swiveling it toward the oncoming blur, finger taking up the last gram on the trigger.

Pounce landed on my shoulders, clinging there and *mrowling* plaintively.

Bloody hell. "*Jesus*, buddy," I said. I stroked his head while I cleared the master bath one-handed.

I went back down the hallway to the living room, Pounce sticking to me like a barbed limpet. I looked through the back window into the patio. Nothing there. I went back to the front door to check the yard one more time, really just putting off what I needed to do next.

There was a voice. Not from the yard, but the floor. Garbled and fluid-filled, but a recognizable baritone nonetheless.

"Whenever you're finished . . . makin' out with the damn cat . . . do you think you could . . . call me a medic?"

CHAPTER 19

Jed didn't fit in a University Medical Center bed any better than he had on a Nha Trang cot.

In a supremely ironic twist of fate, he had taken an identical 7.62mm slug from an essentially identical weapon as that a half century before, in precisely the same location on the opposite side of his chest. The puckered old scar and the raw new hole couldn't have been more accurately placed by laser. He had lost more blood than I probably had in me, but the helo crew had stabilized him and now, a week later, he was recovering astonishingly well for a man of his age, or any age. I had briefly filled him in on Magdalena, Rachel Miller, and the two executed couriers, and was trying to find out as much as possible about the men who had attacked him.

"Rookies," he said dismissively.

"Yeah, well those 'rookies' almost did you in," I said. I was furious with myself, and covering it up with bluster.

"My fault. I moved out of cover at the wrong time. They were just spraying bullets and got lucky." He had about enough breath for a sentence at a time, but filled me in on what had happened.

He'd been in the living room working on a fly rod, and heard a vehicle approach. A glance through the window revealed a black Range Rover with gold trim.

"I knew that couldn't be you," he said, smiling.

He saw multiple silhouettes through the windshield, and moved to lift the Winchester off its rack as doors opened and five men exited, all armed with assault rifles, and jogged toward the house. Kit had barked when the vehicle pulled up; now Jed heard him launch off the porch in response to an obvious threat. There was a burst of fire.

Jed turned the handle on the front door and pulled it inward, but ducked back into the darkness with the rifle shouldered until he could see the men standing with weapons leveled at the opening. He put a bullet through the head of the driver and ducked sideways as a fusillade of automatic fire tore at the house, shattering both windows. Jed moved to one, ducked around it and dropped a second man.

"He must have been in charge, because the firing stopped and there was a lot of yelling and when I looked again the others were dragging the two back toward the vehicle. I don't think they were expecting concentrated resistance."

Jed stepped into the window opening to fire again and at that instant the man who wasn't helping drag corpses let loose a wild burst at the house, one round of which caught Jed.

"It kinda knocked the wind out of me," (*kinda, Jed?*) "and my right arm went on strike and dropped the rifle. So I picked it with my left hand and put a round out the window just to get their heads down again, then did that sort of John Wayne one-handed flip with the lever to chamber another round. Always wanted to try that!"

He grinned about it like he'd been doing trick shooting at a county fair.

"I aimed one-handed and managed to put a round through the neck of the guy who got me."

"Nice shooting, Jed," I said.

He made a face. "Not really—I was aiming for his chest."

I rolled my eyes.

"The room was starting to spin by then and I was getting weaker. I braced the muzzle on the floor and managed to chamber another round that way, then more or less blindly fired another shot through the window to make them think I was still dangerous. The next thing I heard was the engine starting and they left." He paused and smiled again, then said, "Three dead guys must have made a real mess of that Range Rover's leather."

I said: "Hard to tell now. It was torched and abandoned south of Benson. Three decidedly deceased skeletons inside."

Jed nodded with satisfaction. "Anyway, I suspected you'd turn up soon, so I thought the best thing I could do would be to lie still and keep my pulse down." Then he turned serious.

"Kit?"

I said, "I buried him behind the family gravestones."

Jed sighed, and said, "That was the right place. He was a good dog."

I said, "I'm sorry, Jed."

He knew I was apologizing not just for Kit, but for him, for the holes in his adobe and windows and the blood on his Two Grey Hills. For being dismissive and not listening to him and Magdalena—the very people who'd paid the price for my arrogance.

And Jed knew better than to pander to me, to hand me the millennial "it's not your fault" bullshit. He knew I was smart enough to learn from mistakes and not make the same one twice.

He simply nodded, then said, "How is Magdalena?"

That situation had stung more than Jed's. He had at least been able to give back better than he got. Only pure luck had saved Magdalena.

"She's doing well. The procedure to remove the glass from her eye was successful, and they say her vision should be fine. She'll have a few facial scars." The surgeon had actually told me they'd be "unnoticeable," but I was willing to bet Mag would notice them.

Jed knew me well enough to detect the rage under my banter, and to know I was already figuring out what, exactly, to do about it.

With an obvious lack of conviction, he said, "They might decide that injuring us both was enough."

I said, "I don't plan to let it be their decision to make."

He sighed, but nodded. He knew as well as I that not only would two near misses not satisfy them, there was now the added affront of three more dead troops and a Range Rover on which they probably would not be collecting insurance. Instead of teaching me a lesson they'd missed one mark and then had their asses handed to them by an octogenarian, and that wasn't going to sit well with the guys who fed people to jaguars for fun.

But what to do about it?

There was really only one possibility.

Something decisive.

Engaging in any sort of retaliation less than total would only ensure an endless, escalating cycle of violence, with those dear to me as the likely targets again. I had to make sure *everyone* involved in the operation at the lodge was either physically incapable of re-engagement or thoroughly convinced it was not in their best interests.

I was leaning strongly toward "physically incapable."

One of the (several) things I've never understood about the American justice system is its absurdly lenient treatment toward those convicted of attempted—in other words, failed—murder. Killing a human really isn't hard, after all, and there are a hundred ways to accomplish it. Whether you succeed or not you are clearly murderous, so why the massive discrepancy? Attempted murderers are just murderers too incompetent to get the job done. If I were a judge with discretion, I'd sentence the convicted perp to the same term he would have received for a successful murder, then tack on an extra 20 for being a moron.

Sorry, where was I? My point is that, as far as I was concerned, anyone even peripherally involved with an operation that profited from opioid addiction, engaged in on-call hunts for a threatened species, subjected its enemies to a terrifying death by mauling, and, most importantly, tried to murder my friends out of revenge for something I did, richly deserved any fate I might mete out. There would be no such thing as collateral damage here; it was all direct engagement.

I just needed to figure out how to accomplish it alone.

CHAPTER 20

Back at the ranch, I headed up to my place first. The chickens would need me.

Indeed: While the automatic waterer had kept their pan full and the birds hydrated, the feed hopper was empty and they started flapping and cackling as soon as I pulled up. I opened the hutch door and they all boiled out, following me to the back porch and the bulk feed bin with much complaining, except for one that spotted a big grasshopper and took off after it, nabbing and swallowing the hapless thing in one gulp. Normally I would have just spread some scratch around and left the chickens to eat that and then do their normal foraging for arthropods and forbs, but I needed to get back to the main ranch house, so I filled the hopper in the hutch and herded them all back in for the moment. Out front of the house a female whitetail deer and her yearling were standing in the shade of an oak and staring resentfully at the dry water trough there; they continued staring resentfully at me as I filled it, and moved in to suck noisily before I was back on the porch. The wilted geraniums and gardenias there seemed to be looking at me resentfully as well. I watered them, refilled the hummingbird/bat feeders, then headed back down.

A woman who owned an adjacent ranch had taken control of repairs. The windows had already been replaced, and the stucco patched inside and out, although it was not yet been painted. The bloodstained Two Gray Hills rug was in Tucson at a specialist being carefully cleaned. Incredibly, the fusillade of incoming rounds had missed every piece of art on the walls, although the first burst that had come through the open door had obliterated most of the crystal on the bar cart. The Winchester was gone, no doubt taken as evidence by the sheriff's detectives who had investigated the scene. I made a mental note to make damn sure Jed got it back. Civilian weapons tend to disappear into a bureaucratic black hole, even after a justified shooting.

I made some coffee, then sat down in front of Jed's big iMac screen and called up the compound on Google Earth to study it in greater detail than I had at Alberto's.

The place seemed to be divided into three distinct areas. First was the lodge and its cabins—six of them. Situated for dramatic views, it was separated by trees from the kennel and the big fenced cat enclosures, and completely isolated both visually and geographically from the big warehouse to the north, which had its own access road that headed northwest for a short distance and then curved southwest to connect to the entrance road just short of the guardhouse.

I examined the warehouse carefully. Even at the relatively low resolution I could discern a loading dock on the north side, and black tire marks on the concrete from large trucks backing into it. There was a semi trailer parked in one space. On the roof were four small rectangles that I took to be air conditioning units, and adjacent to the west wall was a smaller building and an associated horizontal cylindrical tank—a big one. I guessed this to be a substantial generator for the power supply, probably propane to keep down the noise for the lodge guests.

It had all the marks of a well-organized, climate-controlled manufacturing and distribution center.

Perfect: That would be the first building to go.

I looked back at the lodge. It was fan shaped, with a deck that followed the outside curve. Behind it was a rectangular building I took to be staff quarters, and behind that was appeared to be a maintenance area that included a large array of photovoltaic panels. Below and in front of it was a pool and two tennis courts, and off to the south I recognized the pattern of a trap and skeet range and a long, straight rifle range. I was pretty sure there would be a sporting clays course tucked along the edge of the forest as well.

Above the lodge and staff quarters, behind the solar panels, was a large rectangular building in its own clearing, with a parking lot on the south side containing what appeared to be four identical pickup trucks. I was betting they would prove to be Toyota Hiluxes, and that this was a barracks for the guards and other security personnel. Set farther up the slope was a smaller version of the lodge building, with its own deck presumably looking down on the lodge and the rest of the compound. A driveway ended in what appeared to be at least a four-car garage.

That, I was pretty sure, would be where I found whomever was in charge of the whole operation.

Next, my infil route. Since I'd decided to hit the warehouse first, I had to come in from that direction. Panning back to the main road from Tepache, I followed it north kilometer by kilometer. I found a well-used track that penetrated some way east, but it was too close. A couple of clicks north of it was another that looked much more promising. It was far enough away to hide noise, looked largely overgrown for most of its length, and ended just about two kilometers north of the warehouse and over a rise in the mountains. I knew that sound from a point source (such as a vehicle engine) normally diminishes according to an inverse square law; roughly six decibels for every doubling of distance. Given a typical engine signature of about 65 dB at fifteen meters, plus the added attenuation of the vegetation, my approach should be completely inaudible from anywhere in the compound. About a kilometer and a half south of the track was a slope that appeared to have a nearly unobstructed view of the buildings from about 600 meters. That would serve as my FOP, or forward observation point.

Not for the last time, I wished I could call on one of the six-man British Pathfinder units I'd trained in tracking over the years. These were guys who drove or parachuted into enemy-controlled territory *ahead* of the SAS, using either weaponed-up Land Rover "Pinkies" or blacked out BT80 parachutes. In fact, given the stupendous glide ratio of the BT80s, it's likely a squad of Pathfinders could have done a HAHO (high-altitude, high-opening) jump from a C130 Hercules north of the international border, using HAPLSS (high-altitude parachute life support system) gear, and landed within striking distance of the compound. With a half dozen of them at my side we'd make short work of those fu . . .

Ah. Sorry. Went off on a bit of a fantasy there.

Destroying the buildings presented no challenge. I could do that with materials at hand, or even arrange delayed destruction with a few perfectly innocent-looking odds and ends I could bring with me.

Weaponry to take care of the human element presented a more difficult problem.

It was smart to assume the people behind the operation had access to informants at every border crossing between San Diego and Brownsville. I was also willing to bet they had numerous paid lackeys among the *Federales*. If I crossed the border at any official entry in my own vehicle I could expect to be stopped and have the mother of all searches conducted on the vehicle and my person. I'd seen cars and trucks stripped to the chassis, tires sliced open, upholstery ripped apart, dashboard completely disassembled. If they found so much as a brochure for a Mattel water pistol I could expect to be tossed in a Mexican prison and never see daylight again—and if they didn't find anything there was an excellent chance they'd plant something. It would be the easiest way to get rid of me without getting their own hands dirty.

But going weaponless was not an option either. I would be facing a well-armed enemy, undoubtedly equipped with fully-automatic weapons, and although I had no evidence I had to expect they would be expecting me.

The solution was threefold: I needed to cross the border clandestinely, and I knew where I could do that. I needed a vehicle that wasn't already associated with me in case I subsequently passed a roving *Federale*—a non-U.S.-market Land Cruiser pickup of which there were maybe 50 in North America would be hilariously conspicuous. Finally, whatever firearm I took would have to be concealed well enough defeat a cursory check just in case I was stopped by a random state or municipal police officer.

I printed several color views of the lodge complex, from the "lowest" clear view that allowed me to count trees to one that took in everything from the border south, then headed up to my own place.

Two minutes on Craigslist turned up a dozen beat-up 20-year-old 4x4 Ford F150 pickups that would be ideal low-profile Mexico infiltration vehicles. I called on one with tan paint in a half-dozen shades, half of which looked to be rattle-can—but which sounded to be the best-maintained—and arranged to look at it the next day. Then I opened the gun safe and started perusing the contents. I was pretty sure what I wanted already but it was important to carefully consider each option before rejecting it.

First out was my Steyr SSG 69. The most advanced sniper rifle on the planet when introduced in 1969, with a revolutionary synthetic stock, cold-hammer-forged barrel, and detachable 5- or 10-round magazine, the bolt-action SSG had long since been superceded by more advanced and higher-caliber rifles. But the ergonomics of the Steyr were perfect for me, and I'd had the advantage when I bought it of being able to test-fire a dozen examples. With double set triggers and hand-loaded ammunition the one I kept would print a single ragged five-shot hole at 200 meters—which meant that, mounted with a Nightforce Optics 5.5-22x56 NSX scope and a Harris bipod, it was capable of confident head shots out to at least 500 meters, and center-mass hits at double that.

If my plan had been to assassinate a single boss honcho at the compound and flee, the Steyr would have been a perfect choice. But I had no idea who the head honcho was—that is, beyond the "Che" rumor—and it was virtually certain that I'd be facing numerous hostiles at close range given my plans to wreck the place.

The next three rifles were all variations on the standard 5.56mm AR platform, and certainly had the firepower for engaging multiple targets, given 20- or 30-round magazines. But I simply didn't see any way I could easily conceal such a weapon in a pickup in a way that would foil a search.

I found what I was looking for on a back shelf. It was a pistol—a Glock, the same make as the one Jim Miller had shot me with but a different model, the 31 in .357 Sig. The Glock was inherently a stupendously reliable weapon—I'd never had a single malfunction in the four or five I'd owned—and the bottlenecked .357 cartridge theoretically enhanced feeding reliability even more. Plus it produced the same terminal ballistics as a .357 Magnum revolver cartridge in a semi-auto pistol that took a 15-round magazine. (I also had some 31-round mags but didn't quite trust them 100 percent for combat.)

I'd then added a few things to this example—mostly for fun I'd thought at the time. First, I'd paid the federal $200 tax to legally turn it into a short-barreled rifle (SBR) by adding a collapsible and removable TAC Limited shoulder stock, which lent steadiness that easily tripled the pistol's accurate range. I'd also installed a compact Trijicon RMR 6.5 MOA red dot sight in the Glock's Modular Optics System slide cut. Along with a slightly extended (and threaded) Zev Technologies barrel, the combination meant I could make reliable torso shots out to a full 100 meters. Finally, another $200 tax enabled me to add an Advanced Armament Illusion 9 suppressor.

There's been a stunning amount of garbage written (and filmed) regarding suppressors. In truth they are indeed "suppressors" and not "silencers." Forget the action novel I once threw across the room that described a "silenced" .41 Magnum revolver shot as sounding like "a gum bubble popping." First off, you can't suppress a standard revolver because the cylinder/barrel gap emits both gas and noise in extremely obvious fashion. This author also claimed the silencer actually "enhanced" the velocity of the bullet, which is sheer idiocy. A suppressor only works really effectively on sub-sonic ammunition; that is, bullets traveling under 1,125 feet per second. Finally, forget that gum bubble popping. Clap your hands together and you'll get a close approximation of what a really good suppressor does to the report of a pistol round.

The problem with suppressing the Glock 31 is that nominal velocity for a 125-grain .357 Sig round is in the neighborhood of 1,350 feet per second—far above the sonic threshold. However, I had a case of 147-grain loads for the pistol that clocked just under the limit. The Advanced Armament suppressor would knock a full 33 decibels off the report of that round. What that meant was that if I shot someone in one of the buildings it would be unlikely that a person outside would hear a thing—unless my target shot back, of course.

I wasn't planning to give any of them that chance.

CHAPTER 21

The next morning I drove to my place on the other side of Tucson, which I'd sub-leased to a friend, parked the Land Cruiser, and caught a ride to the address from the Craigslist ad. The truck was perfect: a '93 F150 4x4 that was several shades of tan, with several varieties of dents, and mismatched but okay tires on rusty chrome rims. The engine had obviously not been degreased to look good for a sale, but started immediately and ran perfectly. The cab even had the de rigueur *sarape* seat covers. Sold.

I stopped at an auto accessory store and bought a large plastic fake hood scoop and a couple of smaller fake air scoops, a bondo kit, and some tan flat Krylon that looked to be a close match to at least one of the colors already on the truck. I drove to an outdoor store and bought a roll of Gorilla tape and a case of tablet fire starters, then to a big-box store where I picked up two six-packs of generic soda in half-liter plastic bottles, some dark brown Rit dye, an Oral-B electric toothbrush, and their entire stock of incense sticks of various brands and scents.

Back at the ranch I assembled—or rather disassembled—the weaponry. I wrapped the shoulder stock in chamois and taped it up. Same with the suppressor. The Glock stayed assembled, with the Trijicon sight in place along with a magazine full of sub-sonic hollow-points, and I wrapped it carefully and tightly to ensure the sight didn't lose its zero.

I did a trial fit of the hood scoop and marked its inside perimeter. I taped the pistol and shoulder stock to the hood inside the line. The ATN PS15-4 night-vision goggles were next, sealed in a Ziplock and wrapped in more chamois. I folded up the headset for the ATNs, and managed to cram everything under the scoop, which I glued to the hood, after trimming it to fit neatly. I wanted it to look permanent, so I mixed up some of the bondo and smeared it around the perimeter, then, when it had set, sanded it all smooth and sprayed the whole thing with the Krylon. Some work with a kitchen scrubber soon had it looking like it had been in place for years.

Next I loaded two more 15-round magazines with sub-sonic ammunition, and a further three with normal, 125-grain high-velocity hollowpoints. I figured that if my adventure lasted long enough for me to go through 45 suppressed rounds the game would probably be up and the suppressor would be redundant, and I'd rather exploit the superior tissue disruption of the faster bullets. I wrapped the five magazines, and repeated the earlier procedure with one of the smaller scoops, positioning it on the passenger side of the roof as a jive cabin air scoop or who knows what—I've noticed scant attention to even pretend practicality in the people who are into these sorts of add-ons. A friend once described a truck similarly festooned as looking "like the owner walked through Pep Boys carrying a shit magnet."

The first rule of gunfighting is, "Have a gun." The second rule is, "Have another." So I wrapped up my regular backup pistol, a Springfield Armory Hellcat, with an RMSc holo sight and a full 11-round magazine inserted plus one in the chamber, and stashed it in its ankle holster under the second plastic scoop, along with the suppressor for the Glock.

My reason for the weird concealment plan was simple: The natural inclination of people who conduct vehicle searches—at least peremptory ones—is to look *inside* the cabin, *inside* the engine compartment, and *under* the vehicle. It doesn't instinctively cross their minds that contraband would be hidden in plain sight. Yet it would take me less than a minute with a knife to retrieve the equipment and assemble the Glock and its fittings.

Everything else I was to carry in the truck or on me had to be outwardly innocent. That meant, obviously, that my NIJ Level III Kevlar vest with the ceramic-plate pockets would have to stay home. However, I had a Safeguard NIJ Level II concealable vest just 5mm thick that would at least provide protection from pistol rounds and fit under a shirt. Only a close body search would reveal it.

I also had to skip the ESS tactical vest and its numerous quick-retrieve magazine pockets, but I dug out a photographer's vest someone had given me ages ago, of the type worn by approximately half the male tourists in Africa (I've never seen one on a woman). It would accommodate the magazines easily; they just wouldn't be as instantly accessible. There would be several in each pocket so I'd have to be careful not to dump out the ones I wasn't after while scrambling for a reload. The vest also had two water-bottle pockets and room for some odds and ends I'd need. Unfortunately it was a too-light khaki color, so I gave it a double soak in the Rit dye to turn it as dark brown as possible. It's always better to be too dark than too light.

No Vibram-soled Limmer boots for this job. I needed quiet footwear. Stalking footwear. So I got out the *veldtschoen* I'd bought in Zimbabwe a few years back, which I normally used for hunting. *Veldtschoen* (literally, "field shoe") were developed by Dutch voortrekkers forging their way north from the Cape Colony in the nineteenth century—simple, ankle-height shoes made from whatever leather one could shoot, the upper stitched to a flexible sole. For years you could buy them made to your own feet in Zimbabwe and Zambia for 30 bucks a pair, but then the twee British safari outfitters got wind of them and now they go in their full-color catalogs for $300. I still got mine from the source whenever I was there.

Clothing sorted, I tested the burn time of the various incense sticks I'd bought. I had to do it inside because I didn't want air movement affecting the rate, and as a result the place wound up reeking like Buddha's boudoir. One brand of sandalwood sticks lasted the longest and were remarkably consistent at 28 minutes. Two of them joined with twist ties gave a reliable fifty minutes. I had three dozen of them left after testing, which would be plenty.

There was the problem of how to transport them without breaking. I solved this with a minor flash of inspiration by getting out my set of snake-handling tubes. These are clear plastic tubes of differing sizes, with which one can handle a venomous snake safely by encouraging it to crawl into the tube, whereupon one grasps the body of the snake at the end of the tube. The snake can't turn around so its head is effectively isolated, freeing one to examine it or do rude things to the other end, such as determining sex or implanting tracking chips. I cut off one of the smaller tubes and taped the incense sticks inside, along with some twist ties.

My cover for the way down—thin as it was—would be as a photographer, which had the advantage of being totally legit at any other time than the present. The vest would help. I also filled an old Domke bag that I'd never liked with a selection of outdated camera gear—I was working on the assumption that I might have to abandon the truck, and I didn't want to risk the good stuff. Sadly I had no cheap old tents or sleeping bags to risk—I *loathe* cheap tents and sleeping bags—so I reluctantly stuffed a Hilleberg tent and Western Mountaineering bag in a duffel, along with an ancient but perfectly functioning SVEA 123 stove, and sufficient accessories to make it all look like a legitimate camping kit. A tiny AA flashlight with a red filter. In my toilet kit I made sure to include the Oral-B electric toothbrush, and in a small tool box with sundry pliers and wrenches I stashed a funnel, a cordless Dremel tool with a cutoff wheel and a miniature sanding drum, and a tiny flat strip of steel about five inches long and an eighth of an inch wide.

I'd need something more powerful than even the 15-power Swarovski binoculars for surveillance, so I packed an STX 95 spotting scope from the same company. Its massive objective lens and 20-60-power eyepiece would give me some real reach. With it went a Gitzo carbon-fiber tripod and a fluid head. The scope would be normal, unsuspicious equipment for an outdoor photographer-cum-birdwatcher. I loaded the combination into an old rucksack.

What else? The fire starter cubes, a couple tubes of Super Glue gel. A note pad and pen. I emptied two boxes of large wooden matches, scraped the heads off all of them into a powder, and filled a small Nalgene bottle with it. I had two NATO jerry cans of gasoline for the backup generator that charged the house batteries when long winter storms cut solar gain. One of them was only about three-quarters full, so I poured in three quarts of motor oil, and strapped the can in the bed of the Ford. Five gallons of water in another strapped-down container. I had a stash of MREs but did not want anything in the truck that looked even vaguely military, so I packed some pouched pasta meals and a dozen Tanka Bars. Coffee fixings, of course. I tossed in a first-aid kit that looked normal at a glance— band-aids, Ibuprofen, etc.—but which also included four packs of QuickClot hemostatic dressing in case I needed to plug any significant leaks about my person. I wasn't planning to share them. I put all the small stuff in a black day pack.

Finally I dumped out the dozen bottles of soda, rinsed and let them dry, then put the caps back on and stashed them behind the seat of the truck in a garbage bag.

I was ready to go.

CHAPTER 22

A medical transport brought Jed home the next morning. For the first time, he moved somewhat like an 80-year-old getting up the steps to the house, which sent a renewed stab of guilt and rage through me. I got him settled and promised I'd stick around for a couple of days—a promise I had no intention of keeping. I knew time was of the essence in preventing any sort of follow-up attacks. He thanked me in a way that made it clear he didn't believe a word I said. That evening I called Mary Prude, the next-door-ranch owner, gave her a story about a last-minute job, and asked if she'd mind checking in on Jed. Far from being annoyed at me for abandoning him, she jumped at the opportunity. I was beginning to think she had designs on my elderly but still-dashing friend, despite being 25 years his junior.

I filled all the feeders and water troughs, watered the plants, and set the alarm for 2:00 am. No, I don't have an internal clock like Jack Reacher, but I do sleep well once I've decided on a course of action, so the next thing I remembered was the annoying tinkling of the iPhone. I knew I'd burn a lot of calories over the next few days, so after coffee I scrambled five eggs, cooked a quarter pound each of bacon and sausage, toasted four slices of bread and slathered them with a quarter pound of butter, and downed everything along with a pint of apple juice. It was still pitch dark when I left and coasted past the main house, and just past sunrise when I unlocked the gate at the border and drove onto Alberto's ranch.

Now I faced a dilemma. I did not want Alberto to know what I was doing or where I was going until it was all finished, one way or another. I'd decided the best strategy would be to entreat the guards to keep my passage secret, in the knowledge that the verbal caning they'd eventually get would be preferable to the guilt they'd feel if Alberto insisted on accompanying me and something happened to him.

Since I was in a strange and thus suspicious-looking truck, as I rounded the corner before the first guardhouse and a figure appeared, waiting for me, I flashed the headlamps in the sequence I'd been told to use if I came down at night: one short, two long, one short. The figure—which proved to be Tomás, visibly relaxed. As I pulled up and he saw who it was he burst out laughing.

"*Qué es esto?*" he asked incredulously, waving a hand at the truck. I turned off the engine, got out, and explained the situation and what I wanted him to do. He of course knew the background, and didn't hesitate to assure me he'd stay quiet—but then shocked me by insisting that *he* come with me instead.

"I can shoot!" he said in English, brandishing the HK 416.

Knowing Tomás's military background, I was sure he wasn't boasting, and it was tempting. Touched and humbled, I nevertheless gently but firmly refused. We waited until Fernando showed up, then Tomás led me on side roads well clear of the main house, down to the southern gate to the ranch. He got out of his truck and had a few words with the guards there, who opened the gate and saluted smartly as I drove out.

And then I was on my own. I put on the old straw cowboy hat I'd brought along. I hadn't shaved in two days to give my face some shadow. Between that and the truck there was a good chance anyone driving toward me would dismiss me as local, and not even bother to look at the back of the truck and possibly notice the Arizona plate.

I continued on the dirt road south to Mexico 2, drove through Cananea with my pulse slightly elevated, then headed south on 89, just past Bacoachi where I took a two-lane road east across the hills to Highway 17, then south. Through Nacozari with no drama, then into Cumpas—where, parked off my side of the road and pointed south, was a local police car, the driver outside and leaning against it, watching traffic go past.

There was no way to turn off before I passed him without looking suspicious, so I maintained speed and drove by. He turned to watch, and thus couldn't have missed the Arizona plates. The question was, was he an informant tasked with looking for me, or an innocent local cop just watching the world go by? There was only one way to find out: I turned around, drove back past him, turned around again, pulled in behind his patrol car, slung a camera over my shoulder, and got out.

I walked to where he stood watching my approach. I detected no recognition, no sign of alarm, just normal curiosity as to why a gringo had turned around to talk with him. I affected bad high-school Spanish and asked if I was on the right road to Bacadéhuachi.

"*Voy a* . . . how do you say? *Photographia? El mision? Este direccion?*" And I pointed south.

"*Si, si,*" he said, "*Necessita el Carretera Catorce, en Moctezuma. A la izquierda.*"

"*Ah. Gracias!*" I replied. I got back in the truck and pulled past him. He waved, I waved. I drove around the bend to the south, parked, and walked back to where I could see him—still leaning against his car and watching the world go by.

My pulse settled back down.

I drove on, straight through Moctezuma. Just north of Tepache I turned east on a dirt road that cut through an agricultural area and then curved southeast. About twenty-five kilometers later I splashed through the shallow waters of the Rio Bavispe, then began gaining elevation as the road curved tightly from mesquite scrub and stands of tree morning glories up into oak woodland. By now I was less worried about cops and *Federales* than patrols from the lodge. But the road seemed completely deserted. I was now well south of several locations where I'd recorded jaguars on trail cameras. I wondered if any of them were the animals now being starved in enclosures and awaiting a short and fatal flight from a pack of dogs and men with rifles.

It was past noon when I reached the waypoint I'd marked that indicated my infil track leading east. I discovered why it looked so little-used when I came upon a completely washed-out section of a switchback that hadn't shown in the sat images. I would have had little trouble negotiating it in the Land Cruiser with its front and rear locking differentials and all-terrain tires (not to mention the winch), but the Ford on its mismatched street tires blanched at the obstacle. I was glad for the shovel I'd thrown in the bed. After ten minutes of digging and piling rocks I tackled the slope, but even in four-wheel-drive the right front and left rear tires unloaded and simply spun. I backed off and added a bit of momentum, and this time when the tires spun I gently pressed the brake pedal while continuing to give it gas. This tricked the open differentials into transferring more power to the tires with grip, and the truck bounced up and over the washout.

The track clung to the north side of a slope, well up into shaded Chihuahan and Apache pine forest now, and noticeably cooler than the valley. Mexican jays squawked in annoyance as I passed, and at a bend a Coues whitetail doe and two yearling fawns bounded across the path. At one point an odor wrinkled my nostrils: the unmistakable smell of death, of a decomposing body or bodies. I stopped the truck and got out to see if an animal had died or been killed along the road, but found nothing. A hundred meters farther on the smell diminished and finally disappeared.

And then, with thudding anticlimax, I reached the GPS point that put me directly north of the lodge and its compound. I sat shaking my head, bemused in the knowledge that I could just as well have piled the bed with an assortment of AR15s, thrown in a Gustaf M3 with some anti-personnel flechette rounds, and maybe a .50 BMG for good measure. Ah, well. At least I'd made it safely with the weaponry I had.

I found a spot where I could drive the truck into undergrowth far enough off the track that it would be difficult to spot. I collected some ferns and branches and covered most of the top. With the forest canopy overhead I was pretty sure it would escape notice of anyone not doing a comprehensive aerial search.

Time to prepare the equipment.

First I cut off the fake scoops, assembled the Glock and its shoulder stock, and screwed on the suppressor. I put the magazines loaded with the subsonic rounds in the lower right pocket of the photographer's vest, and the full-velocity magazines in the lower left pocket. I mounted the ATN goggles on their headset, and dropped a spare battery in an upper pocket of the vest, along with the red-filtered mini flashlight, which I would need only if for some reason the ATNs failed, as they had their own infra-red illuminator for use in pitch-black conditions.

I unloaded the jerry can, found the funnel, and carefully filled the 12 soda bottles about halfway with gasoline/oil mixture, screwing the tops back on tightly. I taped them together in pairs, which would prevent them rolling when laid on their sides. I loaded the bottles in the bottom of the day pack, along with the tube of incense sticks, the fire starter cubes, and the bottle of match head scrapings. Two Bic lighters and a box of strike-anywhere matches went in the top pocket. Whenever possible I like to rely on redundant technology.

Next I got out the Oral-B electric toothbrush and the Dremel. Using the cutting wheel, I carefully removed the plastic neck of the toothbrush, which left about two inches of the round metal activating shaft exposed. I switched to the little sanding drum on the Dremel, and carefully flattened the shaft. When I pressed the button the shaft vibrated healthily. Then I used my Leatherman to modify the little flat piece of steel I'd brought, bending one end 90 degrees. Done. I put that stuff in the top pocket of the pack as well, along with the tube of Superglue gel.

The sun was now well down in the west. My plan was to spend the latter part of the night and early morning observing the activity at the compound—I was only interested in what went on between about 0200 and

0700. So I fired up the SVEA, made coffee and filled a thermos, and heated water for a bagged pasta meal. After eating I stretched out in the back of the truck just as dusk fell, set an alarm for midnight, and was asleep within seconds.

A just-past-full moon cast shadows through the trees when I woke up and got ready. I left the truck and headed south. Even though this was a recce I carried the full load of kit so I could isolate any rattles or other issues with the pack and vest—as well as to be prepared on the scant chance the truck was discovered in my absence. The assembled Glock hung across my chest on a sling; the Springfield Armory 9mm rode in an ankle holster. The scope and tripod were in the pack, each in a neoprene sleeve to eliminate clanking. I'd even donned the Safeguard Level II vest. With the ATNs turning moonlight to daylight I had a reasonable chance of spotting any of the local Madrean black-tailed rattlesnakes that might be cruising in search of an ambush point. I'd found the subspecies to be a little more irritable than their northerly cousins, and the last thing I needed was a surprise injection of venom in an ankle.

In a cautious hour I'd crested the last ridge between the truck and the compound, and, searching for a likely FOP, made my way through the trees to a dense copse of oaks about 500 meters from the nearest building, the warehouse. There was plenty of dead leaf litter here to burrow into, and a fallen trunk under which was a gap through which I could see over the entire collection of structures.

I was glad I was not on a CTR, or Close Target Recce, with the British Pathfinder lads. Their observation missions usually involved getting in and out leaving no trace of their presence, and when I say "no trace," I mean no trace. They use cling film and bottles as toilets and carry everything out to avoid leaving any smell a tracker dog could detect, or any DNA that could be identified by hostile forces.

I was on an entirely different sort of mission. I'd be more likely to leave an offering on the front porch of that stylish manager's cabin.

There were only a few scattered lamps glowing on the main buildings and in one of the guest cabins, so I popped on the three-power auxiliary lenses for the ATNs and took a look around. They wouldn't help much from 500 meters away, but I'd be able to see any personnel moving about, especially guards.

And there was nothing. Not the slightest evidence of movement. No standing guards, no one making regular rounds. The place slept, those in residence clearly certain that no one would be insane enough to mess with it. Fine with me.

I settled in to wait for dawn, watching Scorpius arc toward the western horizon over the compound. It was tempting to just head down there right now and lay waste to the place, but I really needed the next few hours of information. Ideally I would have maintained the CTR for at least a week to establish firm schedules and routines, but I didn't have that kind of time. I was too worried that the people behind all this would discover I was no longer home.

The eastern horizon lightened slowly, and soon I was able to remove the night-vision goggles and set up the scope, which poked up just above the log on its tripod. At 20X the buildings leaped closer. I pulled the field notebook and pen out of the vest so I could start recording details and events.

The first thing I noticed was a tower topped with a Yagi directional cellular antenna behind the lodge, which hadn't shown up on the satellite view. There was probably a sat-phone antenna on it as well, and I made a note to cut both cables as soon as I could. I also confirmed that the warehouse, unlike the other buildings, was a steel structure—which could complicate my plans depending on what the internal fittings were made of.

Twenty minutes before sunrise lights came on in the lodge; whoever it was must have entered through the back door from the building I'd assumed was staff quarters, which I couldn't see directly. Soon a vent stack near the back of the building was exhaling a light cloud of smoke. Behind it, back in the trees, more smoke drifted slowly my way—almost certainly from what I had also assumed was the barracks building. Several minutes later a wisp of aroma reached me—faint, but unmistakable.

Bacon.

Why'd it have to be bacon?

My stomach urged me to go down there and shoot may way into the kitchen right then. Instead I unwrapped a Tanka Bar—normally tasty in its combination of dried bison meat and cranberries, but at the moment a pale substitute.

Lights came on inside the guest cabin. Ten minutes later a woman dressed in white restaurant garb came out of the front door of the lodge carrying a tray of something. Bumping up the power on the scope's eyepiece revealed it to be a carafe and coffee cup and accoutrements. She headed up a trail toward the cabin, climbed the steps, and knocked on the door. A barely perceived figure let her in; shortly she emerged and went back into the lodge.

At the same instant as the first rays of the sun flamed the summit of a high peak to the south a deep orange, I heard a noise.

It was a hollow, penetrating, spectral grunting that seemed to fill the valley: *UNH, UNH, UNH, UNH, UNH*. A pause, then again: *UNH, UNH, UNH, UNH, UNH*.

I was intimately familiar with the sound, and it chilled my blood.

It was the call of a male jaguar.

But that wasn't what chilled my blood. This call was . . . different.

Normally a male jaguar's call echoes with the unmistakable assurance of an apex predator, the arrogance of a creature at the top of the food chain. Everywhere I'd heard it—Mexico, Nicaragua, Brazil, Peru—it had that arrogance.

Not this one. This call echoed with—there was no other way to interpret it—despair. Each syllable was more drawn out than the last, and instead of rising to a challenging crescendo, the sequence tapered off weakly and ended, as though the mere effort of the call had exhausted the will of the animal making it.

I had no need to determine which direction the call was coming from to know that it was a caged animal.

I expected the kenneled dogs to light off at the sound, but, oddly, after one or two tentative barks they went silent, as if they were as affected by the call's anguish as I was.

Or perhaps they were just used to it.

Sunlight eased its way into the valley. Presently the guest cabin door opened again, and a white male stepped out. He was dressed in a hilariously cliché outfit that would have looked at home on Stewart Granger in

King Solomon's Mines: khaki trousers, a safari jacket with epaulettes and bellows pockets, with what looked like an Akubra slouch hat on top. I was willing to bet the boots were Russells. He walked down to the lodge, stepped inside for a moment, then sat at an outside table. Soon the same white-clad woman—young and Latina, I could tell now in better light—came out with another tray of coffee, then stood while the man spoke to her. Shortly after she went back inside, the smoke from the kitchen vent intensified. I prepared myself for another onslaught of tantalizing aromas.

Daktari-man lingered over breakfast (more bacon, pancakes, and some savory concoction of potatoes, peppers, and onions, according to my nose) for a good half hour. While he ate I cranked up the spotting scope to zoom in on him. I expected a wealthy physician who spent a lot of time pursuing scarce game animals in far-flung mountain ranges to look fit, but this fellow was rather pudgy. He took off his hat to reveal dark hair showing gray at the sides. The scope picked out some significant hunk of a stainless-steel *über* watch on his plump left wrist, but even at 60X I couldn't identify it. Probably nothing so prosaic as a Rolex. I guessed Breitling or some other mechanical masterpiece with enough extra functions to effectively obscure the big and little hands.

Just as he wiped his mouth and sat back in his chair, another man emerged from the lodge. This one was was Latino, dressed in smartly creased khaki and wearing a long-billed cap, like any one of a hundred safari guides I'd known in Africa. I could easily make out a rather hilarious Emiliano Zapata mustache. The seated man stood up and the two shook hands, then both sat down again. The woman brought another carafe of coffee for the newcomer, and the men sat talking for fifteen minutes. Then both went inside.

I waited, cranking back on the magnification and scanning the compound for any other signs of movement. Presently the two men appeared below and on the other side of the lodge, walking toward the rifle range. Each carried a bag and a long gun. At this distance—they were almost 900 meters away from me now—it was difficult to identify the weapons, but one was definitely a scoped bolt-action, and I swore the other was a double. Now that would be a stylish way to shoot down a trapped, starved, and treed jaguar.

As the men reached the shooting tables under a tin ramada, a man on a side-by-side ATV appeared from the direction of the barracks, rode over to the pair at the ramada and parked, then walked downrange to what I estimated was the fifty-meter line. He was short but built like a tank, and sported military-shaved sides and a flat-top.

The range looked like a simplified version of the classic U.S. military setup, with a deep concrete pit in front of each target where a minder could safely stand, raise and lower the target, and indicate hits with a large colored circle on a stick. Flat-top disappeared into the pit, and shortly thereafter a square target board rose up with what, if I squinted, looked to be a standard NRA GA-53 sighting target in the center.

The two at the table donned hearing protection. Zapata broke open one rifle—ah, definitely a double—dropped in two cartridges, closed it, and handed it to Daktari, who, I noticed, handled it gingerly. Odd if he was an experienced hunter, I thought. After fumbling with it for a few seconds, he shouldered the weapon and aimed it downrange. I waited, then waited some more— *too long, pal*—then the rifle's muzzle jumped upward and the man took an involuntary step backward. I started counting seconds—one, two—at three a percussive boom hit me. Definitely a proper stopping cartridge, whatever it was. I looked toward the target. After a moment a red dot on a stick came up and waved side to side.

A clean miss—of the entire board.

Daktari re-shouldered the rifle. I waited. *Too long, pa . . .* The muzzle jumped again, he stepped backward again. This time a gout of dirt erupted in front of the ditch that sheltered Flat-top. I smiled, imagining his and Zapata's identical thought bubbles. Again the red dot waved side to side.

Zapata took back the double and directed Daktari to sit at the bench. He loaded the magazine rifle with a single round, and arranged a sandbag rest for the shooter. This time there was a distinct lag as he offered some instruction. With the rifle on a rest, Daktari peered through the scope and fired. I watched the rifle recoil—barely a twitch compared to the double—and when the report reached me it was obviously a much milder caliber: a .270, a .243 even. This time the red dot came up and hovered over a spot about six inches below and to the right of the center of the target. Three more shots resulted in a random pattern perhaps ten inches in diameter.

For a fifty-meter group it was laughable, but in terms of shooting a large cat out of a tree at ten feet it would do, and Zapata clapped Daktari on the back as if he'd just rung up a perfect score at Camp Perry.

By now I had had a revelation. This "sideline" canned hunt operation wasn't a *reward* for physicians who were heroes at prescribing opioids and who also were already obsessed trophy hunters. It was its own income stream—they were taking *back* money from the hunting contingent, and clearly recruiting newbies who might never have held a rifle in their lives, but who could be seduced with visions of Hemingway-esque derring-do.

What could it be worth? I knew of a ranch in Texas that raised white elk—merely an odd color morph of the abundant wild North American animal—and charged clients $40,000 to shoot one. Legally. On a fenced property. A hunter in Montana had paid $450,000 for a bighorn sheep tag offered through a special auction. (That was legal as well; additionally, those very substantial funds went towards conservation. But still, 450 grand to kill a glorified goat?) What might someone with a looser moral compass—say, a very wealthy physician who had no qualms about addicting his patients—be willing to pay to shoot a "man-eating" jaguar while being fêted at a picturesque lodge in the Sierra Madre, and then to have the skin delivered to his home in the U.S. to be displayed in some suitably discrete trophy room? Not to mention the client who apparently had an estate large enough to house and hide a live example.

It was brilliant, and virtually without risk—unless (*cough cough*) one of the principals ran into an ornery biologist in the Arizona desert.

It was clear Daktari had been seduced by the pitch, and furthermore upon being offered a choice of weapon had at first elected to go with a legendary double rifle of the type carried by Bror von Blixen, Finch Hatton, and other white hunters mythologized in print and film. But he'd quickly learned what the 5,000 foot-pounds of energy produced by a cigar-sized British express cartridge means to the person pulling the trigger. Zapata no doubt suspected what would happen, thus the smaller-caliber bolt-action substitute.

I was chuckling, but I knew what all this was leading up to—a short, brutal chase of the jaguar I'd heard earlier, and an execution when the dogs finally brought him to bay. The critical question was, when would it happen? I hoped fervently it wasn't today—I had no intention of allowing that animal to be killed, but stopping it would completely destroy the plans I had for the rest of the compound.

Fortunately, Flat-top reappeared from the dugout, and the three climbed into the machine and headed east around the edge of the clearing to where I'd suspected there was a sporting clays course. I lost sight of them, but about fifteen minutes later heard the mild crack of a shotgun, followed sporadically by more. Apparently a leisurely day of recreation was in the offing for the lone guest.

Just then something else caught my attention: the sound of an engine, a big diesel, from the west, behind the warehouse. I swung the scope that way and looked at the Sinn—0820. A couple of minutes later a dusty but newish yellow bus, a 16-seat Bluebird on an F350 chassis, drove in from the isolated road dedicated to the warehouse, pulled into the loading bay area, and stopped. The doors opened, the driver got out. He was dressed in the same khaki as Safari-man, minus the billed cap but plus a holstered pistol. He stood by as 13 women filed off, dressed in blue scrub outfits except for one in dark trousers and a white lab coat. Lab-coat lady climbed a set of steps leading to a door next to the roll-up loading doors, unlocked it, and stepped inside. The women followed in one by one, and each stopped to do something just beyond. I cranked up the scope again, and could see they were donning blue shoe covers. The operation inside was being kept institutionally clean.

The driver climbed back inside the bus and disappeared back down the warehouse access road. A few minutes later another side-by-side—or the same one?—driven by a different, longer-haired khaki-clad male, appeared from behind the lodge and made its way up a narrow track across the valley to the kennel building, which was mostly obscured from my view here. A cacophony of excited barking indicated feeding time. Soon the man appeared again, walking this time, and headed back to the lodge. Then there was only the crack of the shotgun to break the silence. The generator to the warehouse—and its AC units—were surely running; they had to be superbly muffled.

A soporific two hours passed, during which my only amusement came from the occasional gangs of Mexican jays squawking their way through the forest. One group gathered in my tree, spent some time noisily discussing what this odd motionless human could be doing, then squawked away. A Madrean alligator lizard foraged its way through the detritus, clambering over both my arms on its way through. Some time later I felt a light pressure on my legs, which slowly progressed up my back and then off to the side. I turned my head slowly to see an iridescent red, cream, and black mountain king snake winding slowly in the same direction the lizard—a possible meal—had taken.

The shooting had stopped, and shortly after noon Daktari appeared on the lodge deck again and seated himself at an umbrella-shaded table. The waitress brought out a tray of drinks and a menu, and another leisurely meal followed, albeit without the tantalizing drifting aromas—the breeze had reversed itself. I was left to fantasies. Hamburger and fries? Steak? *Stop it.*

What to do after a relaxing lunch? Of course: a relaxing swim. Daktari headed down to a dressing room at poolside, emerged in a pair of baggy trunks, and did a couple of desultory laps before floating on his back and stroking lazily in circles. The woman from the lodge came down with a tray holding some frosty-looking drink, and after he paddled over and took it they chatted for a moment. When she went back to the lodge, another, shorter woman came out, went up to Daktari's cabin, and emerged with a change of clothes, which she carried down to the poolside dressing room and exchanged for the set he had removed. Nice service. At last he got out and redressed (ordinary trousers and a blue shirt this time), then walked back up the path to his cabin and disappeared inside.

For the rest of the afternoon, the only thing of note that occurred was at 1626, when a black late-model Range Rover—why are they always black?—appeared on the road that came down from the manager's cabin and headed west toward the gate at a good clip, spiraling dust behind it. I could see multiple silhouettes inside but nothing definitive beyond that. The speed indicated some sort of urgency, but nothing else followed to raise my concern.

At 1730 the bus reappeared at the warehouse and honked; the women filed out and climbed back in, and the bus left. Just like a typical shift at a typical factory.

Sunset backlit a crimson filigree in the low clouds on the western horizon. A constellation of tiny LED lights came on in the trees and awnings over the lodge deck; another line low to the ground lit the pathway to the cabins. The two women I'd seen earlier came out of the lodge, moved one of the tables to the center of the deck and covered it with a white tablecloth, set it for two, then rolled out a very stylish-looking bar cart.

So far, aside from the armed bus driver escorting the women to and from the warehouse—and that plaintive felid cry from the pens—the scene outwardly gave nothing away as ground zero of a criminal enterprise and two near-fatal attacks on my friends. It could have been any number of high-end sporting lodges anywhere in the world.

Several things were going to shatter that facade.

Daktari strolled down from his cabin, and Zapata joined him on the deck. The two enjoyed a meal comprising enough courses that I lost count (all served by a new bloke in a toque), while the taller of the two women kept them supplied with, first, shaken cocktails, then wine. Zapata told a lot of stories that involved much pantomiming of guns and obvious charging animals—even jumping to his feet a couple of times to add drama—then sat looking attentive as Daktari recounted his own adventures on . . . what? National Geographic cruises? Porsche Experience track days? Hard to tell.

Once the dishes were cleared, the bar lady went inside and returned a few minutes later carrying a tray loaded with mugs and a carafe—coffee, I assumed. But as she stepped toward the table she tripped over something, and the tray went flying, to land at the feet of Daktari and spew its contents. He leaped to his feet, sending his chair over backward. The poor woman froze, but instead of looking at Daktari her head snapped around to look at Zapata, who rose to his feet, placed a hand reassuringly on her shoulder, and motioned her inside while he picked up the tray and carafe. The woman rushed back out with a cloth and wiped down Daktari's trousers while he stood with his hands on his hips. Then she scurried back inside, while Zapata escorted his guest back up the path to the cabin.

When Zapata returned, the woman was on her knees wiping up the last of the spilled liquid. She rose to her feet and faced him as he mounted the steps to the deck. He stepped toward her and delivered an open-handed blow to the side of her head that sent her reeling back into the deck's rail. He then stood in front of her, poking his finger into her chest while she leaned against the rail, hands braced on it, head bowed. Finally he'd had enough and walked off the south end, but not before sweeping the tray and carafe off the table again.

I planned to remember that mustache.

I'd seen enough—rather, I'd seen all I could afford to see time-wise. I needed some sleep before H hour. I packed up the scope and ATNs and backed carefully out of the copse of trees, keeping it between me and the compound until I reached denser forest, as the partial moon was still overhead. Then I headed north toward the truck.

About halfway back I caught the smell again.

Definitely something dead. A soft breeze was now blowing from the west, the direction I'd come from when I noticed the odor driving in. I turned in that direction. I had the ATNs on my head but switched off and flipped up, as the moon provided plenty of illumination in this pollution-free sky. The smell got stronger as I walked west, until it seemed clear I was headed toward more than just one dead thing.

I came to a level clearing. On the far side was an open structure with a tin roof, under which sat a Case backhoe. The clearing was probably sixty meters long and thirty wide. In front of me was a gentle mound of earth perhaps three meters square and shin high, healthily vegetated with grass and shrubs. Beyond it was another, not as grown over. Smaller shrubs. I was following a succession of excavations, from oldest filled-in to, as I could see ahead, one that was not yet covered. There was a large pile of earth next to excavation number three.

The smell was powerful enough to shorten my breath as I approached the open pit. Steps before I reached the lip, two shapes leaped out of it.

If I hadn't been expecting it I likely would have let loose with the Glock. The shapes were small, barely larger than house cats, with bushy tails—gray foxes.

Normally omnivores, gray foxes will on occasion feed on carrion. As the animals bolted for the trees and I stood at the edge of the pit, I could see there were plenty of opportunities here to feed on carrion. The excavation was heaped with dozens of bones, several partial skeletons, and fresher, still-decomposing corpses of animals. I flipped down the ATNs to get a better look at the more or less intact individuals that hadn't been pulled apart by foxes and, no doubt, coyotes and vultures. There were quadrupeds, both canid and felid. The canids were domestic dogs, and the felids were jaguars. The dog corpses were intact, a couple with leather collars still on the neck. The jaguars had all been skinned before being thrown in—and their skulls were missing.

It was easy to see that even canned jaguar hunts were rough on dogs. Several of the canid skeletons displayed crushed front legs and mandibles; the skull of one was essentially in splinters. A rancher I knew whose dogs had accidentally cornered a jaguar in southern New Mexico while he was training them to hunt mountain lions had told me how readily the jaguar had turned on the dogs to fight, in complete contrast to mountain lions, which simply head for the nearest tree.

I looked back at the two covered pits. How many dead jaguars did they represent? The "sporting" part of this operation already could have had catastrophic consequences for the northern Mexico population. Who knew how far south in the country they were trapping animals? Fury welled in me as I tried to piece together how many animals were in this pit, using pelvic bones to tally the loss.

The pile was such a chaos of butchery that it was a moment before I realized there was also a human in there.

The bottom of the pit was about four feet below me. I edged around to a spot that was free of bones, and dropped in.

She—for it was unquestionably a woman, despite the middle stages of decomposition and the work of the scavengers—had been tossed on top of the pile like just another one of the dogs. She was unclothed. I stepped around so I could examine her head, which had been gnawed beyond any hope of recognition or confirmation of any parts that might have been cut off before death. There was, however, enough hair left to see that it was dark, and just about shoulder length. I could also make out the bullet hole just above the foramen magnum.

Once again I fought the impulse to simply walk back down the hill and start shooting. For my plan to achieve complete success I had to stick resolutely to a more deliberate approach. I stood looking down at the woman for a minute, thinking, then said out loud, "I promise." Then I climbed out of the hole and headed back to the truck.

CHAPTER 23

At 0200 I was headed south again with four hours solid sleep under me. I'd left the scope and tripod in the truck, and instead loaded the large rucksack with the 12 filled soda bottles, the incense sticks, and the rest of the fire-making kit. Two of the QuickClot dressings were also in a vest pocket. By 0230 I was overlooking the compound, which appeared exactly as it had the night before. I backed up and skirted the open slope that had been my overview the day before, keeping to the trees on the west side. Even though by this time I was convinced that the lax approach to security I'd seen meant there was little risk of it, I was watching carefully for any remote cameras that might have been positioned on the outskirts of the place.

The trees ended just shy of the parking lot and loading dock of the warehouse. I stopped there, sat, and watched for ten minutes for any movement. I checked the Glock to ensure there was a round in the chamber, the magazine was seated firmly, and the Trijicon sight was functioning. Then I walked across the lot and mounted the steps to the door through which the workers had come and gone. It was a substantial steel unit but, as I expected, I found it locked with a basic five-pin Kwikset deadbolt, the kind Home Depot sells for $19.99. These people were not worried that any petty thief would be insane enough to break in here.

I took off the rucksack, opened the top pocket, and pulled out my hacked Oral-B toothbrush and the bent piece of flat steel. I inserted the shorter bent end of the steel in the bottom of the keyway and twisted it to put slight opening tension on the lock. Then I inserted the flattened operating rod of the toothbrush into the top of the keyway and triggered the button. Its buzz sounded alarmingly loud in the night's silence, but in less than two seconds the oscillations of the rod bumped all five pins in the lock upward into their recesses—and the deadbolt snapped open.

I stepped inside and closed the door, then stood still, listening. Nothing. It was pitch-black inside with no windows to let in even starlight, so I flipped on the infrared illuminator on the ATNs, bathing the space in its eerie glow.

And what it illuminated was a professional operation to package and ship a dozen different perfectly and accurately counterfeited name-brand prescription opioid drugs. At the end where I stood were the finished products, bulk-boxed and ready to be loaded into trucks. There was every popular brand of hydrocodone or oxycodone a crooked doctor was likely to want: Vicodin, Percocet, OxyContin, Nucynta, Palexia, Tapentadol, Norco, Zohydro. Down the center of the building was a double row conveyer belt that dipped under a half dozen stations on each side where various packing operations were performed. I walked to the other end, where the bulk pills and capsules were stored in labelled stainless-steel bins with some sort of electric dispenser on each, controlled by a panel with an LCD screen. It appeared the pills were taken from these bins, counted, and bottled from a stock of appropriately labeled containers in cabinets on each side. Next to each cabinet was a large and complex machine whose purpose I couldn't divine until I looked in their supply bins. They were lined with empty foil blister packs— obviously sealing pills in these was not something that could be accomplished manually. The next station was equipped with a comprehensive assortment of branded sample boxes in which to insert the filled blister packs, complete with "Not to be sold" warnings which I found darkly hilarious.

The entire operation had total redundancy—if anything went wrong on one side the other side could continue producing. It was so thorough, and the pills and packaging so convincing, that my curiosity was aroused. I went back to the bulk bin labelled "Zohydro," the feed hopper of which was secured with a lock that submitted instantly to the Oral-B. Inside was a divided bin, each of which must have held tens of thousands of capsules. I pulled one out. It was bi-colored, and marked "Z330 30mg." The capsules in the other bin read "Z350 50mg." The latter, I knew from the brief reading I'd done, was serious stuff indeed, beyond the CDC guidelines for regular use and intended only for patients in acute, possibly terminal pain. The capsules were to all appearances identical to the real thing. But I was curious about just how identical.

There was a lunch area and a bathroom in the back corner of the room. I pulled apart two of the 50mg capsules and made a small pile of tiny white beads on the edge of the sink. I turned on the tap, caught some water in my palm, and dripped it on the pile.

Immediately it began foaming and expanding, until the residue was a little mound of gelatinous slime. Whoever had made this stuff had gone so far as to incorporate BeadTek technology: an FDA Orange-Book-approved polyethylene oxide excipient designed to make the drug difficult to abuse by inhaling or injecting.

The capsules didn't just look like the real thing; they *were* the real thing except for the fact that they weren't.

I went back into the main room and stood, simply admiring the professionalism of the operation. I had to admit to being impressed.

Now to burn it down.

My biggest concern had been whether there would be enough flammable material in the place to adequately feed a structural-level fire, especially given the steel exterior walls. Investigating now, I found that the substructure of the conveyor belt and station tables appeared to be Baltic birch plywood. That was good, but I needed more. Inspecting the interior walls revealed that they were standard sheetrock, and likely had two-by-six wood studs and insulation underneath. Best of all, the roof structure was exposed built-up OSB rafters with fiberglass insulation bats tacked up between them.

There was also an extensive network of fire sprinklers. Sprinklers don't work like you've seen in movies, where they all come on at once. They're actually individually triggered in order to minimize water damage, usually via a glass tube in each unit, filled with a glycerin-based liquid. The liquid expands when heated to around 150 degrees Fahrenheit, breaks the glass tube, and pops open the valve to the sprinkler.

However, few such systems are designed to be tamper-proof, and I was willing to bet this one was no exception. I walked to the back of the main room and through the door into the loading-dock area. At the back was a bunch of plumbing, including a two-inch-diameter pipe extending from the floor into the ceiling, with a big shut-off wheel in the middle of it. The embossed tin label above it read *Fuego*. Thank you very much. I turned the wheel clockwise until it stopped. I looked around the dock—and hit a jackpot: a pile of wood pallets. Then another jackpot: a propane-powered forklift, with a nice fat 20-pound tank on the back.

I dragged several pallets back into the main room and made a pile under each end of the conveyor assembly, then heaped a dozen boxes full of the physicians' "samples" on top of it. Next I set one of my taped-up pairs of gasoline/oil bottles under each pile, on their sides. I crushed two of the soft fire-starter cubes down into the crevice between the bottles, joined two incense sticks together with twist ties, and stuffed one assembly at a 45-degree angle into each device. Finally I poured a small mound of crushed match heads over the base of each stick. The level of accelerant in each bottle only came up about halfway, ensuring that, once the incense stick burned down and ignited the match heads and then the fire starter, the resulting hot flame could burn through the plastic and immediately ignite the vapor (it's actually gasoline vapor that burns, not the liquid). Once ignited, the flame would instantly melt the rest of the bottle, spreading the gasoline mixture and flames in seconds.

The propane tank on the forklift represented an intriguing possibility for enhancing the fire, but I didn't want it igniting before the wood had a chance to catch. I went back to the dock, turned off the valve on the tank, used the saw on my Leatherman to cut through the flexible line to the engine, then cracked the valve until I could hear and smell a hint of escaping gas. I left it going and closed the door to the dock as I went back into the main room. With a bit of luck the gas would build up slowly enough to create a nice secondary fire or even an explosion when the main fire breached the door.

At last I re-shouldered the rucksack, lit each incense stick, walked out the door and closed it, used the Oral-B to re-secure the deadbolt, then opened the tube of Superglue gel and filled the keyway. If anyone happened to try to get in through the door before the place went up they'd have to do it by force.

I checked the Sinn: 0344. Time to get moving. I switched off the IR illuminator on the ATNs—reverting it to normal starlight mode—ducked around the east end of the warehouse, and ran for the trees that shielded the lodge from view. To my right was the kennel building and the complex of animal enclosures. I planned to come back there. The screen of trees was only a few meters deep, and from the other edge the lodge appeared dark and lifeless. I skirted around to the south to stay in cover for as long as possible, then headed across the open space, skin crawling at the back of my neck. In the greenish glow of my eyepieces everything was still, but I was alert for the possibility of an insomniac going outside for a walk or smoke, or a night guard who hadn't been visible the night before.

I made it to the steps of the lodge, climbed them, and listened at the door. Nothing. I tried the knob and the door swung open, so I stepped inside, closed the door, and listened again. Still nothing. I stepped farther into the room and looked around, but even with the light-intensifying magic of the ATNs the moonlight outside wasn't enough to reveal the extent of the space. I flipped on the IR illuminator, turned to begin a sweep with it, and froze. In the corner ten feet behind me, on a low *banco* above a bookcase, a jaguar crouched, eyeing me.

Adrenalin works on its own schedule, and it's *way* faster than logic. So my pulse jumped and my muscles contracted into defense and firing positions in the split second before my brain realized it was a mounted animal. I walked over to inspect it. It was poised in a perfect crouch, coincidentally aimed right at where I'd been standing. The animal had been in beautiful condition—this was no starved captive. I looked around and found two more, each in a variation of the menacing pose in which taxidermists always stuff predators, even if they were shot out of a tree.

The lodge's great room was a huge fan-shaped space under a soaring ceiling beamed with a spread of massive logs that converged on a semi-circular stone fireplace twelve feet across. An arc of 15-foot-tall windows looked out to the west. Leather sofas and arm chairs formed sociable squares or looked out to the view. In one corner a few dining tables were available when the weather on the deck wasn't welcoming.

And wood. Everything was lovely, flammable wood. This was going to be a lot easier than the warehouse.

There was one tactical issue, and that was the fact that as soon as any fire grew—and it would grow quickly—the glow out the windows would light up the entire field in front and the trees beyond as well, giving away the game. I would have to move quickly once finished here.

Through a set of double swinging doors inset with head-height windows I found a gleaming professional-grade kitchen with a walk-in freezer and refrigerator and an enormous pantry. Past the prep tables and ranges was the door leading out to the staff quarters. I looked up and around on the walls and ceiling, and found and deactivated four smoke alarms. A sprinkler system similar to the one at the warehouse had a similar shut-off valve in the back corner.

Back in the great room I tried another door, which was locked. Out came the Oral-B once more, and the door opened to reveal a small but very tidy gun room. Along one wall was a long bench for cleaning and smithing, along the other was a wooden gun cabinet containing, to my increasing astonishment as I inspected them, a collection of bolt-action rifles and over/under shotguns from the most prestigious makers on the planet—Holland and Holland, Purdey, Westley Richards. It represented hundreds of thousands of dollars worth of of the finest human craftsmanship, and I actually felt a stab of guilt that, if all went the way I planned it, they would soon be so much charred ash and warped steel.

I was about to tear myself away and close the door when I noticed the rifle at the end of the row.

It was a double, without doubt the one I had seen yesterday through the scope, as it still smelled faintly of Hoppe's Number 9 cleaning solvent when I picked it up. It was a Rigby rising-bite sidelock, with the maker's distinctive side plates—and clearly made to order as, besides the traditional rose and scroll engraving, each sideplate was etched with a tiny, exquisitely detailed crouching jaguar. On the bottom of the action was a snarling head. Even in the weird light of the IR illuminator I could see the swirling figure in the walnut stock.

Among the many English gunmakers who had attained prominence during the 19th and early 20th-century heyday of African and Indian hunting, John Rigby & Co. had stood out as the professional's choice; often less embellished than others, but utterly reliable. I'd had a dear older friend in Tanzania, a professional hunter turned game ranger named Finn, who carried an 80-year-old Rigby double that had never once failed him or he wouldn't have survived to be my friend.

The barrels of the one I held were engraved *.500 3" Nitro Express*. No wonder it had nearly upended poor Daktari: the .500 NE was one of the most powerful cartridges on earth, originally intended as a stopper for the largest and most dangerous game. With a 570-grain bullet it produced nearly three tons of muzzle energy. It was, in fact, comically overpowered for shooting anything the size of a jaguar; it would knock one over like a jackrabbit. This rifle, in this context, was just showing off.

It had a leather carry sling. I opened the drawer underneath it; inside were several 20-round boxes of Norma ammunition loaded with Woodleigh solid-jacketed bullets—inarguably the correct load if you were being charged by a cape buffalo.

I slid one of the boxes into an empty lower pocket of my vest, and slung the rifle over my shoulder.

It was a monumentally stupid thing to do. Encumbering myself with an awkward 11-pound load could have disastrous consequences. But I was suddenly obsessed with the idea of saving at least one of these weapons from the destruction I was about to wreak.

Besides, who wouldn't take a bit of a risk to score a rifle worth a hundred and forty grand or so?

Where was I? Ah, right . . . arson. I went back to the main room and set a pair of the gasoline bottles next to a full bookcase (another stab of guilt), and inserted two firestarter cubes and a single incense stick with some of the powdered match head. I looked at the Sinn—0420. The warehouse bottles should be going off in less than twenty minutes, but I knew it would take some time before the fire broke through the roof and gave itself away. I decided to set one more firebomb in the kitchen, light them both, then head for the house on the hill to see if the boss was home—although the exit of the Range Rover the day before had made me less than optimistic. Torching structures and inventory would feel good and put a big temporary dent in profits, but without cutting off the head of the serpent I'd only be asking to get bit in return, worse than last time.

I went into the kitchen and pulled out the fourth set of bottles. In the corner was a commercial-sized deep fryer with what looked to be at least three gallons of oil in it. Perfect. I crouched and set the bottles next to the wall, crushed the firestarter cubes in the crevice between them, and inserted an incense stick.

There was a noise outside the back door.

Something being . . . dragged?

The door opened. The lights came on. The ATNs whited out as I flipped them up, swiveled, and shouldered the Glock. A hand that had reached in and hit the switch withdrew. The door swung open, and a woman backed into the kitchen rolling an institutional wet-mop bucket, holding on to the handle of the mop with one hand and pulling with the other.

This is what I got for doing a one-day CTR on a Tuesday—apparently Wednesdays were early cleaning days at the lodge.

The woman closed the door and turned, and I recognized her as the one who'd been slapped the evening before. Had she been punished with KP, or was this her normal routine?

Since I was crouched, she didn't spot me until I stood up, Glock shouldered and pointed at her and a finger to my lips. She gasped but, to her credit, didn't scream.

"*Quien es?*" she whispered.

"*No estoy aqui para ti,*" I answered, and pointed with my chin in the direction of the barracks and the big house. "*Para ellos.*" I took a chance and lowered the Glock to show I wasn't after her, but those up the hill.

She looked at me wide-eyed for a few seconds, then nodded. She still gripped the handle of the mop, her knuckles white.

I said, "*Necesita ir, ahorita. Rapido y lejos.*" I pointed with my thumb behind me, down the mountain. To my surprise she hesitated, then shook her head.

"*Mis amigos,*" she said, and gestured behind her toward the staff quarters. "*Por favor.*"

I looked at my watch. It was, as I suspected, still advancing.

"*Cuantas?*"

"*Cuatro.*" She held up four fingers as if unsure I'd understand. Was my accent that bad?

"*Cuál es su nombre?*"

"*Elena.*"

I gestured with the barrel of the Glock. "*Vamanos.*" She let go of the mop and turned to open the door. "*Cuidado, Elena!*" I warned her, in case she decided to run. I turned off the light as I exited, and she led me left along a path lit by footlights to the door of the staff building. Inside it was dark except for a couple of night lights plugged into wall outlets. I could see the place was essentially a bunkhouse with privacy screens divided roughly in two by a center wall, I assumed for men and women—an assumption confirmed when Elena flipped a switch that turned on overhead lights, knocked on the wall, and said in a loud whisper, "*Lupita! Fernando! Todos levántense!*" From first one side, then the other, there were shufflings and grumblings, then, when Gloria again said, "*Levántense! Ahorita!*" the shorter woman I'd seen looked out from a cubicle on one side, and the man I'd seen in the toque looked out from the other side, then two other, younger men. Each went from sleepy and mildly annoyed to wide-eyed and instantly alert when they saw me.

"*Elena, qué pasa?*" the older man asked.

Elena looked at me, then turned and whispered, "*Sicario.*" She pointed up the hill.

Awesome. That got their attention, as if my getup hadn't already.

Elena said, "*Necesitamos ir, ahorita.*" And just like that, they moved, throwing on clothes. I still kept a vigilant eye in case there were any sympathizers in the group, but I had a strong feeling there wouldn't be. Once they were dressed and had each grabbed a bag, I turned off the light again and gathered them at the door, where they eyed me sideways, half in fear and half in fascination. They seemed not in the least upset that they were probably about to be unemployed.

I badly wanted to grill them on the personnel up the hill—numbers, armament, etc. But I didn't want there to be any hint that they'd helped me in case there were recriminations later. I was on my own here. Instead I checked the surroundings, then herded them out the door and pointed west. Just to make sure they retained a healthy fear of me I said, "*Si les vuelvo a ver . . .*" and tapped the Glock. They shook their heads vigorously in unison. I didn't think I'd see any of them again.

Something seemed to be wrong with the Sinn—the minute hand was sweeping double speed at least. I flipped down the ATNs, went back into the lodge, and lit both incense sticks. After a squirt of Super Glue in each lockset, I went around the corner to where the antenna tower soared toward the stars. There were two cables running up it, one that parted easily with the wire cutters on the Leatherman; a second that took some concerted effort with the hacksaw blade.

Confident that I'd cut off the place from outside contact, I made a circle to the south and east to loop around the barracks, then angled up to the big house. I had to keep one hand on the Rigby to prevent it clicking against the strap hardware of the backpack but I wasn't about to leave it behind.

As I had estimated from the satellite view, a four-car garage annexed one side of the building, which otherwise was essentially a three-quarter-scale replica of the lodge. One garage door stood open and its bay empty. I poked just my head inside to avoid switching on an automatic light, and the ATNs revealed a Porsche Cayenne Turbo, a Ford Raptor bristling with every pseudo-racer accessory known to man, and a wicked-looking dune buggy powered by a flat-six Carrera engine. The open door betrayed a rushed departure—even a small-time drug lord wouldn't want to have to deal with pack-rat damage to the wiring of a Cayenne Turbo.

In the back of the garage was a wall of Snap-on tool cabinets and diagnostic machines. I looked down and identified the foot-high trigger for the lights, and stepped over it into the garage. My *veldtschoen* squeaked slightly on the polished floor. I moved to the door leading into the house and tried the knob.

It turned in my hand.

At this point I was virtually certain the occupant was gone, but I had no clue as to his living arrangements. Wife? Girlfriend? Boyfriend? Kids? I flipped on the IR illuminator, then pushed slowly on the door, ready to move in at a run if an alarm had been set. But there was no reaction, so I shouldered the Glock and proceeded from room to room, clearing each one in turn until I got to the bedroom.

And there was nothing, no one, and no sign that the luxuriously appointed house was occupied by anyone other than a single male, presently elsewhere in a black Range Rover.

Shit goddamn.

I would have accomplished nothing if I didn't nail the CEO of this place.

For an instant the thought flashed across my mind to run back, extinguish and pack up the devices in the lodge and warehouse, and disappear until I could be certain my primary target was here, but a glance at my watch quickly disavowed me of that idea—the warehouse set would have ignited at least twenty minutes ago. Also, of course, there would have been the slight problem of the Super Glue in the locksets . . .

Nope. I needed a plan B—but first I had to finish the remnants of plan A and take care of that barracks building.

Quickly I pulled open a few drawers to see if there was anything of investigational value to me in them—photographs, for example. No photographs, but I did find something of value: one bureau drawer was stuffed with bundled stacks of $100 bills, a hundred per stack. I grabbed six of them and stuffed them in a back pocket of the vest. That should do to replace Jed's crystal and pay for my new engine, with carrying charges.

As I turned to leave the bedroom, I spotted the poster on the wall.

It was the famous monochromatic print of Che Guevara, made from the *Guerrillero Heroico* photograph of him taken by Alberto Korda in 1960, looking fierce and eminently inspiring after the successful Cuban revolution. The banner on the poster proclaimed the struggle's motto, *"Hasta la Victoria Siempre."* Until victory, always.

I recalled the rumors Alberto had mentioned regarding the head of the operation. If I hadn't been so pissed off I would have smiled.

I left the bedroom and set an incendiary next to the central wall of the house—the construction here was just as wood-intensive as the lodge—and broke two thirds off an incense stick after inserting the fire-starter cubes and dumping some match-heads. A few minutes was all I should need. I flicked a lighter on the end of the stick and thought, *Hasta el fuego siempre, motherfucker.* That *did* make me smile.

As I circled past the main room and its open-plan kitchen, I noticed, amidst a forest of appliances, a massive commercial-grade Faema espresso maker on its own marble-topped island.

Did I have time for a quick . . . ?

Eh, probably not.

I went back out the garage door, but before I closed it a thought occurred. There was a RotoPax gasoline container on a bracket on the external cage of the dune buggy. I unscrewed its central mounting post, removed the cap, and splashed the contents under all three vehicles and in a trail leading up to and just inside the house. I tossed the container back under the Porsche, jumped the photo-cell light switch, and went down the hill at a jog, turning right before the staff quarters to climb up to the barracks. Looking east I could see the rose glow of dawn, and looking west, at the line of trees across the field from the lodge, I could see a flickering orange glow reflected in the foliage. All that wood and oil was catching quickly.

The four trucks I'd noticed on Google Earth—they were indeed quad-cab Hiluxes—were parked in the same spots on the south side of the barracks. It was was a much bigger building than the staff quarters. It appeared to be divided into discrete interior apartments, as along the long wall I approached I counted six ductless air-conditioning units, with a window above each. I checked the other side of the building and found the same arrangement. So I was looking at a potential 12 occupants, which would have been less than cheering odds, except I knew they were down three thanks to my elderly neighbor on Oso Negro Ranch, and from my brief glance at the exiting Range Rover the day before there were at least a couple others gone with the boss, perhaps three. Let's give it seven inside. Not ideal, but I had the advantage of surprise.

There were two entrance doors, one on the south side that fronted a large wood deck set with tables and chairs and a fantastically huge stainless-steel barbecue, and one on the north that accessed a smaller porch. I chose the south entrance, as there was a large blank space on the side walls before the apartments began, so I was pretty sure there'd be some sort of great room where I could assess the situation. Before I stepped up onto the deck, I checked the Glock for a chambered round and firmly seated magazine, and confirmed the Trijicon dot was glowing. Hadn't I just done this a few minutes ago? Yes. I did it again.

I mounted the steps and cautiously tried the deck for squeaks. It was solid, so I sidestepped toward the door, ducking under a large window on the way. The knob, of course, was complacently unlocked—a good thing as the buzz of the Oral-B would have been tactically risky. As I opened the door I realized, maybe not—there was a muted chorus of industrial-level snoring coming from the apartments.

I slid inside and closed the door. The glow from the growing lodge fire along with the brightening sky meant I didn't need the IR illuminator on the ATNs. Under light amplification alone they revealed a large clubhouse-like space with stools and a bar at one end, overstuffed chairs scattered about, a pool table, and several wall-mounted flat-screens. The walls were decorated with posters of variously underdressed women posed provocatively on variously overdressed cars and four-wheel-drive vehicles.

Opposite the entrance was a hallway a couple of meters across that extended all the way to the far wall and the back door. On either side, all twelve doors were closed.

And that was a problem.

There was no way I could go room to room and not wind up creating noise and waking up the rest of the occupants. Even suppressed, the report of the Glock would carry through interior walls and doors. Furthermore, each apartment looked to be a good five by six meters, meaning the interior layout of each could be entirely different based on its occupant's whims. Sure, I could make it into the first apartment and take care of the first of them, but then I'd likely be faced with a half-dozen more alerted that something was wrong.

I felt the stirrings of hesitation. I could think of no way to get the six or seven people in those rooms out into my firing zone without putting myself at high risk of being, at least, holed or, at worst, killed.

The hesitation fueled doubt, a fatal mind-worm for anyone poised to mete out personal justice with a firearm. Could I really be sure of the culpability of everyone in this building? What if there were innocents here, mere worker drones in the system who might not even be aware of the attacks on Magdalena and Jed? Aside from Zapata's casual brutality I knew nothing damning about any of them.

The thought lasted a second, perhaps two, before it struck me with enough force to banish the doubt that I knew all I needed to know about the poor woman in the pit up the hill. And as I remembered my promise to her, I noticed the trophy case.

I'd seen the glass-fronted cabinet on the wall behind the bar but had dismissed it as inconsequential. Now the objects in the bottom of it caught my attention, and I slid behind the bar to look, as the increasing glow from down the hill brightened its contents.

In the bottom of the case were two jaguar skulls arranged with teeth agape. But that wasn't all. Above the skulls were a dozen or so photographs tacked to the back of the case—photographs that showed, in exquisite detail, the victims of the lodge's hired-out retribution killings, post-jaguar, with several men standing above them, grinning and flashing either a thumbs-up or that inane two-finger version.

One of them was Zapata. Another, I was certain, was the one I'd seen on the side-by-side riding to the kennel to feed the dogs, then walking back. And there was Flat-top, from the rifle range.

There were no innocent worker drones here.

The fire glow was increasing, and dawn was coming. If these guys held to the same schedule as yesterday they'd be getting up in just a few minutes.

I turned to go back around the bar and saw another photograph lying on the counter.

It was of me. And Rachel Miller. A telephoto shot of us standing outside the coffee shop.

Apparently she had been followed after all.

I went back to the center of the room and eyed the hallway, thinking furiously. Finally it struck me to set a fire at the front of the hallway, then go around the outside of the building wait behind cover at the back door for everyone to flee and gather there. It wasn't perfect but it might work.

I unslung the Rigby and leaned it against a chair, took off the pack and got out the last two bottles and set them on the floor. Two firestarter cubes went in between. I didn't need an incense stick because I wanted ignition right-the-fuck-now. I put the pack back on, slung the Rigby back over my shoulder, pulled out the Bic, and leaned down to ignite the cubes, holding the dangling Glock out of the way.

The cubes flared.

And wouldn't you know it, the warehouse picked that very instant to explode.

My secondary insurance policy with the propane had clearly worked better than I could have imagined. I had a second's warning as a bright yellow flash lit up the room, and then an ear-shattering concussion blew out the front windows. The noise echoed up and down the valley as the glass showered to the floor.

All hell, as they say, broke loose.

There was a pandemonium of vile cursing and shouting and thumping as I backed off several feet and raised the Glock. The overhead lights blinked on—someone apparently had a master switch in his room. Shit. I flipped up the ATNS. Like it had been choreographed, six doors opened simultaneously and six men burst into the hall, four from doors near me and two at the back—Zapata and Flat-top. Those two and one other were in boxers; the other three were stark naked.

The two naked ones in front were smart enough to come out with weapons, a handgun in one case and an AK in the other. All six turned to look at the flaring firestarter cubes and then caught sight of me, and all six mouths dropped open.

The Trijicon's dot was already on the forehead of the one with the AK—the most immediately dangerous. I fired and he dropped like a stone. I swung to the one with the handgun, who had brandished it sideways and got off two rounds that went wild. I love it when the people shooting at me learned their tactics from television. I dropped him with another head shot. By then the other four had ducked back in their rooms and were screaming at each other and hurling uncomplimentary remarks at me. In a few seconds a guy on the left poked out with a massive chrome-plated revolver—unfortunately being right-handed he had to expose more of himself than was prudent and I put a round first through his left shoulder and then his chest.

Just then the firestarter cubes burned through the plastic of the bottles. There was a *whumpf*, and a four-foot-tall wall of flame shot up, partially obscuring the hand that appeared out of a door on the left and blindly fired a pistol in my general direction. I sighted carefully and put a round through the wrist behind the pistol, which clattered to the floor. The hand disappeared, but I stepped slightly sideways and fired a spread of four rounds at an angle through the wall next to the opening. The wall was just sheetrock and 2x4s and not much impediment to 147-grain DPX bullets. There was a groan, and the guy tumbled into the hall clutching his abdomen. Two more rounds finished him.

Simultaneously to all this action I'd been hearing the two in the back hissing commands at each other, and as I stepped back from the last shots both Zapata and Flat-top dove from their opposing doors, Zapata with an AK and Flat-top with a pistol. Firing wildly in my direction as I ducked sideways they backed up to the door, slammed it open, and dove outside. I put my head back around the corner as they disappeared, and saw they were still in skivvies but had both managed to get boots on. I sent the last rounds in the magazine after them, more in frustration than any hope of hitting them. They were gone.

I ejected the empty magazine, inserted a fresh one from a vest pocket, and racked the slide. Fifteen rounds up. I turned and ran for the door, where the keys to the Hiluxes hung on hooks. I grabbed the lot and threw them back into the spreading fire, then opened the door and exited at speed, straight out and over the rail. I couldn't be sure the two escapees hadn't come down either side of the building. The barrel of the rifle clobbered the side of my head when I landed. Remind me again why had I insisted on taking it? I zigzagged until I was forty meters out, then turned and crouched with the Glock shouldered.

Up the hill, the fire in the big house had already spread into the garage—good; no one would be accessing any vehicles there. The barracks was well on its way to a good burn. And over my shoulder was a beautiful warm glow from the roasting shell of the warehouse.

To my left I spotted Zapata. He was about a hundred meters off, running west through the trees, too far off, too fast, and too obscured for a shot. I wondered where he was heading, then remembered the ATV parked at the kennels across the field. He was either after superior mobility, or merely looking to escape and summon assistance—perhaps from the guardhouse down the road? Immediately I wondered if he might have left his friend to ambus . . .

Yep. I lunged to the right as Flat-top came out from behind the barracks and started shooting—proper stance, and accurate, too—dirt and pine needles gouted around me. I ducked behind a pinyon pine trunk about half as wide as I was, which would do me little good. A round punched into the trunk opposite my head, showering bark. There was no other cover, so I was left facing a simple duel. Fortunately I had the advantage of an optical sight and shoulder stock. I spun into the open and aimed. A shot from Flat-top's pistol tugged at the pack above my left shoulder, but then I had the dot on him. He staggered at the first round and dropped at the second. I put in an insurance round anyway.

I needed to stop Zapata, and he was number one on my list since the real boss was absent. I turned and ran after him. The damned Rigby was now dangerously hindering me, and I reached up to pull it off, but it had snagged on some bit of the pack's strap. I left it and instead worked on the Glock while keeping the white dot of Zapata's boxers in sight. I unscrewed the suppressor and let it drop; it would only be a hindrance from now on. I also pulled out the magazine I'd just inserted and replaced it with one filled with the higher-velocity—and flatter-shooting—125-grain hollowpoints. With the round still in the chamber that gave me 16.

Zapata had hit the huge—and now sunlit—open area between the lodge and the line of trees that concealed the kennel. I was actually gaining on him, probably because I doubted he'd had time to tie his boots. I stopped and sent two rounds after him but missed. He turned while still running and let loose a short full-auto burst with the AK, which went way over my head. Then we were both in the open.

I stopped again and aimed at the running and dodging figure. *Bam.* Nothing. *Bam.* Nothing. At the third Zapata stumbled as one leg went out from under him. He collapsed but came up in a sitting position and loosed another wild burst at me.

The problem with "spray-and-pray" shooting is that every now and then your prayers are answered—even if you're the bad guy. The Glock jerked sideways at a metallic *spang*, and at the same instant I felt a nasty punch in my right chest. I ignored it and fired again—and then the Glock jammed. I looked down to see that one of Zapata's rounds had impacted the slide and caved it inward before expending itself on the Safeguard vest.

Still running at a guy brandishing a fully-automatic assault rifle, suddenly my own arsenal was down to a 12-round backup pistol with a three-inch barrel—and an elephant gun, the cartridges for which were in a box in my pocket.

Zapata was scrambling in a weird sequence of attitudes, trying to get a bead on me again but clearly being hampered by his leg. I skidded to a halt and leaned down, scrabbling under my trouser leg and yanking the Springfield Armory pistol from the ankle holster. I sent three quick rounds in the direction of Zapata to keep him ducking. And then there was nowhere for me to go and nothing to do except to try to outshoot him. At seventy-five meters the 8MOA dot on the Hellcat's sight covered Zapata's whole head, and I was wavering from the run, but I started laying down rounds one after the other. He got the AK shouldered again and I crouched and lunged as another burst went past. Then up again and more rounds—six, seven, eight. Dirt kept spouting just behind him. *Shit.* Two more misses, and another burst from Zapata.

I had two rounds left, and Zapata was steadying himself into an awkward but stable sitting position. I fired, he let loose a three-round burst I heard go past my head.

I fired my last round. The Hellcat's slide locked back over an empty magazine.

Zapata jerked. He looked down slowly, almost contemplatively, and the AK slid out of his grasp. I ran up to him as he slumped and then lay back in the grass. A bloom of blood spread across his bare chest, a small fountain of it welling and receding with his fading pulse. He looked up at me wordlessly, and I knelt down and looked back at him, staying in his space, violating his space until his eyes went vacant.

I dropped the slide on the pistol and stuck it back in the ankle holster, and picked up Zapata's rifle. It was an AK12, the new model, in 5.56mm. Lucky for me—had it been an AK15 in the heavier 7.62 caliber the lightweight Safeguard vest might not have stopped even a ricocheted round.

The rifle was also empty. I threw it down.

I got the Rigby untangled, removed the pack and laid it on the ground, and set the Rigby on top of it. I slid the strap of the Glock over my head and inspected the slide. Clearly beyond field repair, for sure. I dropped it in the pack, along with the ATN goggles. Now I was left with an empty pistol, a broken pistol, and an absurdly overpowered two-shot rifle, virtually useless if anything else came up.

Or so I thought.

Because just then I heard the sound of an engine to the south. I stood up and looked to see the black Range

Rover appear on the entrance road, moving as stupidly fast as you'd expect given that they'd been watching successive columns of smoke rising ahead of them as they approached.

I looked around. I was completely exposed, a hundred meters from cover. There was nowhere to go if someone in the vehicle spotted me—which was exactly what happened. Just before it would have disappeared behind the lodge the driver slammed on the brakes and turned off the road, then accelerated in a big circle directly back toward me. The field was clear of trees but cut with ruts and pocket-gopher holes, so even given the Range Rover's superb suspension it bucked up and down and barely held maybe thirty miles per hour.

Which was still notably faster than I could run.

I yanked open the flap on the lower pocket of the vest and pulled out the box of .500 cartridges, scrabbled at the taped closure, finally simply ripped off the top and dumped the rounds on top of the pack. I grabbed the Rigby and thumbed the lever to break it open. As I did so I heard the engine revs increase. I looked up to see the vehicle coming straight at me, and it occurred to me that they saw what I was doing and were simply going to run me down.

I grabbed a fistful of the fat cartridges and shoved one into each barrel, snapped the action shut and slid the safety catch forward. I kept two rounds between the fingers of my forward hand as I raised the rifle and brought the grille of the Range Rover into its beaded front express sight. The vehicle was now fifty meters and five seconds away. I could see multiple silhouettes inside.

I squeezed the front trigger. The rifle roared and bucked although I heard and felt nothing in the hyper-concentration of stress. A 570-grain solid slammed into the front of the vehicle and a jet of steam shot out the front and billowed over the hood.

It kept coming.

I moved the bead slightly and squeezed the rear trigger. This time there was a tortured shriek of metal and the engine cut out instantly. The Range Rover continued on momentum but it was obvious it wouldn't reach me. The driver hit the brakes and stopped in a cloud of dust—twenty feet away.

The trouble with a double rifle, of course, is that it's a double rifle. If you haven't solved your immediate problem with two shots, there is a forced pause while you reload. I'd seen Finn do this in two seconds flat, but I didn't have his skill. I snapped open the breech and two empty cases arced smartly over my shoulder, trailing smoke. I stuffed in one replacement, then the other, and banged the rifle closed again—but by that time four guys had tumbled out of the Range Rover and had me covered with four weapons. Four, you're aware, being twice the number of rounds I just reloaded. A lot of "*Suelta el arma!*" and "*Sueltalo!*" screaming ensued as I held the Rigby muzzle down—but then one of the men who hadn't been screaming stepped forward, walking right through the firing lines of his comrades.

And goddamn if it wasn't Che Guevara.

Except Che would have been, what, like a hundred if he'd survived the CIA hit in 1967 in Bolivia, right? This character was no more than 40, maybe 45. But he had it all: the olive drab fatigues tucked into combat boots, the black beret with the star in the middle, the wispy beard, and longish black hair curling wildly out around his face, which had the same fierce dark eyes and sensual mouth of the real deal, just made for inspirational posters and murals. Not only that, in contrast to the up-to-date AKs his buddies had leveled at me, he was brandishing a vintage Kiraly-Cristóbal carbine of the type Che had favored during the Cuban Revolution. Where the hell had he even found such a thing?

With the carbine pointed casually at my stomach, he said in near-accentless English, "Just drop it."

I leaned down and laid the Rigby gently on the ground. He might shoot me, but I wasn't going to scratch a work of art. Che raised the carbine in the crook of his arm, muzzle pointed skyward, and cocked one leg so his elbow rested on his hip, just like a guerrilla posing for an AP photo. As he did so the sleeve of his fatigue jacket slid down, revealing the *pièce de résistance* of the whole act: A Rolex GMT Master, just like the one his hero had worn and which the CIA's slippery point man in Bolivia, Felix Rodriguez, had retrieved from Guevara's corpse as a souvenir.

It was all I could do to keep from laughing out loud. But the three other rifles pointed at me helped me keep a poker face.

Che was doing a fair job of looking casual and in control, but I noticed a couple of things. His pupils were widely dilated, and where his left hand had been on the forestock of the carbine it was glistening slightly— his palms were sweating even in the cool morning air. He kept glancing behind me at the warehouse, which was well on its way to burning to the foundation. His three lackeys looked just as spooked.

Che turned back to me and looked me up and down. "I have to say, I'm impressed you were able to make it here without us knowing about it in advance, *Señor* Porter."

Of course I wasn't surprised he knew who I was. But I was immensely relieved to infer he had no knowledge of my connection to Alberto.

He continued, "We heard yesterday that you might have left Tucson." Which explained the precipitous exit of the Range Rover the day before. "But I only concluded a couple of hours ago that you had somehow crossed that mightily reinforced U.S. border without going through an official port of entry."

He glanced back toward the antenna tower and continued, "And when I tried to call and warn my men, for some reason I could not make contact."

I gave him my best look of wide-eyed innocence.

He paused, then said, "Were you actually stupid enough to come down here alone?"

I said, "Why would I need help to deal with you bunch of *pendejo* jerk-offs?" The eyes on the three behind him widened, and I could see fingers twitching on triggers. If Che hadn't been in the line of fire that would have been the end of me.

Che just smiled. "Ah, but here we are, holding the rifles, and you without that beautiful example of the gunmakers' craft you attempted to steal from us."

Which was true, and by now I was aware that my situation was, if I may repeat myself from an earlier chapter, not indicative of a satisfactory *denouement*. You could say that I had Che right where he wanted me. In fact my only slightly cliché strategy at this point was to keep up a witty repartee of insults in the hope it would annoy him enough to keep me around so as to arrange some nasty end later (like, perhaps, feeding me to a jaguar?). Then I could look for a chance to overpower a guard and engineer an escape. Just like something out of a James Bond movie. So:

"At least I can shoot it without getting knocked on my ass like would happen to your three *chicas* back there." Clearly the referenced girls were competent in

211

English because their eyes got wider yet, and fingers twitchier. "And I'll bet I can shoot it better than you can shoot that *Fidelista* relic of yours. Or do you just pose with it in front of a mirror?"

Except it didn't work. Che actually looked disappointed in me.

"What do you think this is, Clayton, a James Bond movie?"

Oops. But hey, at least we were on a first-name basis now. That was a step.

He glanced at the warehouse again, and then over his shoulder at the lodge, the roof of which collapsed with a delightful roar as he watched. A small satisfaction, along with having reduced his manpower by a half dozen and his inventory by 10 or 20 million dollars or so. And he was still sweating.

He turned back and said, "I'm not going to do what the Bond villains always do and take you prisoner so you can overpower a guard and engineer an escape later."

Okay, so my plan was a bit cliché; I already admitted that.

"You *were* stupid to come here. Yes, you've caused some damage, but damage can be repaired. And inventory can be replaced—as can . . ."—he glanced at Zapata's corpse disinterestedly—". . . underperforming personnel. Right now I have too much to do to rebuild what you destroyed, and, sadly, no time to waste cutting you apart piece by piece. I'll have to be satisfied with the fact that you lost. And that you're dead."

He shouldered the carbine and swung it toward my chest. There was the crisp *snap* a bullet moving at supersonic speed makes traveling through the atmosphere—actually a miniature sonic boom. A fine cone of blood and brains blew out the left side of Che's head just under the beret, his already-dead eyes bulged briefly from the hydrostatic shock, and he flopped to the ground like a side of beef cut from a butcher's hook. There was a second of silence, then nearly another, while the three with the AKs stared at the corpse, dumbstruck. Finally the distant rolling crack of the rifle shot. *Six hundred meters*, my brain automatically estimated. My brain also noted that the shot had an auditory signature remarkably similar to that of my Steyr SSG. Which was *supposed* to be home in the gun safe.

In the meantime within that two seconds I'd crouched and grabbed the Rigby. I brought it up toward one fellow who was quicker than his buddies and was tracking his AK back toward me, when his head also erupted. *Fine then.* A short swing to the left, the Rigby roared, and three tons of muzzle energy caught another fellow in the chest. Swing, *BOOM*, and the last one dropped just as he squeezed off a burst that went wide.

Instinctively I broke open the rifle, bent down and retrieved two more cartridges, and reloaded. But there was nothing more, no movement, no more vehicles, and no sounds except the ticking of the Range Rover's ruined engine as it cooled, and the continued, almost concussive crackling of four structure fires. I turned and looked up the hill, toward my own observation point and where that pair of shots had come from. I could see nothing. I gathered the rest of the .500 cartridges, dumped them in the pocket of the photographer's vest, and shouldered the pack. It was time to leave.

But then I remembered.

I turned the other way and jogged toward the kennel and enclosures.

CHAPTER 24

The kennel was a long, low building that obviously included a workshop and storage. It was unlocked; I went inside to check on how the dogs would fare if no one else showed up here for a few days—I wasn't sure how long the lodge employees would wait before curiosity overcame fear, or if the police would eventually work up the nerve to do so. There were twelve kennels, each with interior access to a weatherproof room, but only five dogs—big hounds, all of whom were inside and clearly stressed at the noise and smell of smoke. They eyed me warily as I walked up, and neither wagged nor barked. I noted that there were automatic waterers in each enclosure, so I opened a bin of kibble and scooped a mound into each enclosure. The dogs continued to eye me as I exited the west door.

There was a backhoe along with a couple of smaller garden tractors under a tall awning. The chain-link enclosures were about fifty meters away through the trees. As I got closer I estimated that each comprised a large run of an acre or more, with a much smaller enclosure on my side. The one I approached was empty, which allowed me to inspect it.

Instantly I understood how they controlled the animals. The smaller enclosure contained a water trough, so the animal had to enter it to drink. There was a gate with a solenoid and motor on it, obviously remotely controlled. Within the smaller enclosure was a series of rolling squeeze gates which could force the animal into smaller and smaller spaces until it was completely immobilized. There was a raised chute for loading or unloading an animal from a truck. Hanging from hooks on the fencing were two long cattle prods.

The jaguar was in the second unit to the south.

He'd been locked in the smaller enclosure, apparently in preparation for his final taste of freedom before the dogs ran him down. (With a jolt I realized I'd forgotten all about Daktari, and wondered if he had simply cowered in his cabin while all the commotion was happening. I had no intention of going back to see if *he* had enough food.)

The jaguar, a male, crouched in the middle of the cage and watched me approach. Even before I was close I could see he was underweight, although a layman probably wouldn't have noticed. A healthy jaguar is much stockier than its superficial African *doppelgänger* the leopard, so even partially emaciated it is still a formidable—and beautiful—presence. As I got closer, a low growl rose in his throat, and when I was within a few feet it escalated into an open-mouthed snarl. He did not retreat, but simply crouched lower—and then as I neared the gate to inspect its lock, he leaped at me in a blur and impacted the gate with a crash before backing off and crouching again.

I backed off as well. *Jesus.* The animal had clearly been both starved and abused until its normal overriding fear of humans had vanished. I had planned to simply pick the padlock on the chain that secured the gate and leave it open, assuming the animal would stay away from me until I left. Now I didn't know what to do. I eased forward and leaned down to get a look at the padlock, and saw to my chagrin that it took a tubular key, well beyond my amateur-level picking skills and immune to the Oral-B approach.

I backed off and ran to the kennel, but found no key box anywhere. Obviously this aspect of security was taken seriously. I went back out, saw the backhoe again, and had an idea.

It was a Case 580N, like the one up the hill, with an enclosed cabin and rookie-friendly joystick controls. I'd used one at the ranch and was competent enough to dig ditches, if nowhere near the artist that the guy who taught me was. He could have picked your pocket with his.

The key was in it. I climbed in, closed the glass door, braced the Rigby in a corner, and started the engine. Normally you give the hydraulics some time to warm up, but as soon as the loader and bucket would lift I pulled out and rocked slowly over to the enclosure.

As I had hoped, the size and noise of the machine intimidated the jaguar, which backed into the far corner of the cage as I pulled around and reversed. I could see but not hear him continue to snarl. I swiveled the seat around, took the controls, and slowly extended the boom, dipper arm, and bucket toward the gate. I wanted to hook one of the teeth of the bucket into the chain, but the finesse required was beyond me and I kept crashing the bucket into the gate, further terrifying and enraging the poor animal. At last one tooth hooked the chain. I pressed down with the bucket and the chain parted like a cheap bracelet under a few tons of hydraulic force. With more crashing and fumbling I managed to swing open the gate with the bucket. The jaguar stayed where he was.

Now I faced a conundrum. If I backed away, parked the backhoe, and left the security of its cabin, I couldn't be sure the animal wouldn't come right out after me. But I couldn't very well drive the thing home.

Finally I took a chance. I lowered the bucket to the ground and left the machine idling where it was, close to the gate. Keeping my eye on the cat, I picked up the rifle and slid out the door on the opposite side, watching back through the glass of the cabin. The jaguar stayed where it was, looking up at the machine. I was pretty sure that in short order he would get used to the thing being still and not very noisy, and leave—just, I hoped, not in too short-order. After backing away for a good fifty meters, I turned and headed up the hill, past the still-flaming remnants of the warehouse.

Jedediah Carson sat, knees up and arms resting on them, leaning against the trunk of an oak tree. He was wearing honest-to-God Vietnam-era tiger-stripe camouflage fatigues and, I am not making this up, a dusty, faded green beret sporting the yellow flash of the 1st Special Forces Group. My Steyr lay crosswise in his lap.

He patted it and said, "Nice rifle." He smiled, but he was pale as alabaster and I could tell he was pretty nearly shattered.

I erupted.

"You miserable, stupid old bastard! You could have fucking died coming down here!"

He continued smiling, and said mildly, "Well, you definitely would have if I hadn't."

True as this was, it just made me angrier at that moment, and I continued to berate him for being a miserable, stupid old bastard. He reached behind him, produced an honest-to-God GI canteen, unscrewed the cap, and took a drink. What next, would he break out the C-rations and Lucky Strikes?

Finally I ran out of steam. He *had* saved my life, after all. I looked off in the distance and waved a hand, like I wasn't really impressed, and said, "Okay, look . . . sorry. And thank you."

He snorted. "You think I came down here for you? You forget—these assholes killed my dog."

Never before had I heard Jed use such a low-rent term, and for some perverse reason—call it pent-up tension and subsequent relief at not having been killed by the fanboy of a Cuban revolutionary—it struck me as hysterically funny. I tried to maintain my pissed-off demeanor, but soon my shoulders were shaking with suppressed chuckling, then I was cackling, then laughing, then whooping helplessly and leaning on my knees.

"Besides," he added when I had barely caught my breath, "That damn Mary Prude looked like she was mentally undressing me when she came over."

This triggered another bout of helpless whooping.

When I finally caught my breath again, I said, "And . . . so?"

Jed said, "I figured you'd take a day to recce the place."

I nodded.

"So I drove up and got the rifle. Put a few rounds through it to get the range."

A few rounds through it to get the range? This from the *viejo* who'd just executed two perfect head shots from 600 meters. Of course, one could argue, he'd had extensive experience with the 7.62 x 51mm cartridge. In a self-loading battle rifle. With open sights. A half century ago.

"Then I dug out my old camo and threw a few other things in the truck, and came on down."

I said, "And obviously that *hijo de puta* Alberto told you where to find me."

And then it hit me.

"Wait a minute. He told you where to find me and then let you come down here on your own?"

Jed shrugged.

"What's that supposed to mean?"

A pause, then, "I sort of had to restrain him."

I said, evenly, "Define 'restrain.'"

"I locked him in the wine cellar."

"Jesus. And he just let you do this?"

"Well, no, not really. I had to threaten to put a bullet through the calf of his left leg. Which would have incapacitated him but not done any permanent damage. Then I found Gloria and told her he was going with me for a couple of days, and to take some time off.

"Jesus H. Christ."

"What? I didn't actually *shoot* him. Besides, he'll be fine. There's cheese and sausages hung in there besides all the liquor. I even left him a jacket and a pillow. But we should be getting back. I could use a drink anyway."

I was thinking that the recriminations Jed would face from Alberto would be mild compared with Gloria's towering wrath at being lied to, but decided to let him find that out on his own. I unslung the Rigby and leaned it against the tree to help Jed to his feet.

"Damn," he said, eyeing the swirling figure in the walnut and the intricate engraving. "That's some battlefield pickup. I wondered what you were shooting when I heard it go off. It sounded like a one-oh-five."

He stood . . . and then enveloped me in a hug, clapping my back. After a moment he stepped back with his hands on my shoulders, but instead of looking teary there was an impish gleam in his eye. The old bastard was having the time of his life.

His gaze shifted suddenly as he spotted something behind me.

I turned and looked. Down in the field, just coming out from behind the trees on the east, was a figure. I recognized it instantly as Daktari.

He was walking down the center of the field, looking by turns at the burning lodge and up at the smoke rising from the hidden warehouse. He appeared to be in shock, as he was tripping regularly and weaving back and forth rather than walking in a straight line.

As we watched, he stopped abruptly, as though he had spotted something ahead of him.

And then he turned and ran.

In seconds he was out of sight behind the trees again. Like a suddenly animated patch of sunlight, a yellow-orange flash appeared from the right and blurred across the field. We heard a high, truncated bark of noise, like a howl of terror cut off before it was fully formed, then nothing.

I smiled.

Jed saw it and looked at me questioningly.

I said, "He disagreed with something that ate him."

Jed raised an eyebrow.

I said, "Old Ian Fleming line." And explained who the figure was. Jed nodded, looked down the slope, and said, "*Bon appétit.*"

I did sincerely hope the animal would return to its natural diet of deer and javelina once sated on the hapless doctor.

Rather incredibly Jed let me carry the Steyr. But I swear the brief flurry of action had put a spring in his step as we made our way up the next two rises to where he told me he had parked, just behind my own truck.

I said, "So how did you figure out my infil route?"

He looked at me as if I'd questioned his mental capacity.

"Where else would it have been?"

Apparently ten minutes on Alberto's computer had led Jed to the same tactical conclusion that had taken me two hours.

A little while later he asked, "Do you know where the smell is coming from?"

I described the clearing and the pits and their contents. He just nodded solemnly.

After loading my gear in Jed's F350, I uncovered my truck and left it where it sat, keys in the ignition. I had paid cash for it and hadn't registered it, and I was pretty certain someone would find it who would put it to use, no questions asked or authorities alerted.

Rather incredibly Jed also let me drive (once I'd moved the seat up to where I could actually reach the pedals), and after we'd hit the main dirt road leading back to Highway 17 he reclined his seat and was soon blessedly asleep. Behind us I could still see columns of smoke rising into the air, yet we passed no incoming vehicles. It seemed the place was strictly *prohibido* no matter what might be happening.

I remained on edge as we passed through Moctezuma and Cumpas (no cop this time), then back through Nacozari and over to 89, up through Cananea. Not until we were on the dirt road leading to Alberto's ranch did I begin to relax. In addition to being furious with Jed for risking his life to follow me, I was worried that he'd brought a truck easily traced to him. But there was zero evidence of any kind of alert—no police, no suspicious loiterers by the side of the road. The operation I'd just torched seemed to exist in a universe separate from the normal goings on in Mexico. Which was the way I'd found so much of the country—just getting on with life and partitioning the subtext of violence and corruption.

Fernando was at the gate and waved us through with a grin; obviously he had no clue that anything was amiss —the gate guards often went days without seeing Alberto. About a kilometer before the main house we passed the tidy compound where Gloria lived. It was far enough off the road that she couldn't see who was—or wasn't—in the truck, but she waved from the porch. I waved back cheerily. Jed had woken up and waved too. *Yeah, you just wait, pal,* I thought gleefully.

We pulled up to the hacienda and parked just at sunset. Jed got out—stiffly—and we walked in through the patio gate and the big sliding glass door, through the guest lounge and the five-star kitchen. Jed pulled a set of keys from his pocket and unlocked a door, then we went down a flight of steps and along an arched corridor built with local stone to a second, heavy mahogany door. Jed put in a key and turned, and swung the door inward.

Alberto sat on the pillow Jed had so thoughtfully provided, leaning against the far wall. Arranged geometrically around him were the partially gnawed corpses of a huge wheel of cheese (a nice sharp cheddar by the smell) and a two-foot-long salami. It looked like a large fastidious rodent had invaded the cellar. Clearly Jed had neglected to leave a knife or cheese slicer. Also scattered about were several opened bottles of wine. At least he had a glass.

Alberto peered at us rather myopically and said with exaggerated precision, "So, has the Governor commuted my sentence?"

I realized he was half sloshed—the first time I had ever seen Alberto the least affected by alcohol. As we walked in he looked vaguely cross-eyed daggers at each of us in turn. Jed, never one to apologize for something he'd done that he thought was the right thing to do, said, pointlessly, "Well, we're back."

Alberto said, "Are you expecting me to toast the fact?"

I took over what was aiming to be a sniping contest and said, "Alberto, look, we're really sorry for this." Jed looked sideways at me as if to protest the "we're" part.

I continued, "We were only thinking about you. We already took advantage of your home and hospitality. We didn't want to do anything more to endanger you *or* your people."

Alberto, looking at Jed, said, "Threatening to shoot me doesn't indicate much concern for my welfare." But he seemed mollified. And all three of us knew perfectly well that imprisonment was the only way Jed could have prevented him following us down.

I picked up one of the open wine bottles—still partially full—and looked at the label, then gaped at Alberto.

He lifted his chin and said archly, "If I am going to be locked in my own wine cellar I am not going to drink cheap wine." By which I assumed he was referring to, like, low-rent $100 bottles of California cab.

I sniffed the bottle—and recoiled at a rank, sulphurous odor. I looked at Alberto, who waved an arm around the cellar and said, "What else was I supposed to piss in?"

I realized I was holding what was undoubtedly the only empty bottle of Chateau Petrus that had ever been used as a chamber pot. I set it back down. Carefully.

Jed held out a hand, and Alberto, after scowling at it, took it and stood up. He seemed to be recovering his senses and equilibrium, and said, "So?"

I gave him a two-minute version I could expand on later, winding it up with fires and explosions and the jaguar and Che. Mention of the latter made him smile, pleased that the intelligence he'd offered and that I'd laughed at had proven true in its own way.

He said, "Good. So that's it then."

Just then we heard a noise behind us.

Gloria was standing in the doorway.

I froze. Jed froze. Alberto froze.

Hands on her hips, she looked at the mess on the floor, and at Alberto, and said, "*Qué es esto?*"

Alberto walked over, took her by the arm, and led her just outside the door, talking softly. About 10 seconds in her head snapped around to look at Jed. *Hoo boy, here it comes.* Then she continued listening. Finally she tugged her arm free and marched back into the cellar, up to Jed—and then threw her arms around him and laid her head on . . . well, about on his solar plexus.

She whispered, "Tenk you, Yed."

I thought, *Oh for God's sake.*

CHAPTER 25

Gloria took "Yed" by the arm and led him back upstairs while Alberto and I followed meekly. She sat him at the family table and rushed off to her kitchen with a stern warning to him not to move.

Alberto went to the liquor cabinet and brought back the Ron Zacapa XO and glasses. He poured doubles for each of us.

I raised my glass, thought for a moment, then smiled and said, "*Hasta la Victoria Siempre!*" Alberto smiled, too; Jed just drained his glass and reached for the bottle. I wasn't about to remonstrate with him.

Over the next hour I told the story in detail, while Gloria stuffed us with *posole, chilaquiles, carne asada*, and *flan*. Jed and Alberto asked incisive questions at every step, marveled at the sophistication of the drug operation, shook their heads at the slaughter represented in the pits, and actually applauded solemnly when I described the warehouse explosion and the subsequent firefight. Alberto made me go out and bring in the Rigby so we could all inspect its magnificence in leisurely detail. It had somehow survived my rude treatment without a scratch.

Finally Alberto said, "And, so . . . is that the end of it?"

Jed looked at me, too; I suspected he already knew the answer.

I said, "Not a chance."

Alberto looked crestfallen.

I went back to the encounter with Che.

"He put on a suave act, but underneath it he was flapping. Dilated pupils, sweaty palms. He couldn't keep his eyes off the buildings going up in flames. Consider what I'd done from the perspective of an operation raking in tens of millions of dollars per year: Up to that point, the loss was merely buildings, inventory, and a few expendable troops. In the big picture, all very easy to replace. But Che didn't act like he was going to have to replace them; he acted like he was *responsible* for them. And even though he pretended to joke about it, I think he really was terrified that I'd somehow escape if he didn't cap me right then. He was desperate to make sure —for *someone*—that at the very least he hadn't fucked that up. If he'd actually been the boss there's no way he would have passed up the opportunity to hang me by the thumbs and skin me alive. He was scrambling to do damage control.

"He was certainly high up in the organization, perhaps even a number two or three, but I think his responsibility was strictly for that facility. Everything I saw indicated it was a discreet operation devoted solely to the drug packaging and shipping and the canned hunts—along with the gruesome little sideline for the cartel. The bomb in Magdalena's truck? That came from somewhere else, and I think someone else was running the couriers in the U.S. and had instant access to the high-power attorney from Phoenix."

This sobered Alberto, although Jed the warrior took it in stride.

Alberto said, "So what will you do?"

"Avoid losing the initiative."

"How?"

"I don't know just yet. Whatever happens next, I'm going to make sure it happens on my terms. But I haven't figured out what that will be. What was it Mencken said? 'For every complex problem there is an answer that is clear, simple, and wrong.'"

Jed and I were both fading by that point, so we went to bed. I figured I'd be lying awake for some time replaying the day and evaluating my options, but the next thing I was aware of was the aroma from the mug of *café con leche* Gloria set on the bedside table.

Jed was still in an annoyingly ebullient mood—fueled by a protein-heavy Gloria breakfast—and tried chatting on the way home (he'd climbed into the driver's seat when we left; I didn't even bother arguing), but soon gave up as it was clear I was in a nether world of strategic considerations. Of course when we got back to the ranch there was no way he was going to let me "help him get settled." He dropped me at the upper house but ordered, "Come down for dinner."

Chickens. Deer. Hummingbirds. Geraniums. Difficult to say who acted most annoyed at my three-day absence. To be fair it seemed like a lot longer to me, too. I fed and watered, collected eggs, went inside and put the Rigby in its new place of honor in the safe, along with the cash I'd liberated. Remembering Jed was currently weaponless except for an old Smith and Wesson revolver, I pulled out a generic AR15 and a couple of full mags to take down the hill. I was decidedly over the hubris I'd originally displayed in relation to the situation, and while I was confident whoever actually controlled the whole operation would have plenty to do for some time before they turned their ire back in my direction, I was taking no chances.

Then I sat down at the computer and opened Google Earth.

Rather than examining the mainland south of us, I panned west, to the Sea of Cortez—the fingerlike, 700-mile-long extension of the Pacific Ocean that divides the Mexican mainland from the Baja peninsula.

A result of the same tectonic fault line that will one day tip Los Angeles into the ocean, the Sea of Cortez—or Gulf of California—started forming only around five million years ago when the peninsula began to tear itself free from the mainland. The resulting dead-end sea supports a huge number of endemic aquatic and littoral species—Jaques Cousteau referred to the Sea of Cortez as "the world's aquarium." And the 37 major islands within the gulf—some of them protruding remnants of mainland terrain, others volcanic—support their own endemic terrestrial species: snakes, lizards, and mice that sometimes exist on only a single island.

The long and narrow nature of the Sea of Cortez results in extreme tidal ranges—up to thirty feet at the northern end, the third greatest in North America. I panned the view to about a third of the way down the gulf, where three islands—Tiburón, San Esteban, and San Lorenzo, called the Midriff Islands—form a loose chain from the mainland to Baja. Each of these is separated by about fifteen miles from the next, yet the constriction is enough to supercharge the tidal currents surging between them. In fact the channel between San Lorenzo and Baja is known as *Salsipuedes* ("leave if you can"), and the narrow passage between Tiburon and the mainland is called *Canal el Infiernillo* ("little hell channel"). When an incoming tide boiling through these passages slams into waves created by seasonal northerly winds, the combination produces directionless, chaotic seas and whirlpools that easily swamp small craft.

I'd done some work on each of the Midriff Islands —assisting an anthropologist friend on San Lorenzo, tagging rattlesnakes on Tiburon, and surveying the endemic chuckwalla—a two-foot-long lizard—on San Esteban, the island right in the middle of the chain, farthest from either coast.

I zoomed in on that one.

Roughly square-shaped, about four miles on a side, San Esteban rises jaggedly from lowlands on the southeast coast to highlands in the northwest; a single major drainage called Arroyo Limantour, normally dry, divides the island roughly in two. Vegetation is Sonoran Desert scrub—giant cardón cacti, the heavier relative of the saguaro, tower over elephant and ironwood trees and smaller shrubs and cactus. Several species of lizards, a single species of rattlesnake survive here, as well as just one terrestrial mammal—a tiny deer mouse, *Peromyscus stephani*. Sea lion colonies dot the shore here and there.

In centuries past another terrestrial mammal also lived here: a small band of Seri Indians managed to scrape out an existence, hunting the big lizards, pelicans, and sea lions, and traveling back and forth to the much larger Tiburón Island and the mainland in canoes made of bundled reeds. They were finally driven off in the 19th century when Spanish and then Mexican soldiers and ranchers were doing their best to annihilate the entire tribe.

I zoomed in farther, to the southwest corner, where a long gravel spit turns the island into a capital Q. This was where I'd landed on my previous trips, as one side of the spit or the other was sheltered from all but southwesterly breezes and waves. The Seri called this spit *Coftécöl Iifa*, which roughly translates to "Big Chuckwalla Peninsula." Chuckwallas were an important food source for the Seris; I could never figure out if they thought the spit looked like a lizard's tail, or if one of them just happened to catch a big-assed chuckwalla there.

From the spit a canyon sliced north into the higher elevations. I confirmed my recollection of the west coast as being mostly cliffs, with few safe landing spots and little access to the interior. I remembered standing on one of them, looking over the channel to the west, which plunges to a depth of 2,000 feet or more, as a high spring tide raged against a 30-mile-per-hour northerly wind, whipping the channel into a murderous froth.

Zooming even closer to slightly blurry individual-tree level, I confirmed another recollection: One of the cliffs was topped by a loose slope that slanted up to a rocky crest. From the crest it appeared the view of the water would be cut off to about fifty meters from shore. If you stepped off the crest onto the slope you'd likely precipitate a landslide that would carry you right over the edge. Reaching the shore any other way—such as to a safe landing spot for a boat—would take at least thirty minutes.

I left Google Earth, called up the U.S. National Weather Service website, and looked at the long-range forecasts for California and the Four Corners region. It predicted that a series of low-pressure systems would be moving east off the Pacific Ocean across California over the next few weeks, following each of which high pressure zones would develop in northern Arizona, Nevada, and Utah. The forecast showed beautiful dense atmospheric puddles of 1025 millibars and higher stalling over the Great Basin Desert.

Perfect.

I had a plan. And that plan was to make sure the people behind the attacks on my friends didn't just die —they were going to *disappear.*

I put the computer to sleep. Outside, the sun was just a few degrees above the horizon. The Land Cruiser was still in Tucson, so I shouldered the AR15, pocketed the mags, and walked down the hill. After being greeted/assaulted by Pounce I got no answer to my hail, so I hung the rifle on the hideous deer-foot rack and walked through the house to the back patio. Over the wall I caught sight of Jed, sitting in a chair on the other side of the row of gravestones, in front of the wood marker I'd put up for Kit. He had a glass of whiskey in his hand. I was about to back up and give him time alone when I noticed there was a second chair, an empty glass on it, and a bottle on the ground next to it.

I opened the gate; Pounce jumped off onto the wall. Jed reached down, retrieved the bottle, and poured three fingers into the second glass. I sat, we lifted our glasses silently toward the marker, and sipped.

"You know, he had never made a hostile move toward any other human. He just knew something was wrong with that bunch."

I nodded. I didn't apologize a second time because Jed didn't need it—a single sincere one was enough for him.

I said, "Remember when Sally used to be able to get him to eat asparagus by pretending she was going to feed it to Pounce when he refused it?"

Jed smiled. "Yeah, he was kind of a knucklehead that way."

"Or how about when he pissed off that momma javelina and she kept chasing him until he jumped on the patio wall to get away?"

"Yep; well no knucklehead move there. That was *smart.*"

We reminisced through a refill of the whiskey, then Jed fired up the barbecue on the patio and grilled two venison steaks while I made a salad, sliced some bread, and opened a bottle of red. As dusk deepened to night we ate on the big plank table on the patio by the light of kerosene lamps, and talked about nothing having anything to do with the last few weeks. Pounce sat on the table between us, calmly accepting bits of venison as an entitlement. Jed told me the cat had taken to wandering about the house uttering quiet, questioning *mrowls*, looking in all the places Kit used for naps.

Finally my chain-yawning got the better of me and, after helping wash the dishes, I headed back home. I paused at the door and turned.

"By the way . . ."

Jed said, "You've got a plan."

"Yep."

". . . . and?"

I said, "I plan to do something that will represent such a massive 'Fuck you' that they won't be able to stand it. They'll have to rise to the challenge personally or look like complete pussies."

"What would that be?"

"Easy. I'm going on vacation."

"Let me guess. Back to Mexico."

I smiled. He rolled his eyes at me.

"And this time," I said, "I can guarantee you won't be able to follow me."

He raised an eyebrow. "And you've somehow convinced yourself that's a good idea?"

CHAPTER 26

The next morning I did a quick search online and ordered a Flexible Flyer snow saucer—one of those disks kids use to slide down hills in winter. Unlike the vast majority of them these days, the Flexible Flyer is made from steel—I needed the strength, and I wanted the biodegradability.

Next, I emailed a proposal to the Explorers Club to be granted Flag Expedition status for a study on Isla San Esteban; purpose, to conduct a population-density survey of the San Esteban deer mouse, *Peromyscus stephani*, and compare it to densities of the San Esteban rattlesnake, *Crotalus estebanensis*. I had completed several flag expeditions for the club and was sure the application would be approved quickly.

Two more emails went out to editors of magazines I'd worked for in the past—one a British publication devoted to ocean kayaking, the other to an American conservation quarterly—proposing articles covering adventures in the Midriff Islands.

Still online, I bought a liability-only policy for the Land Cruiser from a Mexican-insurance broker in Tucson (they won't cover an older vehicle like mine for collision or theft). I needed a weather window so I paid for a month.

After lunch I walked down the hill, and Jed drove me into Tucson to pick up the Toyota. My sub-lease tenant friend was at work, so when Jed left I got to work myself.

The canvas hood covering the bed of the Land Cruiser was stretched over a hooped frame I had reinforced with diagonal struts. On top, four small velcroed flaps covered welded-in bases for a pair of Yakima cargo bars, which I retrieved from the garage and mounted, along with a set of kayak saddles.

Back inside, I unhooked a rope from a wall-mounted cleat and lowered a boat to the floor.

It was a sea kayak—the longer, more stable, ocean-going relative of the nimble whitewater craft. This one was a kevlar/carbon model from the British maker P&H, a Cetus HV: eighteen feet long and twenty-three inches wide, the highest-volume single they offered. I liked it because of the generous cargo volume, which had allowed me to carry enough gear—and, critically, water—to be self-sufficient for two to three weeks on earlier Sea of Cortez trips. It had an adjustable skeg under the stern, which helped tracking and compensated for weather-cocking in strong breezes. The cockpit was separated from the front and rear storage compartments by waterproof bulkheads, making the thing essentially unsinkable—assuming, of course, it remained unriddled by small-arms fire. Hatches fore and aft accessed the gear. I'd installed a bilge pump operated by a lever just behind the cockpit, but with the spray skirt in place it was rare anything more than a few ounces of water got inside, even in rough weather.

In a long case I found the paddles—graceful two-piece things with carbon-fiber shafts and laminated wood blades. Just 28 ounces each and thus energy-conserving to use all day. I always carried an identical backup paddle strapped on the kayak's deck, rather than a cheaper emergency spare, figuring that if I ever lost my main paddle it was likely to be in dangerous conditions—exactly when I wouldn't want to have to rely on a cheap paddle.

A duffel held a spray skirt, a Stohlquist Keeper PFD (personal flotation device), which incorporated large pockets useful for survival supplies and odds and ends, and a shortie wetsuit top and bottom. People think of the Sea of Cortez as a warm-water oasis; in fact upwelling from the deep trenches on the Baja side keeps the temperature in the hypothermia range even in summer.

Another duffel, about three feet long by twenty inches wide and ten deep, contained a piece of gear critical to my plan. It weighed 35 pounds and wouldn't come close to fitting inside the kayak, and I wasn't yet certain how I was going to manage it, but in the bed of the truck it went.

There was more. A half-dozen 10-liter Ortlieb water bags, durable and easier to stow when full than rigid containers. As a backup, a Katadyn Survivor 06: a compact, hand-pumped desalinator incorporating a micro-membrane that could turn sea water into drinking water, albeit at the glacially slow rate of a liter per hour—barely enough to offset the sweat produced working the thing, but enough to survive on.

What else might I need? A titanium cookset, titanium utensils, and a three-ounce isobutane stove with several cartridges. A pile of roll-top dry bags for gear and clothing. A roll-up 50-watt solar panel for recharging my GPS unit and VHF radio. Emergency flares and a marine-specific first-aid kit.

I carried the kayak out, slid it up over the truck until it dropped into the saddles, then climbed up top and strapped it down. With everything else in the back I was ready to go, after leaving a note for my friend so he wouldn't think we'd been burgled.

When kayaking where I had to carry all my water I never bothered with specialized foods like freeze-dried meals. I stopped at a grocery store and stocked up on pouched pre-cooked entrées I could either eat cold or heat in a pan of boiling water which I could subsequently return to my supply or use to make coffee. I also stocked up on pouches of fruit and cartons of fruit juice.

Back at the ranch by late afternoon, I parked in front of the big house. As I got out, Jed strolled out on the porch, took a look at the kayak on the roof, shook his head, and walked back inside. I followed him in, with a large black cat on my shoulder.

"I want to make a fish stew for dinner," Jed said without preamble. "Let's go catch some."

We carried fly rods out to the big pond and started casting the little poppers the panfish seemed to view less as food than as intruders to be destroyed. The fish seemed to move around the pond in a school at random; to connect you just had to keep casting and moving until you found them.

"I heard a bullfrog in here last night," Jed said. "I'll have to get out the .22 later." Bullfrogs were an inimical non-native species here; one would invariably turn into hundreds if left alone. It was a mystery how they got from one isolated cattle tank to another, but if left to breed they'd wipe out all the native amphibians. Of course Jed was fully aware his panfish were non-native as well, but they couldn't grow legs.

"So tell me about this plan."

I had no intention of telling him the actual details of my plan; he would have shot me in *both* legs. Instead I gave him a vague, sanitized version that he clearly recognized as being vague and sanitized.

"What makes you believe they won't just send troops after you?"

"Because of the way Che acted. He was obviously expecting the Hammer of the Gods to fall on him. The three guys with him in the Range Rover were just as spooked, and they shouldn't have had any sense of personal responsibility or fear of punishment. It seems clear from what Hinwood said that this operation isn't actually part of the Sinaloa cartel; it's its own entity that the cartel seems to be happy to leave to its own devices except for collecting their cut and borrowing a jaguar now and then. So it makes no sense for top management—however many of them there are—to be more than one step above Che. And given the mathematics of the barracks rooms I think that between you and me we've taken care of just about all the troops."

I paused, then added, "And if I'm counting correctly I think I'm ahead on that tally?"

Jed said, "Spoken like a man who was doing his shooting from ten feet away."

I grinned and winked at him, then continued. "Even though the Sinaloa people seemed happy to let them be, I'm willing to bet that once they're gone the cartel will just slot their own people into the operation. In the end the only way I'll have affected them is to increase their profit margin. Who knows, I might even wind up on their Christmas card list."

Jed: "Yeah, *if* you're around to be on *anyone's* list.

"I'm going to have total situational control."

"In a damn kayak."

I said, "Trust me."

He would have rolled his eyes, but just then the fish started biting.

CHAPTER 27

In just two days I got a reply from my friend in the Explorers Club that he had gotten my flag application approved, and that Flag #81 was on its way via FedEx. I also got emails from the magazine editors saying they would look forward to my articles.

If my time in Mexico went as planned, I'd have some explaining to do as to why I had produced neither a noteworthy study of insular predator-prey relationships nor any fascinating travel stories, but I wanted to play the in-your-face I'm-on-my-way-to-Mexico act to the hilt, and I wanted it to be authentic just to mess with heads even better.

I added a page to the news section of my website, *claytontporter.com*, which I kept active for people who followed my articles and photography. I announced and detailed an upcoming expedition to Isla San Esteban in the Sea of Cortez. Likewise on Facebook and several forums of which I was a member. Dates were still in flux, I noted, in order to exploit the best weather window. Perfectly true: I was keeping an eye on those lows drifting in off the Pacific.

Finally I called a reporter for the online news source Tucson Sentinel, who had been bludgeoning me with requests for an interview about the encounter with agent Miller and the subsequent assaults on Magdalena and Jed. The incidents had made a brief splash before receding into the background noise of newer stories. I'd been happy to leave it that way, but now I wanted a fresh splash to further rattle cages.

I met the guy, a veteran newsprint man named Tony, who looked exactly like how Dashiell Hammett would have described a "grizzled" reporter, at a dive bar on 9th Street and 2nd, and gave him a rousing tale which he actually scribbled on a steno pad with a thoroughly-chewed 99-cent Bic pen while downing four or five shots of Jack Daniels—I lost count. I could see his longhand and it was as rock-steady at the end as it had been at the beginning. I couldn't have landed the pen on the paper after that much alcohol. He looked up and said, "No fucking way" about 10 times during my account. By the time I finished he was champing at the bit to get to a computer to publish the story—I envisioned a coffee-and-ketchup-stained Vic Commodore 64. I followed him out to his car: a 30-year-old Volvo with a 20-year-old Earl Scheib paint job, unmarred by a single undented body panel. Two fast-food containers tumbled out the driver's door when he opened it; a glance inside revealed an accumulation probably started by Earl. I'd been going to gently suggest calling him a taxi, but once he started the engine I decided it was unlikely the Volvo could attain speeds sufficient to seriously injure anyone he hit, including pedestrians. He disappeared in a half-pint's worth of oil smoke.

The weather was not yet cooperating, so the next day I drove to Ajo to see Magdalena. So far I had only spoken to her on the phone shortly after the incident, and she'd still been loopy on painkillers. Now she was, predictably, already back to work, but off that day.

A rental Camry (what else?) sat in her driveway. The scorched and vegetation-free spot in front of her house gave me a renewed jolt of guilt and anger. The door still had a piece of plywood tacked in where the glass had been, but Magdalena opened it before I knocked. She was barefoot, wearing tattered Levi's and a chambray shirt, and the patch over her left eye reduced me to instant, self-indulgent tears despite my prior promises to myself to remain cool. She stepped out onto the porch and embraced me.

"It's okay," she said, "This is just to ease the irritation. It's going to be fine; my vision is already almost back to normal."

I said into her ear, "I'm sorry I landed here. And I'm sorry I didn't listen to you. Or Jed."

She backed away, gripped my shoulders with her hands, and glared at me with the one eye. "Oh for God's sake, Clayton, don't be stupid. Where else would you have gone? And who could have predicted how they would react?"

As I recalled she had in fact predicted more or less precisely how they would react—she had simply been mistaken about whom they would react *at*.

We went inside and I sat on the living room sofa while she brought us glasses of lemonade. She sat next to me and filled me in on her treatment and recuperation thus far. There were two stitched cuts on her forehead, otherwise only superficial and mostly healed nicks. She made light of the stitched wounds.

"I can hardly wait 'til someone I don't know asks me about them, so I can say casually, 'Oh, those? Near miss with a car bomb.'" Knowing Mags, that wasn't all just bravado; I hadn't known a woman since Jack as beautiful and as completely unaffected by it.

She fixed me with another cyclopean glare. "So, where've you been?" She knew me well enough to know that I wouldn't have waited this long to come see her unless something else had been significantly more pressing.

After what she had been through there was no way I was going to insult her intelligence, either by lying to her or keeping things from her. So I gave her pretty much a blow-by-blow—or shot-by-shot, if you will—account of the action in Mexico. Although her visible eye got wider as my account progressed, she said not a thing until I got to the part when Jed showed up, whereupon she covered her mouth with her hand and whispered, "Oh, Jed."

Sometimes I swore my chief rival for the affections of any woman in whom I had a potential romantic interest came from a guy 40 years my senior. *Wasn't he past the average life expectancy for an American male?* I thought sourly.

I brought the tale to an end with us back at the ranch. Magdalena looked at me for a moment, then said, "But that's *not* the end, is it?"

Her perceptiveness didn't surprise me. I explained my theory about the hierarchy of the operation, which she listened to thoughtfully before nodding.

"Yes, that sounds logical."

Somehow, coming from Magdalena, that erased any doubts I might have had. I gave her the same vague, sanitized version of my plan that I'd given Jed. She looked even less convinced than he had. But again, the perceptiveness:

"You really have no choice, do you? You can't spend the rest of your life looking over your shoulder. And it's not like you can expect help from law enforcement on either side of the border."

I said, "I don't care about looking over my own shoulder. It's your shoulder and Jed's I'm worried about."

She said, "Is there anything I can do to help?"

I said, "Jesus, Mags, I think you've done enough!"

She waved a hand dismissively. "Hey, all I did was get blown up."

I took her to lunch at a little cafe on Ajo's old central plaza, and we chatted about the wildlife of the Cabeza Prieta that had been my original reason for being there all those weeks ago. The proprietor knew Mags well and fussed over us both. We both decided on BLTs, fries, and cokes.

I asked if she'd looked into a new truck yet. She laughed.

"Do you know the insurance company tried to tell me that 'car bombs were not a covered eventuality?' I told them fine, I'd hang up and call my friend who's an investigative reporter for the *L.A. Times*; he'd love a story like that. Change in attitude. I have a new one on order."

She tried her best to squeeze more details out of me about my proximate strategic plans. I was having none of it. One, I didn't want her shooting me in the legs either; two, I had more than a vague notion that no one close to me should know any details that could somehow be extracted from them. I was for damn sure not going to underestimate the other side this time. If I could have convinced them to go I would have sent Jed and Mags off to a nice vacation to Iceland together.

On second thought, I would have sent them somewhere separately.

After coffee and some way-better-than-decent pecan pie—on the house—we walked back outside to find Border Patrol Deputy Chief Jeff Hinwood leaning against the ARB bumper of the Land Cruiser. He was in uniform and had a fresh flat-top.

He grinned. "I was pretty sure I recognized this thing. Hard to miss." We shook hands, and he tipped an imaginary hat to Magdalena, which I thought was quaint.

"I'm glad to see you out and about," he said to her. Then to me, patting the hood of the truck, "All fixed?"

I nodded. "New engine. An upgrade, actually."

We chatted for a few minutes. He said that the investigation into Miller had hit a dead end—"Literally," he said, smiling at me—and the U.S. was getting no cooperation from the Mexican government regarding the opioid/jaguar operation.

"In fact," he said, "It's already pretty much a cold case. And the assaults on Magdalena and your friend are out of our jurisdiction." He sounded relieved to be putting such a nasty bit of publicity behind the service.

He looked up at three circling turkey vultures. "Speaking of which, where were you anyway when all that went down? And what've you been up to? I called you a couple times a few days ago to see how you were doing, but got voice mail. Never got a call back."

Magdalena said, "Welcome to the club."

I said, "I was at a friend's when the attacks happened." Completely true of course; he didn't need to know it was in Mexico if he hadn't talked to detective

Reid. "Not sure why I didn't get your messages later." *I might have been burning down a few buildings at the time*, I didn't add.

"*MmHmm.*" He kept watching the vultures. "You wouldn't be planning to do anything stupid about this, now, would you?"

I said, "Well, I rarely *plan* to do anything stupid. Although now and then it does work out that way."

He smiled. "I just don't want you taking matters into your own hands. You were lucky the first time, but these are obviously nasty people. Let's just assume they'll be satisfied with the damage they already caused. Anyway, it's good to see you both." He shook my hand again, tipped his imaginary hat to Magdalena, and strolled off down the covered walkway of the plaza. I couldn't see where he was parked.

We got in the Land Cruiser. "'*Lucky*,'" I snorted. Magdalena patted my arm and said, "There, there," while smirking.

I said, "You want to walk home?" She just buckled her shoulder harness and continued smirking.

Back at her house, she removed the patch once we were inside. The eye was still inflamed, but otherwise it looked okay. I was relieved. She excused herself to put in some drops.

"Mind if I check the weather on your computer?" I asked. She made an exaggerated show of ducking her head to look out the window at the clear blue sky. Comedian.

"Sure," she said. I called up the forecast while she was in the bathroom. When she came out I had just called up the isobars for California and the Great Basin Desert to the east. She looked over my shoulder.

I said, "I have to leave."

Magdalena said, "Story of my life." But as I said good-bye at the door she hugged me fiercely and kissed me tenderly on the lips.

"You know what I have to say," she said.

This was a long-standing duel. Call it superstition on my part—and hers.

"Don't do it," I said. She said nothing, but after I started the truck, backed out and put it in gear, I made the mistake of looking to where she stood on the porch watching.

She mouthed the words, "Be careful."

Shit.

CHAPTER 28

Back home I called up the forecast again. The weather patterns had accelerated, and a high was already stalling north of Las Vegas. That one was too late for me to exploit, but the following low-pressure system that would trail its own high was right behind it.

I got an email delivery notification from FedEx that Explorers Club Flag #81 had been delivered to my commercial mail drop in Tucson. I had no intention of picking it up and taking it with me; it would stay safe right where it was. However, I posted on my website that it had arrived and that I would be heading to Mexico in two days.

I published an itinerary for those who wanted to follow along (or who, say, might want to follow me). I would drive to Bahia Kino, on the east coast of the Sea of Cortez, and from there north to a Seri Indian village called Punta Chueca. I had several friends there developed through years of studies and explorations in the Midriff region.

Punta Chueca is only about a mile by sea from *Isla Tiburón*, the largest island in the Sea of Cortez (and in fact the second-largest island off the west coast of North America, after Vancouver Island). But the channel in between is the shallow and current-swept *Canal el Infiernillo*—and indeed it can be a little hell when currents and waves collide. After parking the truck and launching the kayak at Punta Chueca I'd paddle straight across the channel and down the east coast of Tiburón, around several promontories and then west through a passage north of the diminutive *Isla Turners*. From there it was a 15-mile open crossing to San Esteban, dicing with the three potential nuisances of wind, waves, and current. I planned to base camp in the valley on the southwest corner, near the gravel spit.

I detailed my study equipment for the students of natural history who followed the site. Three dozen Sherman traps—cunning collapsible live traps for capturing small rodents; in this case that endemic mouse. Three dozen passive integrated transponder (PIT) tags—grain-of-rice-sized devices I could inject subcutaneously into captured rattlesnakes using a large hypodermic needle. A PIT tag requires no power but reacts to the proximity of an antenna, which records the identity of the tag and thus the individual animal. It's a relatively low-tech and non-invasive method for relocating and tracking individual animals, although nowhere near as sophisticated as GPS-based trackers.

The tracking antenna and its batteries and waterproof case. A snake hook and snake tongs, plus the snake tubes for safely immobilizing the snake while sexing it and injecting the tag. Bags for temporarily holding snakes. Sexing probes: rude but harmless little stainless-steel ball-ended devices inserted into the cloaca to positively identify male or female. Several min/max thermometers to record air and substrate temperatures. Two scales, one for mice that might weigh twenty-five grams, another for snakes that might weigh 1,000 or more.

Of course I actually planned to take none of this stuff. The list was all for effect.

Now I put together the kit I really would need, in addition to what I'd already picked up.

A large Mystery Ranch rucksack. The ATN night-vision goggles. A pair of 10x42 Zeiss binoculars—I'd be moving around a lot, and quickly, and needed to save weight, and I wouldn't need the big power of the Swarovskis. A 500-foot spool of mil-spec Type IV paracord, 750-pound test—50 percent stouter than the common 550 version. A remnant of a roll of Gorilla tape. A hacksaw with two spare blades—a sturdier unit than the emergency blade on my Leatherman. A Lixada stainless-steel four-claw folding grappling hook that was rated to hold 850 pounds, but only weighed 26 ounces. At the eye on the end of its shaft I attached a small stainless shackle and Ronstan pulley.

I set the Motorola 9575 satellite phone batteries to charge overnight, along with the Garmin handheld GPS. I wouldn't need the latter to tell me where I was, but if all went well I might need to tell someone else where I was. In their small transport case I'd also be carrying an Olympus voice recorder with a playback speaker.

What else? A dark green boonie hat—and a spare—for sun protection. A tin of dark camo face paint. A pair of Israeli Defense Forces Palladium desert boots with lugged soles for hiking but all-canvas uppers that wouldn't be damaged by getting soaked. Lightweight, light-colored, and fast-drying nylon trousers and shirt for paddling, dark cotton clothing for land. A pair of double-gradient Bausch & Lomb Aviator sunglasses to cut glare off the water, with a leash. A small mirror on an extendable stalk, which I normally use for checking bird nests for eggs. A quart of household bleach, which I decanted into a narrow-mouthed one-liter Nalgene bottle. Several empty Nalgenes to fill with water from the bulk Ortlieb bags. My Helle Temagami sheath knife, which I touched up so it was razor sharp. Sunblock? Check. I added a case of Tanka Bars to the foodstuffs; they would keep me going if I ran out of the pouched meals. And a simple hobo fishing kit with line and hooks.

I also tossed in a folding Wrist Rocket—a slingshot with a wrist brace that allowed the use of much more powerful elastics than the common version—along with two dozen .44-caliber steel balls for ammunition. I'd found it useful for driving off camp-raiding baboons in Africa and numerous similar tasks. It could easily kill small game.

My remaining camping gear, in addition to what I had collected in town, was simple. I wouldn't need a tent, but I had a sil/nylon tarp in case of rain. Likewise I didn't need a regular sleeping bag; I had a lightweight fleece envelope that would suffice. Coffee? Hell yes—I wasn't going to let a few homicidal drug lords keep me from coffee. However, as a nod to tactical realities I pre-ground it rather than packing the handheld burr grinder. Also, sugar was no problem but cream was pretty much out of the question. Maybe I could milk a sea lion or something.

The last thing I did was tuck a couple of my liberated hundred-dollar-bill packets into the Toyota's strongbox.

In the evening I walked down to the main house, where I found Jed in the shop working on gluing up a new fly rod. I had always thought it closer to magic than craftsmanship that six strips of bamboo could be cut, tapered, and glued together into a nine-foot-long wand with a hexagonal tip barely an eighth of an inch in diameter. I stood silently and watched; I knew Jed knew I was there and would speak when he could break concentration.

In a minute or two, without looking up or flipping up the magnifying lenses, he said, "Leaving?"

"Tomorrow morning, early."

He was silent for another minute. Then, without lifting his head: "If you screw up and leave me alone with Mary Prude I'll rip out your geraniums and burn them, and feed your chickens to the coyotes."

I knew Jed wouldn't feed the chickens to the coyotes, but I wouldn't have put it past him to rip out the geraniums and burn them. He had stooped to abysmally low tactics.

I tried a single, weak riposte: "I wonder if I should call Mary and let her know I'll be away?"

Didn't work. "Do that and the gardenias go too."

Bastard.

He went back to concentrating on the rod, and I knew Jed well enough to leave rather than expect more, or to hang around for dinner and try to pretend everything was normal. This send-off was Jed's way of hiding his emotions, and it was better to accept the rough camaraderie for what it was.

Except that at 5:00 the next morning, when I left in the dark and drove past the lightless main house, the Oso Negro Ranch gate was standing open, and the Land Cruiser's headlamps caught Jed standing off to the side with one hand raised in farewell.

CHAPTER 29

No sneaking over the border this time—I wanted the most public crossing available, in Nogales. I topped up the fuel tanks with diesel, skipped the less-trafficked Mariposa Road gate and headed straight downtown for the big one used by tourists looking for souvenirs, "authentic" Mexican food, cheap prescription drugs, and affordable dental care. At 7:00 a.m. there were only a few cars headed south. I drove past the heed-this-or-else "No firearms in Mexico" sign and two incurious U.S. Customs officials, then bumped over the baby-head speed inhibitors and under the awning leading to the inspection station.

Like other Mexican crossings, this one had a green or red light that triggered randomly as each vehicle passed —green meant proceed, red meant stop for an inspection and search. The Chevy truck ahead of me and the battered Volkswagen Golf ahead of it both got green lights. I let the clutch out and eased forward past the photocell trigger.

The light flashed red.

A bored-looking uniformed 19-year-old carrying an HK G3 rifle that had seen better days before he was born barely glanced sideways as he continued chatting to his buddy and waved me into the inspection lane.

Then his head snapped around and he looked straight at the Land Cruiser. His eyes widened.

I had bet heavily on what would happen next.

The kid stepped aside and waved me vigorously into the lane leading out.

My window was rolled down. As I idled past him I raised my hand and said, "*Gracias*!" He said nothing in reply, just swiveled to keep staring at me as I drove by and out onto Avenida Obregón.

It occurred to me I had seen the exact same expression on people who had just got their first look at a corpse.

Despite the fact that I had certainly just burned a bridge behind me—I could be sure the border guards had been warned not to let me back across—I smiled as I headed through Nogales and onto the highway heading south. I had not only confirmed that my plan was working, the bait had been swallowed whole. The splashy, thinly disguised "Fuck you" had been the perfect taunt. They had accepted the challenge.

And that meant I was in control.

They could have chosen any number of ways to neutralize me once I crossed the international line. In fact simply proceeding with an inspection and planting something in the Land Cruiser—a gun, drugs—would have got me out of the way instantly. Instead they had thrown the gauntlet back at me.

Hasta la Victoria Siempre, I thought.

I was relaxed—and hungry—enough to stop in Imuris at an old favorite cafe, *Taquería la Familia*. The grill was already up and running and I inhaled a half dozen *huevos con chorizo*, grilled *cebollas*, and a half-liter bottle of Coke. Strictly out of habit I sat at a table on the patio with my back to a wall, and kept an eye open for any passers-by acting strangely. It would have been easy to hire some street thug to walk up and plug me as I sat there with the Land Cruiser parked blatantly out front, but I knew it wouldn't happen.

I continued south, staying on the toll road to save time, contrary to my usual obsession with avoiding toll booths. At Hermosillo I turned west on *Carreterra 100* and was soon out where the Sonoran Desert scrub was only starkly broken by impossibly green fields of cotton, sorghum, watermelon, and grapes, irrigated with water sucked up from the depths of the earth.

In another hour I crested a rise and got the first glimpse of the Sea of Cortez, a Tanzanite-blue slash across the horizon. I skipped the bypass road and drove through *Kino Viejo*, then began passing the faded-white beach houses of *Kino Nuevo*, a hardscrabble tourist town split more or less democratically between Mexican and U.S. citizens. With no natural harbor Kino had escaped invasion by both the yachting crowd and large-scale commercial fishing operations; its part-time residents were mostly happy to drink beer and watch the sun set over the gulf.

Just after the Tienda Six market I turned right on the road to Punta Chueca. The sea dropped from view as the road curved through forests of cardón cactus and ironwood trees, then popped up again on the left, with the mountains of Isla Tiburón across the channel. In a half hour I rounded a bend onto the long downhill straight that leads into the Seri village of Punta Chueca.

The Seri People, or Comcáac as they call themselves, are an anthropological and historical enigma. They share their language with no other mainland ethnic group, and are vaguely thought to have immigrated from the Baja California peninsula centuries ago, gradually shifting across the intervening sea by island-hopping in reed boats. What is certain is that they fiercely resisted subjugation from, first, the Spanish, and then the Mexicans after independence. Seris saw the fat cattle and sheep brought by Europeans as a convenient new food source, and Europeans saw the Seri as sub-humans deserving of extirpation: from 1845 to 1870 the state of Sonora offered a cash reward for Seri scalps, and even after that was rescinded the killing of Seris went on with impunity. By the beginning of the twentieth century their numbers were down in the low hundreds; at the end of the millennium they had rebounded to perhaps a thousand, but their fiercely independent lives had been circumscribed by laws and external population and economic pressures. Now most of them lived in two villages on the coast of the Sea of Cortez: Punta Chueca and, about thirty-five miles farther north, El Desemboque Sur.

To augment the fishing that had sustained them for centuries, the Seri became famous for their exquisite ironwood carvings and finely wrought basketry. But even the income from the ironwood art was demolished when Mexicans in Kino and elsewhere began reproducing it in bulk using power tools, also decimating the supply of suitable, long-dead trees. In combination with the disruption in their small-scale fishing from large commercial operations, this left the Seris struggling with poverty and drug use. I had led some photographic tours to Seri country years before and had made sure the participants spent money generously on carvings and baskets from craftsmen and women I knew, and this had fostered several lasting friendships.

I drove slowly down the main street, waving at a couple of people who recognized and hailed me. Just past the soccer field I turned left on the last road before the beach and the town's tiny artificial harbor. A block south I stopped in front of a tidy white house, in front of which was a shaded palapa where a man a few years younger than I sat polishing an impressionistic carving of a road runner. He stood up as I switched off the engine and got out.

"Clayton!" The Seris often had trouble pronouncing my first name, so simply swapped it to the easier "Cleh*tone,*" accent on the second syllable. Not like I could say anything—in years of trying I had learned maybe 20 words of the impenetrable Seri language. We conversed in Spanish, which most of them spoke fluently.

"*Jorge, como estás?*" We shook hands warmly.

Jorge was one of the few younger Seris who had managed to maintain an income from fishing, while also developing a fine eye and hand for carving. I'd helped him secure the patronage of several high-end craft shops in Tucson and Santa Fe. The same shops represented his wife, Marta, who was a superb basketmaker. With the extra income they'd been able to send their son and daughter to a high-quality boarding school in Hermosillo.

Marta had taken their truck to see the children, so Jorge was home alone. After we had chatted for a few minutes, I asked after his boat.

"It is running well," he said in his decent English, which he liked to practice on me because he knew I'd correct him.

I asked if I could see it. He set aside his tools and we walked down to the beach where his panga was pulled up onto the sand.

The panga used in Mexico is sometimes referred to as the Yamaha panga, not because of the engine that is the predominant choice of power plant but because Yamaha supposedly developed the design in the early 70s for a World Bank project intended to standardize an inexpensive but seaworthy working boat for the Third World. Built of thick fiberglass able to withstand being run up on beaches year in and year out, twenty-two feet long with a five and a half foot beam, the panga has a stable V-hull and a broad, flared bow for flotation when fishermen are drawing in full nets. Jorge's had a 40-horsepower Yamaha outboard, and a small steering binnacle with a wheel set amidships, which improved balance when he was the only one aboard. Like all the pangas I'd ever seen, the hull showed heavy use but the engine was impeccably maintained. The owner's life depended on it.

I turned to Jorge and said, "I'd like to buy it."

Seris are typically imperturbable regarding commerce; they've long been used to taking any opportunity available. But he smiled and asked, "What about your *juguetito*?"

The Seris loved referring to the kayak as my "little toy," and thought me insane for tackling the open waters of the gulf in it—even though, as I teased them back, their ancestors had crossed over from Baja in canoes made from bundled grass.

I said, "I'm buying it for someone else. What would it cost you to replace it with something as good or better?"

He thought, then said, "The boat, that is no problem." He paused again, then, "There is a 60-horsepower engine that would be better . . ."

I smiled. "How much for both?"

This time he thought for considerably longer, then named a figure.

"*Bien*," I said.

I faced him and said, "Some people are going to come. They will want to rent or buy a boat. You tell them this is a gift from me. Answer whatever questions they ask. Give them anything they want. Do you have extra cans of gas?"

He nodded.

"Give them those too. Food, water, whatever they want."

Jorge said, "These people. Bad or good?"

"Bad. Very bad."

"What will you do?"

"I have everything under control. Don't lie to them about me or anything else. Tell them whatever they want to know."

It was getting late in the afternoon and I needed to launch. We walked back up to the Land Cruiser and Jorge climbed in the passenger seat while I drove it back to the beach; then he helped me unload the kayak. At the water's edge I loaded the front and rear compartments with equipment, food, and water, and secured the halves of the spare paddle to the front deck.

The last thing to do was securely strap down the awkward 35-pound duffel on the rear deck, and then lash the Flexible Flyer snow disk on top of that, while Jorge watched, mystified, accompanied by now by a gaggle of Seri kids as well. I was actually less concerned about the weight of the duffel than I was about the snow disk, as its large surface area would catch wind and waves. I didn't want to lose it, and I didn't want it to capsize me. Rolling back up would be virtually impossible with that much mass and resistance on top of the boat. Fortunately the breeze was mild and the tide was nearly ebbed. It was several days to a new moon so the amplitude would not be troublesome for the main crossing to San Esteban.

I opened the Land Cruiser's safe and pulled out the banded bills. I handed one bundle and a good chunk of another to Jorge. I was smiling to myself picturing the reaction when Jorge told my pursuers I had left them a boat as a gift. They'd undoubtedly guess where I'd got the funds, too. It was all about rattling the cage and making them angry. Angry people don't think straight.

I said, "If the people who come don't return in three days, and I don't return either, I need you to drive my truck to a ranch near Cananea. Can Marta follow you to bring you back?" Jorge nodded. I pulled another $500 out of the bundle and handed it to him. Then I dug a notebook and pen out of the center console and wrote directions to Alberto's place.

Jorge, perceptively, said, "What about the vehicle the people come in, if they don't return?"

I smiled and said, "That's your problem." I was picturing Jorge picking up his kids with, say, a black Range Rover at the end of term. I seriously doubted he'd be left with the key fob, but Jorge would figure something out.

We shook hands again. I donned the PFD and zipped it up, then slipped the spray skirt over my head. The clear water of the little bay lapped at the bow as I slid into the cockpit and fastened the neoprene edge of the spray skirt around the rim of the cockpit. With the paddle in my hands I nodded to Jorge, who shoved me off.

As the kayak cleared the beach he called after me softly, *"Buena suerte, mi amigo."*

CHAPTER 30

There is a magical moment in any boat, but especially in a small one, when you first feel the craft sever itself from land and dance on top of the water, defying and yet as one with it. I dipped the paddle blades and the kayak surged silently ahead. The built-up embankment of Punta Chueca's tiny harbor slipped past on my right, and as I moved into the channel the slight swell lifted and lowered the boat. Rather than paddle straight across to Tiburón I aimed southwest to clear a spit and mangrove estuary, then it was a long run down the straight east coast.

To my right I spotted the canyon in the interior mountains that accessed one of the only permanent springs on the big island. The early Seris carried water down from here in clay pots made so thin and light they were referred to as Seri Eggshell pottery. On the trail to the spring you could still find scattered mounds of shards where some unfortunate water carrier had dropped a pot—undoubtedly, one assumes, on the way down with a full one.

Up in those same mountains, I knew, was a healthy population of bighorn sheep, introduced to the island in 1975. Actually it proved to be a reintroduction after scientists found evidence of an ancestral bighorn presence. The current population served as a reserve for the mainland animals, and was also managed for very exclusive trophy hunts under the auspices of the Seri, who formally own title to the island even though it is also a government-decreed nature reserve. Did I mention expensive legal hunts some time back? These went for $90,000 each, with half going to the Comcáac community.

I didn't mind the hunts in theory—the Seris needed the funds and with no serious natural predators the bighorn could easily outstrip Tiburón's carrying capacity —what I did mind was that vehicles had also been introduced to the formerly pristine island, first by the military and then by the outfitters whose rich clients didn't want to have to hike too far to do their shooting. And as each year passed, the guides connected and extended the tracks farther. An island that could have remained a gleaming jewel of environmental preservation had been violated.

Sorry, where was I? Right: in a *juguetito*.

The sun was heading down and I wanted to get around the south end of the island before dark, so I'd been stroking along pretty briskly, staying about 300 meters offshore. One of the damn roads came right along the beach here, and I did not want to be spotted by some random military patrol. Fortunately, in contrast to normal sea kayak safety protocol, I had ordered the Cetus with a white hull and blue deck, which effectively disappeared in the ocean from a surprisingly short distance away. My PFD, too, was faded blue. So I was pretty sure I'd be missed by anyone not specifically looking out to sea, *unless* the sun glinted off a paddle blade. So I kept my eyes open behind me as well as in front.

At last I rounded Punta Ast Ah Keem, the towering knob at the southeast corner of the island, after the road had turned inland. I pulled up on a gravel beach in a cove around the corner just at sunset. Beyond the storm tide crest of heaped pebbles was a low sandy spot out of view from the water, so I ferried all the gear up there (including 132 pounds of water in the Ortlieb bags), then shouldered the 60-pound boat and carried it up and over the ridge. It was easy to flatten out and disguise my footprints in the gravel, even though I was certain no one would be after me for a day or two.

Despite being in tactical condition-yellow with the knowledge I would soon be chased down, it was impossible not to be happy to be here. A six-inch surf lazily rattled the beach pebbles. I could clearly hear the intermittent blow of a whale as it traversed from east to west a few hundred meters offshore. Coyotes yapped from the interior.

However, I wanted to be back on the water well before dawn, so I fired up the stove, boiled some water, and heated a pouch of beef stroganoff. When the water had cooled it went back in a Nalgene bottle to drink. I ate some fruit as well, then spread out the sil-nylon tarp on the sand, pounded out depressions for my hips and shoulders, and laid out the fleece bag. The PFD made a nice pillow, and within minutes I was asleep.

When I launched at 4:00 the next morning, the waning crescent moon hung in the eastern sky, still giving enough light to see in the pollution-free air. The tide was at its lowest ebb and would be flowing back north as I paddled, but not quite yet with the full velocity or volume it would reach at new moon. And the early morning air was still—something I counted on to not last.

Even after I rounded the last southwest corner of Tiburón and stroked out into the 15-mile channel that awaited, the moon didn't perfectly illuminate the larger swells that rolled in from the north, so I had to pay close attention. I had once tried paddling with the ATN night-vision goggles on, but despite their dual objective lenses and binocular vision, it was too unsettling, for me anyway.

I knew the tide would start carrying me northward soon, so I stopped, shined a flashlight on the bow-mounted compass, and lined up 225 degrees with a prominent star above the horizon. I estimated that would be a point just south of San Esteban—and indeed, as the horizon lightened and I finally could make out the island's dim silhouette, I appeared to be aiming to miss the island altogether. "Ferrying," as this angling across a current is known, feels like a completely illogical strategy, but it works.

Slowly the sea lightened from black to the steel gray that is somehow more intimidating than the black from an 18-foot-long boat. But I loved this time of day on the water. The outline of San Esteban gained clarity, the last stars disappeared, and the distant, tallest peaks of Baja California burst into gold fire. In what felt like seconds the steel gray sea morphed into deepest cobalt. A northerly breeze began to pick up as sort of a table of contents of what was to come, and the incoming tide lifted the gentle swell to a couple of feet. Perfect paddling conditions.

The water around the kayak exploded.

I snapped my head to the right and left, as a pod of at least twenty bottle-nosed dolphins leaped free of the surface and churned the sea getting looks at me. Was there any doubt they were grinning at having startled the shit out of me? None, the assholes. They clearly had covered the last 200 meters submerged so as to maximize the effect when they surfaced.

They circled and leaped around the kayak for a few minutes, until it became obvious I wasn't going to speed up to twenty knots and give them a wake to surf on. Then they disappeared off toward Baja.

By now I was in the middle of the channel and the tide was flooding. The southern tip of Isla San Lorenzo was slowly disappearing behind San Esteban, which meant I was still being carried north. I swung the bow another ten degrees south, which stabilized the view. While I was still certain I was well ahead of any pursuit, I turned frequently to check the horizon behind me. Not that it would have made any difference—if a panga caught me out here all the pilot would have to do is run me down with that inch-thick fiberglass bow. No need to waste ammunition.

In the distance ahead I caught the faint sound of a whale's blow. It came closer and closer until I could spot the condensed exhalation with each surface and breath. As it passed not fifty meters off my port side I recognized the long profile of a fin whale, the second largest on earth and a year-round resident of the Sea of Cortez.

By 10:00 I was just off the coast of San Esteban, only about a kilometer north of my intended aim—the ferry navigation had worked. I turned south but stayed well offshore to avoid the tidal-current vortices curling around the corner, then curved back to paddle along the precipitous coast, past a small group of sunning sea lions, to the "Big Chuckwalla" gravel spit at the southwest corner. The gravel beach there was pretty steep and there was a small but dumping surf pounding it, so I paddled around to the other side to land.

The first thing I did after dragging the boat out of the water was to dig out the binoculars, run down to the end of the spit, and check the eastern horizon—and the northwest, just in case someone had been clever. Nothing there, and I didn't expect anything until tomorrow at the earliest.

I now had a lot of work to do as quickly as I could accomplish it. The kayak and gear would be extremely vulnerable for the rest of the day as I whittled away at moving stuff, and I would sometimes be miles away.

I unloaded everything and carried it up the wash until it was at least out of sight of a passing boat. Kayak, big duffel, and snow disk too.

Then, first, water: I had six 10-liter Ortlieb bags of water, which I needed to disperse and hide as widely as possible. Water was life. The Katadyn Survivor desalinator would keep me alive, but barely. I needed lots of hydration for what was to come.

I put two of the bags in the Mystery Ranch rucksack, along with a dozen Tanka Bars, and headed north up the wash. It was a short drainage; it topped out a kilometer later and I looked over a hill to a northward-flowing drainage that led into the huge central watershed of Arroyo Limantour. I headed down that one to a spot I'd found before where there was an overhang hidden behind a thick copse of the shrubby elephant trees that are a dominant plant here. One bag went in there with a half-dozen Tanka Bars, after I'd shined a light in to make sure no San Esteban rattlesnakes were dozing inside. I'd have to take the chance that one of the endemic mice would find the bars and drag them off one by one, or chew through the Ortlieb. Then I continued down to the central drainage—broad and flat, and relatively lush with ironwood trees and rock figs—and jogged up it, toward the northwest corner of the island, keeping to the rocks on the side to avoid footprints. There was another good hiding spot there, on the crest of a hill with a spot to watch for pursuit.

I detoured on the way back to the boat to check the cliffs on the west coast. As I remembered and as the satellite view had shown, there was one about halfway down that had a loose slope angling sharply toward an abrupt edge. It was difficult to judge heights from here but the edge looked to be about thirty feet above the water. I also couldn't tell if the sea came right up to the base or if there was a rock apron—I'd check that later.

Now came a critical part: I clicked the timer on the Sinn, and booked it for my landing beach as quickly as I could move.

Eighteen minutes. I figured I was in better shape than the people who would be after me. Give it twenty-two, maybe twenty-five. It was still going to be interesting.

On the next water run I first carried the snow disk up to the cliff. Nearby was a narrow vertical cleft in the rock where I was able to wedge the disk and hide it with rocks piled above. Then I carried the two Ortlieb bags and more pemmican bars down and across the arroyo and up again to one of the highest volcanic peaks on the island, around 1,800 feet tall. From there I could spy on a large part of the island and almost half of the arroyo.

Two more trips got the rest of the gear away and concealed, including all the electronics and my camping equipment. I picked a shallow, sand-bottomed cleft only a kilometer north of the spit and beach as my bivouac, because I hoped to stay close and keep surveillance on my terms, not theirs. The spot also overlooked the channel to the west. Not far away I buried the spool of paracord, the hacksaw, grappling hook, and the pulley, which I wouldn't need until later.

Now I faced another vital task.

I carried the kayak back to the west side of the spit. Rather amazingly for this late in the day, the sea was still calm and the breeze mild. I lashed the big duffel back onto the rear deck, donned the PFD, climbed in and secured the sprayskirt, and launched. The boat was *way* less stable with the duffel on top and no gear inside, so I paid attention as I paddled up the west coast. Cormorants eyed me warily as I stroked past; gulls and brown boobies squawked and circled close until they figured out I wasn't tossing offal off the stern like the big fishing boats. The sun was heading down in the west, lighting up the multi-colored strata of San Esteban's rugged silhouette.

I stayed well offshore and kept my eye on the clifftops until I spotted the one with the loose slope. I knew it was the correct one because I'd noted at its northern end a particular, tall cardón cactus..

I turned and stroked for the cliff. There was a pair of car-sized boulders awash at its base, but otherwise the bottom dropped off sharply; it looked to be at least ten or fifteen feet deep a kayak-length from the rocks. Excellent. I turned south, staying close to the wall, watching for a break, something large enough to crawl or walk into. But there was nothing for a good 200 meters. Too far. I turned around and paddled back north. There was a crevice, but only a foot wide. Farther on another, slightly wider. Then a deep gouge in the face, four or five feet wide—but with no bottom; the mild swell gurgled in and out of it. The sun was angled wrong so couldn't see into the shadow to determine if there was a place to stand or land. If there were I'd need access to the rear deck, so I raised the skeg on the kayak to allow maximum maneuverability, spun the boat at the entrance, and stroked backward hard to drive it in. As the stern shot between the walls I had to snatch the paddle alongside the kayak to prevent the blades catching on either side of the cleft and yanking it out of my grasp.

Even though the swell was mild it immediately crashed the kayak into the rock on the left side. I stuffed the paddle under the deck bungees and extended my arms. I could reach the rock on both sides, and was able to steady the boat and walk it backwards, looking over my shoulder. About twenty feet in there was a jumble of small rocks, and a rubble-choked shelf above that. I kept walking the kayak backward until the stern was knocking against the rocks, where I was able to use handholds on one side to steady myself and step out of the boat into knee-deep water. Crabs scurried away from my Israeli boots as I dragged the kayak up to where it wouldn't re-float itself, then turned to explore the cleft.

It got no wider than it had been at the entrance, which would be something of a logistical problem, but it would work. The cleft dead-ended in a near-vertical wall another twenty feet in, and there was a lot of rockfall around. Excellent.

I unlashed the big duffel and carried it above the high-tide marks on the rocks. There was a good sized boulder there that concealed it completely. I left the other items I'd need, then piled more rocks over the lot. Only someone who ventured it all the way in there could find it. You certainly couldn't make it in a panga.

Now I needed a place to hide the kayak. I climbed back in, scooted my way out of the cleft, and paddled north. There were several large sea caves on this side of the island, but I wanted an open ravine, if possible one with foot access to the interior. Not far south of a hammer-shaped spit the Seris had used frequently for camping and foraging, I found a short inlet and ravine that would work. I beached the kayak, carried it back into the V-shaped cleft, and tucked it under the south wall. After piling boulders in front I walked back down to the water's edge and looked back, then did some adjusting. Only a tiny patch of the deck was visible; I was sure no one could spot it from offshore unless they were looking in exactly the right spot.

I climbed up the steep slope and emerged near the upper sources of Arroyo Limantour. The quickest way back to my camp was to follow the arroyo partway south and then go up the side canyon where I'd hidden the first water cache. Along the way I ran into a thick stand of the endemic agave that was a major food source for the San Esteban Seri. Nearby I found several pits that had obvious human origins—these were where the Seri roasted the agave hearts to render them edible. I couldn't recall these as being mapped yet, so I made a note to tell my anthropologist friend Tom about them, to add to his extensive database.

By the time I got back to my bivouac it was near sunset. I jogged down to a crest that overlooked the spit. No one there.

Ready when you are, I thought.

I was starving after the day's running and paddling hither and thither, so I walked back to camp, lit the stove, and heated two pouches of beef stew. I followed that with some fruit for dessert. Then I climbed up the ridge and sat looking west over the channel, Isla San Lorenzo, and the dark low silhouette of Baja. Venus burned like a flare low over the peninsula; above me was another obvious planet. I lay back and looked through the Zeiss binoculars, and could just make out the oblong shape that identified it as Saturn and its rings. Poor Galileo had gone to his grave thinking Saturn was simply an oval planet.

I lay there, forcing myself to think of nothing but the splendid solitude, as the violet Belt of Venus—the shadow of the Earth on its own atmosphere—faded in the east, and stars emerged from the heavens one by one until it was completely dark.

Few places in the developed world retain night skies as dark as those on the Midfriff Islands. The summer Milky Way laid a phosphorescent wake across the western horizon. Paul Bowles wrote of night in the desert as " . . . a woman wrapped in a cloak of burning stars." When I led student trips in the desert I would have them lie on their backs, heads inward in a circle, and stay quiet, urge them to just look straight up until they perceived nothing but themselves looking up at the universe. Then, when they had been quiet for some time, I would interrupt and say, "Okay. Now, instead of feeling yourself looking up, imagine instead that you are looking *down*." This inevitably drew gasps of awe, sometimes of terror.

I lay there and counted meteor trails until my pulse had settled to its normal resting rate of 45 or so, I pulled out the ground sheet and fleece bag. But first I powered up the Iridium phone and checked the weather via SpotCast.

My pulse quickened. The forecast showed a low pressure system off California, slowly easing its way onshore. It looked like I had about three days before the conditions I hoped for made it this far south.

Ready when you are, I thought, before dozing off.

CHAPTER 31

The morning's moon was a fingernail hanging above Tiburón, soon lost in the glare of dawn. It was just a couple of days before new moon—when the sun and moon were aligned on the same side of the earth—which would mean maximum tidal flow.

Had I actually been here for research the day would have started well: As I was wandering around with a cup of coffee (sugar but no cream; insert 50-percent unhappy face here) listening to the desert birds, I spotted a fine three-foot-long male specimen of *Crotalus estebanensis*—the endemic rattlesnake—winding its way through the undergrowth. Probably heading back to a shaded overhang to wait out the heat of the day. I started to walk on by, but then a thought hit me.

It was remotely possible I could find a use for a venomous snake in the next day or two. After all, look at the great job a harmless one had done for me.

The last thing I wanted was to endanger a member of a species found nowhere else but a single island. But still—while I was pretty sure I held all or most of the cards, the oldest rule of warfare is that no battle plan survives contact with the enemy. I went back to my stash of equipment and emptied a coated nylon dry bag. Since I didn't have any snake-handling tools with me I found a more-or-less suitable stick and quickly pinned the snake's head, which sent him (it was a male) into a fit of writhing and rattling. I gently but firmly grasped just behind his head, lifted him up and guided the rattling end into the open dry bag, tossing the head in last and quickly rolling up the opening. The bag was full of air and snakes don't use a lot of oxygen, but I used the tip of a blade on my Leatherman to poke a dozen half-inch slits. The rattling had already subsided when I stashed the bag under a ledge where no sun would reach it.

I debated heading east to a high spot from which I could scan the channel between San Esteban and Tiburón. There was a possibility they would try to outflank me by landing at the wide beach of Arroyo Limantour—where, had it been later in the season, I might have also expected to see a Lindblad Expeditions ship pull up and anchor. The company ran Sea of Cortez tours that included a hike on the island and Zodiac excursions around the coast.

No. I was counting on my quarry being arrogant— and pissed off—enough to head straight toward where I'd advertised I'd be. Especially after I'd bought them a boat. Also, I needed to conserve water. So I set about doing what I was good at doing anyway: waiting and watching.

First I checked the forecast again. Still looking good for what I needed in two to three days.

I built an FOP (forward observation point, if you'll remember) under an ironwood tree at the crest of a ridge about 200 meters from the mouth of the drainage. The spot was shaded during the day, which would be good both for comfort and concealment. I built a short tunnel with branches and debris that would allow me to squirm forward and get my binoculars on the area without any possibility of reflections or backlighting. It only covered my head and shoulders but that was all I needed; the rest of me would be behind the crest.

Above the FOP was a partly shaded, more comfortable rock perch that looked over the drainage as well as the channel to the west. I sat there to spend the day. During the morning and early afternoon a couple of fishing boats passed by well off toward San Lorenzo, and, surprisingly, a good-sized sailboat on a northerly course, a ketch at least fifty feet long. Most likely headed toward Bahía do Los Angeles, a popular yachting stopover with a sheltered harbor, good restaurants, and a superb little museum.

I heard scrabbling under a rock ledge behind me, and turned to see one of the San Esteban chuckwallas, apparently simply bored, crawling from one recess to another. As a defense against predators, chuckwallas developed the habit of wedging themselves into a crevice and then inflating their bodies, making them difficult to pull out. It worked well until Seri kids came along. They'd simply carry a sharp stick and puncture the wedged lizard, then haul it home to add to the family larder.

By 5:00 I was beginning to wonder whether anyone would show up that day. If I were them I wouldn't want to be setting up a perimeter after dark. By 5:30 I was certain.

And then of course they showed up.

I heard the drone of an outboard, squirmed quickly back into the little tunnel, and trained the binoculars on the tall sentinel rock that stood at the water's edge on the east side of the beach.

Jorge's panga appeared, cruising slowly toward the base of the spit in perfectly calm water.

There were four men in it. One was seated at the steering console with a weapon slung across his back. The other three were arranged in a triangle in the bow, braced with rifles up and pointed at the beach. No third-world AKs for these guys; they were brandishing tacticalled-out AR-type carbines—spendy HK 416s I was willing to bet, with full-auto capability. Co-registered optical sights, vertical forward handgrips, underslung weapon lights. Thirty-round mags. The works. They were dressed in disruptive desert camouflage with matching boonie hats. Wraparound ESS ballistic glasses. No doubt they were wearing armor under the camo.

And they weren't just dressed up to do selfies in the mirror; they were clearly pros—ex-military contractors. Mercenaries. The three in the bow were sweeping right and left with their muzzles, perfectly splitting the field of fire.

And that was a problem.

No, not the fact that they professional operators. I had that covered.

The problem was that there was no way these guys were the masterminds of the drug and hunting ring. They were—as Jed had suggested as a possibility— troops. Top-level hired mercenary troops, but troops.

Had I misjudged them? This so did not fit with my psych evaluation that I ducked behind cover and turned my head to check six and make sure no one was sneaking up behind me.

I turned back. The panga headed for shore, the three in front still sweeping. The guy at the helm gunned the engine at the last minute to run the bow well up the beach. The weapons of the trio in front didn't even waver as the boat hit the gravel and ran half its length out of the water. They leapt out and moved apart rapidly, duckwalking, muzzles still sweeping back and forth, up and down. Nice work.

The engine cut out.

At least, *that* engine cut out.

Because I could still hear another.

Not another outboard, or an inboard for that matter. In fact it sounded like a . . .

Yeah.

Just as I placed the sound signature, a helicopter banked around the bluffs to the east where the panga had emerged, no more than fifty feet off the water.

It was a Robinson R44, the little piston-powered civilian model popular with doctors and other well-to-do amateur pilot-owners who all too frequently wound up killing themselves in the things. I'd ridden in several of them on wildlife surveys, never altogether comfortably.

I had several stream-of-consciousness thoughts in rapid succession, perhaps not all of them what you might expect from your typical action-novel black-ops hero.

First: *Hey, no fair!*

Second: *Is aerial gunning for biologists legal in Mexico?*

Finally, something reasonably perceptive on a tactical level:

If they fly this direction instead of landing, I'm fucked.

Seriously. I was completely concealed from the ground, and nearly completely exposed from the air, with no cover in sight aside from scraggly desert trees. I definitely wouldn't fit where the chuckwalla was snoozing.

Fortunately the helo flared in above the panga, curved north into a broad area of the wash, and settled onto a flat expanse of sand and gravel. The bow gunners from the boat moved smoothly up on either side and in front of the craft, still sweeping; the helmsman had secured the boat and was standing back, covering the high ground with his own weapon. He was talking in what looked to be a normal voice, and at one point reached up to adjust something at his ear, so the four apparently had discreet two-way radio headsets, probably the excellent Silynx C4OPS units.

The Robinson's six-cylinder Lycoming engine doesn't need the extended rundown time of a turbine. The pilot rolled the throttle down to 75 percent, waited to make sure the cylinder-head temperature was normal, then throttled all the way off, disengaged the clutch, and cut the fuel mixture to shut off the engine. As the rotor wound down two people climbed out.

And there they were.

I was only mildly surprised at who "they" were.

I resisted the urge to call out, "*Bienvenidos!*" The constantly sweeping muzzles of the other four sort of . . . muzzled me.

The forward gunners backed toward the pair, weapons still traversing, and while one kept sweeping the other two helped pull several equipment cases out of the rear seat and walked back toward the panga, where the helmsman was now unloading a huge mound of duffels, water containers, ice chests, and Pelican cases, including a long, flat one. The gunmen pointed out the numerous footprints I'd left and made no effort to conceal—I *wanted* them to know I was here and not on the other side of the island.

With two contractors standing guard, the other two finished unloading the boat, carried the gear above high tide line, and began pitching a camp—the first components of which were, while I gaped in astonishment, a pair of canvas wall tents like something right out of my South Rift field station. Chairs, tables, stoves followed. Canvas wash basins on tripod legs? Yep.

Then they did something interesting. One of them brought a pile of four-foot-long sections of rebar from the boat, and started hammering them in the ground in a semi-circle inland of the tents. Then he unloaded a pile of what looked like conduit, each maybe eight feet long, and slipped them over the protruding ends of the rebar.

Suddenly I got it, and my hunch was confirmed when he then unrolled about 50 feet of nylon, eight feet wide, and began unfurling it along the poles, using what appeared to be sewn-in loops. In a few minutes, the tents were invisible from my perch.

It was a simple anti-sniper screen.

Considering that I could easily have brought along the Steyr SSG given my wave-through at the border, it was a smart move. But I hadn't been confident enough that I'd be allowed through without any search at all to bring a rifle.

In any case, I had plans for this group more interesting than simply trying to pick them off one by one. And I didn't intend to leave any corpses where they could be found.

After the screen was up, one man went back down and hammered in a sturdy anchor stake for the panga and tied it securely.

One thing I'd noticed so far: At no time was there not at least one man out front with a rifle at low ready scanning the wash and hills, and he generally kept moving as well.

That I wasn't worried about.

The helicopter. *That* I was worried about. Their embarrassingly unsportsmanlike move had completely upended the tactical situation. I could script what would happen tomorrow morning: They would leave two guards in camp, remove the four doors from the Robinson, and the other four would pile in and scour the island for me with three automatic rifles at the ready. There were plenty of places I could hide from an aerial search—among them some of the caves the San Esteban Seri had sheltered in—but my situational control would vanish. They'd already set up a stylish safari camp. Next they'd be hunting. I'd be on the run, and my movements would be severely restricted given the speed and altitude advantages they would have. My end game would be impossible to implement.

I was beginning to feel like Sanger Rainsford on Count Zaroff's island.

Nope. The helicopter had to go, and right the fuck now—the sooner I moved, the better, before they got comfortable with their surroundings. "Move first," one of my instructors had pounded into me. Then he'd repeated it. "Always. Move first."

I looked at where the Robinson sat, about thirty meters north of the camp. Close, but perhaps not too close. Everything would depend on how many guards they stationed there that night. One, and I had a chance. Two, and it would be almost impossible. It was a certain bet they'd have night vision equipment.

It was also a certain bet that no ordinary distraction would work with these pros.

The sun went down, and soon the camp was illuminated with LED lanterns and I could see the glow of a lit stove. The guards swapped duty. One went down to stand over the boat and another walked up and positioned himself close to the helo. He had a night-vision set already strapped to his head, but—if I was making it out correctly in the fading light—it was a single-tube version with only one objective lens. That would hamper his perception compared to my binocular vision with the ATNs, but he'd still have equal light-gathering assuming they were Gen 4s like mine.

But it seemed only one guard was to be on duty at the Robinson.

I eased back down from the crest, turned, and jogged north along the ridge to my bivouac. The last evening light was fading as I quickly downed a couple of Tanka Bars for energy, liberally applied the dark camo paint on my face, strapped on the ATN goggles, made sure the Helle knife was in its sheath on my belt—and, last but not least, retrieved the dry bag containing the rattlesnake.

CHAPTER 32

I crossed to the east side of the wash, where the vegetation was thickest, and turned south. The ATNs magnified the stars' glow enough so it was as though I was walking in the light one gets just before dawn, except with that characteristic greenish tinge. The guard at the helicopter would have the same view. I had one advantage: Night-vision goggles have zero peripheral vision, thus as long as he wasn't looking directly my way he wouldn't catch me out of the corner of his eye. But then when I had to look down to watch where I stepped I couldn't see him either. I had to hope he wouldn't have an infra-red illuminator on or there'd be no way for me to hide.

I stopped behind a shrub high enough on the east flank of the wash so I could evaluate his movements from about seventy meters away. He was not slacking— he never sat down or took his eyes off the terrain—but after a while I detected a repetition to his movements around the helicopter. He spent about five minutes on each side before swapping. The regularity might help keep him alert, but it would also help me get closer.

I waited a while longer, until the lanterns were extinguished in the camp. I couldn't wait too long or I'd risk running into a shift change. Given the number of gunmen I expected they'd do three-hour shifts. I'd left the Sinn at the bivouac—even though I was wearing a long-sleeved shirt I couldn't risk having the watch peep out. The luminescent hands and dial markers would glow like a flare through NV goggles.

It was time to move.

Now I had a problem. When I removed the rattlesnake from the dry bag it was inevitably going to piss him off again, meaning he'd start rattling. And I needed to get within ten feet or so of the guard to effect my scheme.

I put the bag on the ground, loosened the roll-top flap, and slowly bled the air out of it until it was flat and I could make out the shape of the snake inside. When it moved in a way that revealed the head I pressed down just behind the lump. Sure enough, he started buzzing furiously, but the bag muffled most of it. Now I had to stick my other hand in the bag and try to grasp his head from the back—a fraught operation at the best of times, much less blind. But I managed that, and then I slid my other hand in, found the rattle, and grabbed that to still it. I pulled the snake out and left the bag.

Cool. Now I just had to sneak up the last seventy meters on a trained, armed, and alert operator while clutching an annoyed pit viper.

Fortunately, as is usual with snakes, the initial thrashing soon subsided and he switched to calmly but determinedly trying to squirm out of my grasp. Which meant that a good portion of my situational awareness had to remain directed at my right hand, lest he manage to get that head free by an inch or two and turn around and nail me.

I eased down the slope into thicker cover. Each step required a sequence of operations: look down to ensure the next placement wouldn't make noise, look up to ensure I was out of the guard's line of sight, take the step, and reaffirm that the snake's head was still secure between my thumb, fore, and middle fingers. One step. Five. Ten. Fifty.

Finally I was opposite the starboard side of the helicopter, only thirty meters away. I checked the camp; all seemed quiet and dark. There were three jatropha shrubs between me and the machine that should provide cover when the guard was on my side; that meant five minutes to move silently between each one when he was on the other side. I had help from a light surf that provided background noise, as well as a zephyr of breeze that lightly stirred the vegetation.

First one. I made it there and crouched with my head down so I was just a blob behind the bush. I heard the guard walk to the near side of the helo, where he stood silently—no fidgeting, no humming to himself. When he moved around again I looked up cautiously, then eased my way around and went for the second shrub. This took worryingly longer due to the crunchy gravel of the wash bed now under my boots, but I crouched again just a half-minute before the guard came around.

Again he was quiet.

For about two minutes.

Then he walked toward me.

I was already motionless, but I got motionless-er, if that makes sense. I envisioned a sequence of moves if he came all the way to my shrub and spotted me—fling the snake, grab the Helle knife from the sheath, go for his throat in the faint hope I could slash it before he yelled. Or fired.

He crunched closer; he was probably at the first shrub by now. He stopped.

I heard a zipper. Followed by a drawn-out splash.

He walked back and was quiet again before circling once more. I moved.

The last shrub was the most dangerous because, 1) it was soaked with piss, and, 2) it was fully in his field of vision when he was on my side, and anything that changed would create a jarring note. I was in all-dark clothing and the jatropha shrub was fully leafed-out, but it was no larger than an oil drum and there was little leeway either side for the guy to step without spotting the extra silhouette. I crouched but kept my head raised just enough so I could watch his feet and lean either way if needed.

I was really glad he had chosen his previous interval on this side to pee.

He came around and took up the starboard position. I could see his feet shift slightly as he looked each way, swiveling to scan a full 180 degrees. This interval felt at least ten times as long as the preceding ones, but finally he circled once more.

I stood and slowly stepped around the bush. A light increase in the breeze tousled the vegetation and gave me extra sound cover for the last few steps, and then I was crouched against the right side of the helicopter. The snake gave a sudden violent twist that damn near wrenched the tail loose, but then it subsided again and went back to quietly squirming.

I rose and looked through the canopy. The guard was watching the hill above the west side of the wash. He was standing right at the front of the cockpit. I stood fully upright, leaned right, and had a clear view of the back of his head around the sloping front of the perspex windscreen. I waited until he had swiveled to watch northward, then, when he turned back west, I stepped toward the front of the machine, wound up, slung the rattlesnake underhanded in a high arc toward him, and ducked back behind the canopy to evaluate the results.

The instant the snake left my hands the rattle went off full bore—a harsh, metallic *bzhzhzhzhzhzhzht!* The guard spun, and his augmented monocular vision was filled with the sight of a snake flying through the air at his face.

Ophidiophobia is a surprisingly common syndrome. More people admit to being afraid of snakes than admit to a fear of heights. Or even clowns. And once it's there, it's damn near impossible to get over; I've tried with several otherwise macho friends with decidedly mixed results. And even if you're not particularly susceptible, the sight of a flying rattlesnake might tip you over the edge.

It certainly did this guy. He drew in a huge breath that was nearly an inverted scream on its own. The rattlesnake landed across his chest and shoulder, writhing. The guy dropped his rifle on its sling and grabbed for the snake, which twisted and buried its fangs in the side of his neck before he could fling it away.

That huge intake of breath came out in a shriek, and he turned and ran stumbling for the camp, screaming unintelligible Spanish.

Before the shriek ended I was in motion.

Behind the helicopter's cockpit was the upper aft cowl door, secured by two toggled Dzus fasteners. I twisted them and flipped the hatch down. Inside was the transmission system of the Robinson's Lycoming engine. There were any number of ways to disable the machine, but I need one that would work in the next 15 seconds, and I knew what it was.

The engine drives the Robinson's main and tail rotors through a sprag clutch and a pulley that in turn drives four identical belts, made of cord-reinforced rubber—basically oversized, glorified fan belts.

And I had a very sharp knife.

I pulled the Helle from its sheath and reached in with it. The space was tight, and I had to swap the knife to my left hand while worming in with the right to grab the belts in turn. The clutch was disengaged so the belts were loose, which actually made them harder to cut. In turn I pulled each one taut and went at it with the knife.

As I was cutting I was listening to the sudden chaos in camp. The guard was still babbling the same thing over and over, and finally my Spanish caught up with him:

"FLYING SNAKE! FUCKING FLYING SNAKE!"

There was much shouting and cursing on the part of the others, but as yet no one seemed to have grasped that it was anything but a fucking flying snake—and the bite on the poor bloke's neck would be making itself obvious by now given his racing pulse. I had no doubt the riled-up rattler had given him a full dose of cytotoxic venom, and in the neck it was going to be a serious situation.

The last belt parted. I closed the cowl door and twisted the fasteners, then ran straight up the wash to put as much vegetation as possible between me and the camp. Once I was out of range I turned and climbed the west bank to my FOP. I'd left the three-power lens converters for the ATNs here, so I popped them on and settled down to see what would happen.

I could still hear the bitten guard blubbering, but his rant had subsided to outbursts of painful curses that even from this distance seemed to be growing slurred. The venom would be destroying his red blood cells and initiating tissue necrosis. His body would be trying to fight the attack by flushing the area with lymphatic fluid, inducing swelling that itself would be life-threatening given the location of the bite. Most rattlesnake-bite victims survive even with no treatment; given anti-venom the survival rate is 99.9 percent. But most snake bites are on extremities, and this victim was nowhere near possible treatment.

They definitely wouldn't be flying him anywhere.

Two gunmen appeared from opposite sides of the sniper screen, rifles shouldered and blazing-bright LED weapon lights sweeping the landscape. The ATN's circuitry shut down so I took them off and switched to the Zeiss binoculars.. The two headed straight for the helicopter, waving the weapons right and left and up the slopes on either side. Finally they'd caught on. They reached the machine, and one covered while the other looked around in the cockpit with a handheld flashlight. Then he started opening hatches and shining the light in each one. When he got to the right-side aft cowl door, he looked, then called his buddy over. Even if you knew nothing about machinery it would be obvious something was amiss in there with the ends of four belts flopping loose.

The two stepped from the port up to the front of the helicopter and raised their rifles. One yelled something back at the camp, and then the night was split by the hammer of full-auto fire as they hosed down the vegetation of the wash. Sixty rounds gone in two and a half seconds; they reloaded in stylish synchronicity and blasted another sixty rounds at the surrounding slopes. One round actually whined off a boulder a few yards from where I had ducked.

A nice show of firepower but really quite useless. And unprofessional. I'd made them mad and they'd let it get to them. That meant I was back in control.

From the sniper screen the other operator and the two principals emerged at a run, each of them carrying a carbine at ports arms. They converged on the helicopter and one of the gunmen showed them my drivetrain modifications. The pair met my expectations by taking it way cooler than their hired pros. They conferred with each other, looked up in my general direction, then turned and walked calmly back around the curtain. About five seconds later there was a single shot. The moaning and babbling of the snake-bit gunman ceased.

Sweet. One down. Five to go.

I ducked behind the ridge, gathered the equipment, and headed for camp. I knew the principals wouldn't let the gunmen do what they probably wanted to do and rush out after me, so I was safe until the early morning. And I was starving.

CHAPTER 33

When I woke up at 4:00, Orion was rising over the eastern hills of the island. The constellation always lifted my spirits.

I checked the surroundings with the ATNs to make sure no early searches had been launched, then made coffee. I decided coffee with sugar but no cream was less than half satisfying, so I took it black. Then I kitted up and headed back toward the FOP, keeping to the seaward side of the ridge, just my head high enough to scan for movement on the other side, and moving slowly enough that it took me nearly an hour to cover the kilometer between me the my goal.

I approached the observation point on my belly, squirmed my head and torso into the little hide, and lifted the binoculars over the edge. In the predawn dimness the camp was wide awake and in motion—I could see shadows thrown across the sniper screen from lantern light. Soon two gunman emerged, carrying the corpse of a third down to the panga, where they tipped him unceremoniously inside. One then loaded an unevenly shaped boulder from the base of the rocky slope and tossed that in as well. They untied the mooring line and climbed in, started the outboard, backed off the beach, then turned and gunned it straight offshore for a few hundred meters before cutting the engine to an idle. They were tiny even through the binoculars at that range, but they appeared to do some wrestling with the rock and some rope and then heave the corpse over the side, where it disappeared.

The boat came back in and nosed the beach. The gunmen jumped out, disappeared behind the screen, and returned several times with various cases and four rifles. They jumped back in, then the two principals walked down and climbed in. The boat backed away, turned, and motored slowly back east, disappearing around the sentinel rock.

I considered this development. Were they fleeing? That, too, would be counter to my reading of them. Had they wanted to send for more troops they could have just sent one man. Fetching another helicopter? That seemed unlikely as well—I hoped.

I thought some more, then put two things together. They were almost certainly out to do a circuit of the island in the hopes of finding my kayak. It made sense to start on the sunlit east coast even though it was farther away.

The other thing I put together was the obvious fact that I'd seen only two gunmen.

The beach and camp sat quietly in the rising light. There was no movement. I was pretty sure the guy wasn't sleeping in.

The back of my neck began to tingle. I considered the odds that he had circled around behind my position. But that didn't make sense. There was a big expanse of terrain where I might have been; the odds would have been scant that he would have spotted me—and, more importantly, I was willing to bet they'd be loath to send one man off alone on a scouting mission in terrain with which I was familiar and he wasn't. I was confident they had more respect for me by now.

Nope. I was certain the other gunman was still somewhere right here.

Now my forehead began to tingle.

Without moving the binoculars, I began to scan within their field of view the shaded east slope of the drainage. At the mouth it rose at a shallow angle, cut by ravines, but inland there was a jagged knoll that offered a towering view over a sweep of the drainage and western slopes—including the crest behind which I crouched.

The tingling grew more pronounced.

Millimeter by millimeter I moved the binoculars to the left to take in the knoll. I peered at several likely sniper's vantage points, and settled on three that looked like spots I'd choose if I wanted to enfilade the approaches.

Then I watched and waited.

An hour passed.

Then another.

Nothing. No movement.

Another hour. The morning's coffee was making its presence known.

Then I saw it. The tiniest movement as something shifted in a gap under a car-sized boulder that leaned over a dip in the steep rock face.

I froze my attention on that spot. The movement again—an object, barely resolved at this distance, long, straight, thin.

I held the binoculars in place while I ducked my head behind the crest, then pulled them back too and slithered out from under the hide. I nodded in admiration: He had very nearly outlasted me in stillness.

An urge seized me. I looked around for a couple of branches. I removed the boonie hat and placed it on one, then wedged the binoculars in the fork of another and held both branches so the hat crouched atop the instrument. I crawled sideways to a spot still well-shaded by the tree, then ever so slowly raised the hat and binoculars above the ridge.

Five seconds later there was a *crack* and the boonie hat flipped backwards off the branch. A second later, the crashing report of the rifle reverberated up and down the rocks. Something substantial—not .50-caliber-ish substantial, but certainly .338 Lapua-ish substantial. The size of the hole through the front and back of the hat corroborated my instincts.

Another urged seized me. I crawled back to the crest, then raised my left fist, its back toward the shooter and middle finger erect. A half second, a second, then I yanked it back down as the air cracked again a foot over my head and the rifle crashed.

Yes, I know what you're thinking.

I smiled, then immediately ducked back deeper into the depression—a good thing, as two seconds later a .338-ish round punched through the rubble six inches below the crest, stinging me with a spray of sand and pebbles.

I smiled again. Keep them angry; keep them off balance.

I raised an arm and gave a quick wave to let him know that, yeah, I was till there, un-punctured, then gathered up my kit, tipped the ventilated boonie hat back on to my head, and hiked back north on the other side of the ridge. I knew the shooter wouldn't leave the camp unguarded, so rather than watching my six I concentrated on not leaving tracks that could be followed later.

I was also willing to bet the shooter would ditch his empty cases and tell his returning comrades he had spent an uneventful morning, rather than admit to missing with three rounds and being flipped off by their quarry.

I kept an eye on the water. The sea was more active today—a northerly breeze raised regular whitecaps that punched against the still-strengthening incoming tide. A preview of things to come.

I reached the bivouac without sighting the panga, so I took a break to heat a meal. While I ate I tried to estimate how long it would take to do a thorough search of the coast. At least half of it was impossible to land on and thus easily bypassed. In other sections there were narrow beaches but no place to hide anything as large as an 18-foot kayak. The mouth of Arroyo Limantour on the east coast was wide and easy to land on; they would have stopped there to check for tracks. Most of the north coast was inaccessible. By now it had been nearly five hours since they had launched.

Hmm . . .

I stood with the binoculars, and there they were, still about a kilometer north of me. Heading south—and moving at a good clip, way too fast to still be searching the clefts and caves on this side. They cruised right past the slot under the cliff where I'd hidden the big duffel.

That could only mean one thing.

I waited until the boat passed me and disappeared around the bluffs to the south, then jogged up along the ridge to the ravine leading down to the kayak. One more scan with the binoculars to make sure they hadn't doubled back, then I clambered down to where I'd left the boat.

It had been throughly, vindictively smashed. A kevlar/carbon P&H Cetus is designed to withstand a lot of abuse, so it had taken serious effort and some good-sized boulders to trash it this comprehensively. Even the primary paddle had been splintered.

I smiled.

I was still in control.

Now I had to solidify it with one last bit of carefully timed mechanical mayhem.

Tomorrow, I was betting, the crew would embark on a concerted cross-country manhunt, knowing I was now trapped on the island. Even assuming they left someone to guard the panga, given four of them and one of me that would theoretically put me on the defensive again. My advantage would be that I was familiar with the terrain and had water and food caches scattered about, meaning I could travel lighter and faster. But it also meant tonight had to go perfectly.

One thing was certain: It would take more than a flying rattlesnake to distract them this time.

I returned to the bivouac and dug out the Olympus voice recorder, then hiked back up the ridge to a ledge above a steep, loose slope of scree and volcanic boulders about fifteen feet high. I took off my rucksack, sat on the edge, turned on the recorder, then sat quietly, picturing in my mind the coastal hills on the west side of the spit. I was pretty sure I could make it from a spot more or less directly above where the helicopter sat, along the seaward side of the crest, and down to within a couple hundred feet of the tent compound.

I closed my eyes and envisioned every step that would take in real time, and added five minutes for placing the recorder.

Eighteen minutes in I held the Olympus, still recording, and jumped off the ledge onto the scree. The rocks tumbled and crashed against each other as I rode the slide, trying to avoid having this turn more realistic than I intended.

Just as I reached the bottom and the din subsided, I screamed. A short cry of agony that I cut off by sheer force of will. Or at least I hoped that's what it sounded like. I kicked a couple of rocks to make a bit more noise, then clicked off the recorder. A playback of the last bit sounded pretty darn convincing, but the speaker wasn't exactly made for projecting so it would have to be placed really close.

I walked back to my stash, fired up the Iridium phone, and checked the weather.

A beautiful high-pressure system was stacking up over the Great Basin and Four Corners area, while low pressure was to predominate for several days over the Sea of Cortez. I had about forty hours before the combined effects would reach the Midriff Islands.

I called up tidal activity. High tide in Bahía de los Angeles, on the Baja peninsula about twenty miles north of me, was due at 10:50 a.m. the day after next. That meant it would be flooding northward where I was between about 7:00 and 10:00. At just a day after the new moon it would be a strong one.

Perfect.

That put tonight's operation on even more of a must-accomplish basis. Tomorrow I'd need to make sure the group stayed in pursuit of me all day, after which I'd have to elude them through the night, and then lure them after me one last time—much, much closer—the next morning.

I fueled up with two servings of beef stew—the most nutritionally complete meals I had. In the buried cache where I'd already stashed the equipment I wouldn't require immediately—the folding grappling hook, the spool of paracord, hacksaw, Garmin GPS, desalinator, and fishing kit—I added the sat phone, stove, cook kit, and the rest of the pouch meals. I reburied everything and inspected the site from all angles until I was satisfied the cache was invisible. I loaded everything I'd need for the next forty hours in the pack—water bottles, first-aid kit, spare batteries, the fleece sleeping bag. On a whim I tossed in the folding slingshot and ball ammunition—it could be useful for creating a distraction, or even as a weapon. Food was going to be fruit pouches and Tanka Bars. And no coffee. (I allowed my lower lip to tremble just for a moment at the thought, then told it to harden the fuck up.) In the removable back pocket of the pack, which could be converted to a fanny pack, I stashed the ATNs and the bottle of bleach.

After stopping at my first water stash to check on the Ortlieb sacks and pemmican bars (still unchewed), I traversed northeast, down across the big arroyo and up again to the high point near where two other Ortlieb bags were hidden. A short fin of rock at the top, shaded by an ironwood tree, offered a broad view southwest from under cover, and an escape route down the north slope if needed. I removed the external pocket from the pack, put a liter bottle of water in it next to the ATN goggles, the voice recorder, and the liter bottle of bleach (let's not confuse those bottles), slung the Zeiss binoculars over my head, and stuffed the pack under a ledge that wasn't visible from below. I strapped the pocket around my waist, re-applied face paint, and headed back.

By nightfall I was surveilling the camp from a peak farther away than my FOP, and safely out of sniper range. Through the binoculars I could see the contractors moving around a lot in and out of the cover of the screen, as if they were preparing for some significant activity. Yet always at least one was out out front with a rifle, and one was standing near the boat. I felt safe in assuming that the principals wouldn't have wandered off without their attack dogs.

Now I had to get just about as close as I got last time.

I descended to the bed of the wash, where vegetation shielded me, and began working my way south, stopping frequently to listen for continued activity. It was now dark enough to swap the binoculars for the ATNs and spool them up. Despite the instant clarity, I was doubly cautious not to get caught out by the tunnel vision of the optics. At a hundred meters out I went to my hands and knees; at fifty meters I went to my elbows and belly. Fortunately the gunmen were working by lamplight and even the posted guard didn't have an NV headset on, so his nocturnal vision would be shit.

I had to decide where to place the Olympus recorder. It needed to be close for the sound to carry effectively, but if they found it—at least if they found it quickly— they'd know immediately they were being conned and would turn their attention the wrong way for my needs.

An obvious spot suggested itself—under the helicopter. They'd be unlikely to look there when they heard something that sounded like a landslide. I squirmed that way, keeping the machine between me and the lights. I could see under it so it was easy to keep track of the activity, and in a few minutes I had my head stuffed under the cockpit and was scooping a pocket in the sand to stand the recorder upright and pointed at the camp. Once it was oriented, I took a deep breath, hit "play," and turned the volume to maximum. Only a slight hiss was audible.

I had eighteen minutes.

I backed out, checked to make sure the helicopter was between me and the duty guard, then crouched and stepped carefully for the shelter of the vegetation. A hundred meters later I took a sharp left and climbed the ridge, then doubled back south once I was over the crest. I poked my head up at one point and found everything still normal. At this point my main worry was to keep from starting a *real* avalanche, so I made haste slowly, as they say.

In ten minutes I was at the south end of the ridge line, overlooking the spit and, to my left, the camp. The guard at the boat was leaning against the bow; his rifle was hanging across his chest on its sling but he was alert and scanning regularly. However, because of the well-lit camp in front of him he had no goggles on either. That would be a big help. The sea was almost preternaturally quiet, which was bad and good—bad for my approach, but good for the recording that was about to play.

I crept down the opposite side of the ridge, and eased my way along the base of the slope above the high tide line, until I completely ran out of cover about forty meters from the panga. On one knee, I eased the bottle of bleach out of the fanny pack. I was farther away than I wanted, but all would depend on the reaction to . . .

There was a crashing, knocking, sliding cacophony— the heads and rifles of the two on duty snapped up— then a short, agonized cry of pain, cut off by sheer force of will. Hey, I *did* sound convincing. The poor little Olympus probably blew out its speaker but it sounded convincing, too.

The camp erupted in a shouting, scrambling frenzy. The front guard and my guy at the boat both sprinted up the wash, yelling, weapon lights on and jerking around furiously. Within seconds the other three sprinted after them, and five cones of blinding LED illumination turned night into day over a half square kilometer of the valley and hillside.

I sprinted too, straight for the boat. Over the gunwale, back to where the outboard was mounted. The helmsman had properly tilted it up to get the propellor out of the water where it couldn't drag on the bottom as the stern swayed with the swell, but I needed it down, so I dropped the Nalgene, pulled the catch and lowered the motor level. A quick glance behind me; everyone was still moving up-canyon. I reached around behind the engine cover and pulled the latch, then tilted the cover all the way over toward me. Oil filler? There. I twisted off the cap, grabbed the Nalgene and unscrewed its cap too, then carefully tilted it against the filler opening. The bleach gurgled down the tube. I got about two-thirds of a liter in before it came welling back out, so I capped the bottle and capped the filler tube, hoping it would be enough, but—critically—not too much. I flipped over the engine cover and reached back to latch it.

A beam of light stabbed the air over my head. I turned—someone was coming back my way, and quickly. The sniper screen was shading me at the moment, but in a few seconds whoever it was would be around one side or the other and I'd be pinned. There was no time to run either way along the beach. I grabbed the Nalgene and slipped over the stern of the boat into the cool chest-deep water.

And remembered the motor was still down. Shit.

I heaved myself up on the transom, trying not to splash water inside, pulled the catch, then slipped back down and raised the shaft housing until the motor was in its storage position again. The light was coming around the west side of the sniper screen as I slid back down and turned to see the bright white Nalgene bobbing away from me. A frantic lunge secured it and I ducked behind the boat just as it was floodlit with a weapon light. The beam held steady for ten or fifteen seconds.

Would whoever it was who'd been smart enough to check their six be satisfied with that?

Nope—footsteps crunched down the beach, and the boat rocked slightly as someone stepped aboard. I held on to the Nalgene—since it was half empty it was trying mischievously to bob to the surface—and ducked around to the starboard side of the craft, just my nose and eyes out of the water an inch or two from the hull. I cocked my head to make sure the damn ATNs didn't smack the fiberglass. Fortunately they were waterproof so I didn't have to worry about dunking them.

The footsteps clomped sternward and stopped at the motor. There was a long pause, a metallic noise, and the barrel of a rifle appeared above me as it was laid against the coaming. A clunk as the motor dropped level again. Then—*goddammit!*—the whir of the electric starter and the motor growled to life. I sincerely hoped whoever it was wasn't planning on a night patrol. Just checking to make sure it hadn't been tampered with? If so it had better be a short test. I held my breath in every meaning of the word as the motor burbled.

C'mon . . .

The motor stopped. More noise as it was raised again, then the footsteps clonked back to the bow and crunched onto the beach, fading away as I breathed again.

But I was still stuck. The search was still on, and the weapon lights were angling in every direction now, including toward the beach. By now they'd all be pretty well convinced that the noises had been a diversion and would be looking for *why* there'd been a diversion.

A couple of minutes later two sets of footsteps crunched toward the boat. They stopped short as a conversation ensued, one assuring the other that the boat was okay. The footsteps retreated to the camp, where a thorough search seemed to be being conducted.

I needed to leave, and there was only one way to go: out to sea.

I emptied the Nalgene, re-capped it, and stuffed it into the front of my pants, then floated onto my back and stroked slowly outward, keeping just my face above the surface. The buoyancy from the empty bottle helped keep me parallel to the surface and made progress quieter. Shadows danced across the water from random sweeps of flashlights, and I waited to be pinned in a beam. Twenty meters, then thirty, then forty.

Confession: I was a little creeped out doing this. There were sea lion colonies up and down the coast of San Esteban. Where there are sea lions there are usually sharks. And the thought of ending my days being ripped apart like a meat pie by a giant fish is not high on my list of preferred ways to go. Let me get taken down by a nice warm-blooded lion, or stomped by an elephant, or even chomped neatly in two by a hippo. Cold, lidless death from the unseen depths? Uh uh.

(Yeah, go ahead and laugh, like my friend Tommy, the Recon Marine whose hobby was free diving around the Farallon Islands, where great white sharks come big as school buses. But he ran the other way when I tried to hand him the beautiful eight-foot black mamba I caught while we were on a patrol in Tanzania. Everyone has his own *bête noir*.)

A hundred meters out I decided I'd gone far enough. My legs were getting serious heebie-jeebies and the theme from an old movie was playing in my head. I turned and stroked eastward—I didn't want to add to my exposure time as live bait by having to swim all the way around the spit to reach the west coast.

I swam for about 300 meters, angling back toward shore, then crawled gratefully out at the mouth of a ravine leading inland. Legs still attached.

The route was unfamiliar so the initial going was slow, and it was near midnight by the time I got back to the hill and the pack. My clothes were dry and my boots had stopped squelching, but I was still chilled—the temperature felt to be in the high 50s thanks to the low pressure system. And I was again starving, and rueing the stove and meal pouches I'd left buried at the bivouac. Four Tanka Bars and two pouches of fruit at least quelled the worst pangs. Then I spread out the fleece bag, climbed inside, and arranged the pack as a pillow. I drifted off counting the bright streaks of a meteor shower.

Everything was now in place. All I had to do was draw the group after me tomorrow, and keep them after me for twenty-four hours.

CHAPTER 34

Don't think about coffee.

Coffee.

You thought about coffee.

I lay in the bag in the pre-dawn dark, seriously considering running back to the bivouac and digging out the makings. What had I been thinking? Watching the stars to distract myself didn't work. Orion was no longer a hunter drawing a bow; instead it looked like a cosmic French press with a curved handle. The Pleiades were a sprinkle of sugar ready to be stirred in.

But the Milky Way was below the horizon, spoiling the hallucination.

I shook my head to clear it.

How about some water?

Gee, thanks.

I hydrated joylessly. Food? Tanka Bars. And, oh, look —*more* Tanka Bars.

I set about organizing and silencing the pack for the next day and night. First I swapped out—by feel—the lithium-ion battery in the ATNs. I got out the medical tape from the first-aid kit, tore off a strip, and laid a dozen and a half of the .44-caliber steel balls for the Wrist Rocket in a line on the sticky side, then laid another strip across the top and pressed it all together so the balls couldn't click together. The balls and slingshot went into an easily accessible side pocket. I rinsed the ex-bleach Nalgene and filled it plus two other liter bottles from the Ortlieb stash, then rolled them in the fleece bag to prevent them clonking and to partially silence sloshing. I would have been better off, tactically speaking, with a hydration bladder, which wouldn't clonk *or* slosh, but I seem to remember mentioning how much I hate those things. I put the tin of face camo in another side pocket—there was no point in applying it now and expecting it to last through a day of sweating. A dozen pemmican bars and a half-dozen fruit packs went in the top flap pocket, along with my stalk-mounted inspection mirror and the first-aid kit, from which I pulled one of the QuikClot dressings in case I needed it in a hurry.

I wiped down the ATN goggles and the binoculars, both of which had survived their swim with no issues. The ATNs went on my head, the binoculars around my neck. I cinched all the straps on the pack and shouldered it, snugged the waist belt, and shook back and forth. With all three water bottles still full there wasn't a sound; I planned to drink a liter at a time to avoid half-full noises. I tipped an Ortlieb to my lips and guzzled as much as I could take to get a head start, then stuffed it back under the rocks.

After thinking about it, I was pretty sure I could predict what the secondary strategy against me would be —given the catastrophic loss of their primary strategy to a flying snake and a sharp knife.

Of course they could simply leave and take the chance I'd die of thirst and/or starvation before a fisherman or Lindblad ship chanced by. San Esteban suffered from a distinct shortage of timber suitable for impromptu boat building. But there was plenty of wood suitable for signal fires—and they had no way of knowing what sorts of backup supplies I had, up to and including the satellite phone.

No. They couldn't take that chance—and besides, there was no way they'd leave at this point without having another crack at me. Not after I'd delivered another solid kick to the hornet's nest.

The radio headsets I'd detected when the operators landed were a clue. My bet was they'd leave one gunman to guard the panga. Of the other two contractors, one would be the sniper, carrying either just his long-range weapon or, more likely, a carbine as well. With radios on everyone the four of them could spread out far enough to cover a front 200 or even 300 meters wide while remaining in discreet audio contact and near enough to close up rapidly should the need arise. The gunmen would be on the flanks, and probably out in front by about fifty meters, so the formation would take a broad U shape.

One could argue that on a rugged island four miles on a side such a hounds-versus-fox game could go on forever. But both sides knew the scenario was set up for an eventual confrontation; the only question was when and how it would come about.

I could have stayed where I was, on the high ground, with long but sweeping views toward the southwest. But I had a slightly risky plan that required me to be closer when they appeared—and that hinged on estimating *where* they would appear over the high ground after climbing up from the coast. I thought I knew where that would be. So I headed downhill toward the big arroyo, then traversed west across several shallow valleys to an open slope about 2,000 meters across the broad drainage from the spot I had in mind.

And settled down to wait, while the big French press in the sky slowly faded. Soon I packed away the ATNs and began scanning with the binoculars.

The sun cracked the horizon and tipped San Esteban's peaks in gold fire. I watched, mesmerized, as the light eased its way down the slopes to ignite trees and shrubs, one by one, then, when it reached the broad expanse of Arroyo Limantour, flung a sudden carpet of luminescent green across the heart of the island.

I turned the binoculars back toward a certain ridge line and waited. An hour later I smiled.

A man appeared. From 2,000 meters and at 10x the figure was ant-sized, but I could discern that in his arms he cradled a long-barreled rifle topped by a long, fat scope, while over his shoulder peeked the silhouette of a carbine. I nudged the binoculars to the right, and several seconds later another man appeared, this one with just an assault rifle at port arms, about 200 meters west of the first man. I moved the binoculars to the space between the two contractors, and first one, then the other of the principals appeared. About fifty meters behind the point guards. A broad U-shaped formation. I smiled again.

They were all now in desert-pattern camouflage and matching boonie hats. Very stylish—and effective; when any of them stopped moving they blended in well with the scrub. However, it seemed that only the sniper rifle had a decent camo wrap; the black assault rifles revealed themselves with any movement at all. It's surprising how sharply sunlight will glint off a barrel and receiver, even from a mile away.

I was sitting under a small ironwood tree on an otherwise exposed slope. It was about 120 meters to cover over the top. I had chosen this spot on purpose, as well as that 2,000-meter separation between me and them.

I needed to trick them—convincingly—into thinking I had unwittingly exposed myself. I wanted them chasing me, but they needed to believe I was really on the run rather than baiting them deliberately toward some trap.

And to do that, I needed to let their sniper take a shot at me. And just hope he missed.

It was the only way to be convincing, because no matter how I might have fooled them before and no matter how much they would be on their guard for more tricks, they would know that *no one* would be stupid enough to deliberately expose himself to a sniper.

I know what you're thinking. But stay with me.

The craft and technology of sniping had advanced considerably since 1967, when a Marine sergeant named Carlos Hathcock mounted a two-foot-long Unertl scope atop a tripod-mounted Browning .50-caliber machine gun, set the fire selector to single, and killed a Vietcong soldier 2,250 meters—1.4 miles—away. It was a record that would stand for 35 years, until a Canadian soldier named Aaron Perry, on duty in the Middle East, beat it in 2002—with a highly specialized .50-caliber rifle—at 2,310 meters. That record was extended by another Canadian, Rob Furlong, just days later, to 2,430 meters. (Someone once asked me why the Canadians were so good at killing people from so far away. I replied, "They're Canadians. They're polite. They don't want to bother anyone with the noise.")

For several years the record stood at 2,475 meters, courtesy of a British soldier wielding a rifle made by

Accuracy International, in .338 Lapua. Then in in 2017 that number was obliterated by an unnamed, yes, Canadian shooter, who dropped an ISIS militant at an unbelievable 3,540 meters—over two miles.

Consider the physics of that shot, made with another .50-caliber rifle. At that distance the bullet's flight time was almost ten seconds. Since bullets do not travel in a straight line, but in an arc due to gravity, the sight line has to be adjusted accordingly. For a .50-caliber bullet to be on target at 3,450 meters, the top of its trajectory would have been 140 meters—450 feet—above the ground. No scope can compensate for that much drop; it would have been entirely up to the shooter to put his crosshairs over the correct spot in mid air in order to make the hit.

That's not all. Besides wind drift, the shooter actually has to compensate for the spin of the earth, which continues to rotate under the flying bullet. Shoot eastward at those distances and your shot will impact slightly higher; shoot westward and it will impact slightly lower. Then there is earth curvature, bullet spin, temperature, humidity . . .

Sorry—where was I? Oh, right. Shit.

Such stupendously long shots are mind-blowing, but those shooters were, first, in the top .001 percentile of their craft, second, they were all in solid emplacements with solid rests, and, finally, they had spotters who could accurately laser the exact range and monitor crosswinds. Under hasty and impromptu field conditions, a 2,000-meter shot was stupendously long—but, I hoped, one that would be tempting enough for my man to try.

I couldn't tell what brand of rifle he was carrying, but it was almost certainly some high-end model from Accuracy International or the like. It would be heavy, at least 15 or 16 pounds with a scope, and he'd been humping it up from the coast, along with a carbine and, no doubt, a pack filled with water and food. The exertion would affect his accuracy no matter how fit and good he was, as would the fact that he'd have no time to range me. I would also be moving, although slowly so as to appear unconcerned.

All in all I figured I had about a 90 to 95 percent chance of escaping un-holed.

It was now or never. I cinched the shoulder straps of the pack, stood, and began striding briskly uphill, a man on a mission but not rushing.

CHAPTER 35

That tingling sensation I had when I was first looking for the sniper was nothing compared to this. It felt like there were a dozen centipedes racing up and down my spine and neck. The skin on the back of my head tightened so much I could feel it in my face.

I was wearing the only terrestrial clothing I had, the dark stuff. Great for nighttime concealment, and fine in the day if you stay in shadow, but moving against the tan and russet slope it should show up in stark contrast. Which was, ironically, what I wanted.

I climbed. The crest of the slope drew closer, now about 100 meters above me.

I climbed another thirty. I'd been in view for about a minute and a half.

A football-sized volcanic rock ten feet upslope and five feet to my right evaporated, shrapnelling me with edged flakes.

Er, fuck. That was closer than I expected.

Funny, the guy hadn't *looked* Canadian . . .

I spun around and pretended to search desperately for the source of the shot, then turned again and ran uphill as the *boom* reached me a full four seconds later. I didn't have to look convincing any more; I wanted out of there. If he was as good at working a bolt as he was at shooting he had time for at least a couple more shots.

Number two blasted a gout of dirt six feet to my left.

Whose idea was this again?

I started jinking wildly left and right, and urged the damned Israeli boots to move faster. But I had an idea even as I ran. I reached down and pulled the Helle knife from its sheath and held it in my right hand. I was twenty meters from the crest. If the next round landed just right . . .

It did. I felt the wind of the damned thing's passing as it went on to hasten the erosion of another of San Esteban's boulders by a few millennia.

Immediately I spun, threw myself to the ground, and plunged the point of the Helle into my left forearm about a half-inch deep. Blood welled as I stood and staggered upwards, limping; within feet it was dripping off the ends of my fingers and leaving a fine spattery trail. I tumbled over the crest to shelter before the next round could bracket the first three.

Perfect.

I scrambled back up and peeked over the top from behind a shrub. The four had abandoned their tactical spread and were coalescing into single file at the double to get on my trail. The contractors were in the lead, and I wondered if the principals would let them forge ahead after me or if they'd stick together. I was betting they'd be smart enough to stick together. Whatever—they were doing just what I wanted them to do.

I turned and started north. I let the arm continue dripping for now, although I'd need to be careful if it continued not to lose too much blood. The puncture wound stung but wasn't anything but a scratch, really; it wouldn't even need a QuickClot dressing, just a bandage. I had poked with the blade lengthwise along my arm to avoid unnecessary muscle-tissue damage.

I was about two kilometers from the north coast of the island, a precipitous rampart of bluffs and cliffs and a few narrow beaches. There were a couple more valleys and ridges and an eastward-curving source of the arroyo between me and the area where I wanted to lead the group.

I figured one or both of the contractors would be trained in man-tracking, so I left a trail that would be easy to follow but not obvious. With each step I twisted my left foot to give the impression of an injury, and kept the blood dripping along that side. I increased my pace to stay well ahead of them but, in case they were *really* good, kept my stride short so it would appear I was moving slowly.

I made it down the next canyon and up to the next ridge. In front of me now was the larger valley that formed one of the sources of Arroyo Limantour. I hustled down the slope, shoved my way through the thickets of jatropha, ironwood, and elephant trees in the watercourse, and climbed the north slope, heavily studded with agaves whose dagger-ended leaves I made sure to avoid.

I looked back across the valley. It was about 1,000 meters to the crest I had ducked over. I wanted them to spot me again so they'd think they were gaining, but no way was I going to risk another shot from the "Canadian." So I positioned myself just below the top of the next ridge and waited. The drip from my arm had

313

slowed, but I put pressure on the hole to stop the flow for the moment.

I estimated they'd be about ten minutes behind me, and nine minutes later the sniper appeared over the ridge, looking down at the blood trail. I turned and limped up the last dozen steps to the top and looked back just as I ducked over. The other three had gathered and the second contractor had just pointed me out when I disappeared.

Okay, I silently telegraphed at them. *How about a little game of hide and seek?*

The ground was rockier now and I was able to increase my speed to a jog to put some distance between us without leaving telltale marks. I let off the pressure on my arm and it dropped a fresh splatter of O-positive to keep them roughly on track. There was one more shallow canyon to negotiate, and then I was up top looking north over the coastal cliffs and the Sea of Cortez. I angled sharply right over a hill, calculating that the change in direction would confuse them enough to give me the time I needed, then dropped rapidly down onto a broad, sharply crenelated bluff of rhyolite with a lip that dropped almost vertically to the sea. A full kilometer wide, it was cut by dozens of narrow crevices that started as inch-deep scars and gradually grew to several meters deep but sometimes only one or two wide when each ended abruptly at the face. Some of them forked into two or three slots. Some were a few meters long, others 100 or more. Most had enough eroded rock to support small shrubs and even a few elephant trees on the bottom. The crevices were convoluted and undercut so that, looking down into them, you couldn't tell if you were seeing the bottom or just a shelf beside which might be a hidden secondary, deeper slot. I didn't know if the slots were artifacts of the original volcanism that formed the island, or the results of eons of erosion. But they comprised a maze in which—even given a search party of four—I should be able to hide for at least a day with little risk of being discovered.

My arm had almost entirely stopped bleeding; I actually had to give it a pinch—*ouch*—to open it up again. I ran around the upper ends of the slots to give the impression I was passing them, and indeed continued on for a couple hundred meters to sprinkle a diversionary blood trail. Then I ran back into the middle of the slot complex, picked one, and dropped into it where it was a couple of feet deep, making sure I didn't inadvertently sprinkle any blood here, or disturb the substrate.

The slot deepened quickly until my head was below the lip, then went on deepening until the sky was just a blue slot. A few meters later a sort of shelf angled out from one side of the crevice, which completely blocked the view of the sky—and, of course, of the bottom if one was standing on top. As the slot deepened yet more toward its opening at the cliff face, it twisted and turned so one couldn't see straight ahead for more than a few meters. It was cool and dim, and the floor was compacted rubble that didn't readily show footprints. I walked out to the mouth, where the cliff dropped straight down for about thirty meters to truck-sized boulders awash in the rising tide. Sticking my head out and looking left, I examined a series of hand and footholds that could be used as a traverse to the next slot—a risky but potentially useful bailout route, as anyone not willing to use it in pursuit would have a two-minute backtrack to get out, and I knew the next slot was much shorter.

Confession: I was cheating. I'd been here before.

Several years earlier I had served as a guide for an arachnologist friend whose specialty was the genus *Loxosceles*—commonly called the brown recluse even though the actual brown recluse was a single species restricted to the central U.S. We'd come out in Jorge's panga, and while she scoured debris piles for spiders I'd gone exploring and stumbled upon this maze.

Barring an outlandishly foul stroke of luck, I knew I was safe for some time, so I settled down to rest, far enough back in the slot that the noise of the surf was barely audible, where I could hear anyone passing by. I got out the first-aid kit, extracted a gauze pad and tape, and bandaged the knife puncture. I cleaned off my arm with water from one of the Nalgenes, making sure to rinse the blood well into the rubble so no stain would show when the water dried. Then I drank the remainder of the water in that bottle. I rolled down my sleeves to hide the white bandage. I was about to open a Tanka Bar when I heard voices.

It had taken them a while to get back on my track, but now it sounded like they were moving right along—and arguing. I couldn't make out anything being said but voices were obviously raised, probably berating whoever got the blame for the delay and probably getting pushback. I smiled. Good—anger creates loss of concentration and reduction in critical thinking skills. The voices continued along my blood trail to the east. Now it was a question of whether they would keep going once the blood stopped, or return immediately and begin searching the slots.

If they did start searching, I was thinking they'd do it individually, both to cover more of the area quickly and because several people crammed in one crevice in single file would be tactically awkward.

I had two possibilities for silent defensive weaponry with me. First was the knife, of course. But that would require direct physical contact, and despite what you've seen in movies it's extremely difficult to kill someone quickly and silently with a knife. An occiput strike—a brutal point-first stab to the top of the spinal column just under the skull, or through the occiput bone itself just above—will do it, but that's a fiendishly difficult move. A slash across the throat sufficient to sever the windpipe along with the carotid artery will also do it, but again if you bugger it things will get loud and messy. Well, they'll get messy anyway with that one, but you get my point. So to speak.

The knife had been riding on my belt; now I removed it and secured the sheath to the PALS webbing on the front of the pack's left shoulder strap, where it was instantaneously accessible.

I dug into the pack and got out my other option: the Wrist Rocket slingshot.

I know what you're thinking, but don't laugh. After installing a more powerful set of bands on mine, I had chronographed those .44-caliber steel balls at 260 feet per second. A hit in an eye socket at that velocity would almost certainly penetrate through to the brain, and a forehead strike would at the very least render a target unconscious. When I employed mine on baboons and other camp raiders I used hard clay balls that burst on impact, to avoid the possibility of seriously injuring the animal.

The problem with a slingshot is that they're not accurate beyond about twenty, maybe twenty-five feet. Since there is no spin imparted to the projectile it doesn't have the stability of an identical ball fired from a rifled barrel. I'd practiced on cans until I could reliably send them flying at twenty feet; beyond that the projectiles started to yaw significantly. In the confines of these slots, however, twenty feet would be all I'd need. I unwrapped the steel balls from their tape strips, put two in each side pocket of my trousers, and hooked the slingshot through the left shoulder strap of the pack.

I settled down to wait, and finished getting something to eat—you already know what it was. If a chuckwalla had crawled by I would have been sorely tempted to spit-roast it.

As the Sinn's little hand swept into afternoon I started to wonder just how far the group had gone on beyond my last blood drops. There was plenty of coastal range for them to waste time on, but at some point whoever was the dedicated tracker would notice there had been no sign whatsoever for a long time. Not far to the east there was a short arroyo that emptied into a narrow crescent of beach; beyond that were more hills, then an abbreviated gravel spit at the northeast corner of the island. They wouldn't go that far, and the only other logical area where I could be hiding was this one.

Still, I'm good at sitting quietly, and I kept it up, while benefitting from the rest. I stayed hydrated, peed once off the edge of the cliff to avoid leaving sign in the crevice, and kept the pack on my shoulders, ready in case I should need to bolt.

Another hour passed, then another. Could they possibly be this incompetent? I didn't think so, and kept waiting. My watch passed 1500, then 1600.

And then I heard a noise.

It was the faintest scrape of one pebble over another, but the sound ricocheted down the rock walls to reach me. I looked up and waited, and a few seconds later the light filtering down indirectly from the slanting sun changed, dimmed, just for a second, and nearly imperceptibly.

Someone was standing on the western edge of the slot, directly above where I sat.

CHAPTER 36

To be honest, I was more than a little relieved. After all, the plan required me to be in close proximity to the group early tomorrow morning. I didn't *want* them wandering off to the east coast.

After some thinking I was pretty sure what was going on. They had followed my blood trail and then probably continued on for some time, but had realized there was no more sign of any kind. Logic would have led them back to the maze. They couldn't be sure how badly I was wounded, although I hadn't left anything like a serious blood trail.

However, rather than immediately start the potentially risky business of clearing the crevices, they had decided to set an ambush, to see if I'd show myself after several quiet hours had passed. I had to nod in admiration—it was a better plan that what I would have done in their place. I figured they had formed a strategy to return silently and spread out at intervals along the bluff, hoping I'd prairie-dog so one of them could spatter my brains on the rhyolite. Well, that wasn't going to happen. The question was, how long would they maintain the enfilade before trying something else? If the sniper had his way and was sure I was in here he'd be happy to wait for days. Snipers are used to that. The other operator would likely be just as patient, but would the principals? They might prefer to start sending their attack dogs down the holes sooner rather than later.

In the meantime, as long as whoever it was stood right above me, even my stomach growling might give me away. I tried not to think about the packets of beef stew I had stashed back at the bivouac. I tried not to think about coffee. I tried not to think about Gloria's enchiladas, or the omelets I made with my own chickens' eggs and Dubliner cheddar, or . . .

Stop it.

I had to hand it to them, they were patient. Only the outlandish coincidence that had led one of them to stand right over me had given away the game. The light above me began to fade as the sun neared the horizon.

I heard a soft, muttered curse above me.

Huh? That was a weird break in discipline.

The reason became apparent several minutes later when I heard muted footsteps approaching.

The newcomer stopped above me. He spoke *sotto voce*, but I recognized him as one of the principals.

"No creo que está aquí."

The first one—an unfamiliar voice; one of the operatives, and noticeably pissed off, but still whispering —replied: *"No. Esta aquí en alguna parte. Necesitamos ser pacientes."*

"Han pasado seis horas!" His voice was getting louder, and the operative actually shushed him.

"*Y es possible necesitamos seis mas horas. En la noche saldrá. Posible temprano, posible tarde. Tome algo, come algo, observa, y espera.*"

There was a long moment of silence that oozed tension, then the footsteps receded, albeit noticeably louder than when they arrived. The contractor sneeringly muttered a few choice words under his breath, of which I only caught "*chingado*" and "*pendejo.*"

So. The pros had correctly surmised I was here and had set the ambush. But the principal hadn't the patience infused by training and had convinced himself they were on a futile mission. He'd been told in no uncertain terms to go back and wait. The contractors were surely pissed to have lost one of their own and to have had a helicopter disabled under their noses. A professional insult. (*Just wait til they try the panga*, I thought.) The three pros would be happy to slap a month-long siege on San Esteban to rout me.

After another hour of silence a barely perceptible change in the light, along with a whisper of substrate being compressed, revealed that the pro had moved off, I presumed to another vantage point. I took advantage of his departure to get out the ATNs and strap them on, and button up the pack again. And there things remained as night fell and the slot descended into complete darkness.

Now that I knew the tactical situation, I needed to figure out to get out of here in a few hours, get them on my trail a lot closer than last time, and lead them where I wanted them.

But there was a problem with that "a lot closer than last time" part: the sniper. He'd proved to be no slouch, and I'd be stunned if he didn't have a night scope mounted on that rifle by now. There would have been only a sliver of moon tonight, almost lost in the glare of the setting sun, and then just starlight. But the right scope would still allow accurate shots out to several hundred meters, which was about the amount of lead I was hoping to maintain. Too risky.

There was a 50-percent chance that the gunman who'd been standing above me was the sniper. I wondered how far off he had moved.

I decided to find out. *Move first. Always.* I reached into the top pocket of the pack and pulled out the inspection mirror on its telescoping wand. It was an excellent tool for checking birds' nests for eggs, or reflecting sunlight into rock crevices to look for reptiles. I stood, lowered the ATNs and turned them on, and crept silently back up the slot to a spot where the lip was only just above my head. I extended the wand on the mirror, and inch by inch raised it about the edge.

I saw rocks, hills, stars. I adjusted the angle until I could see horizontally across the bluff, and began swiveling it in a circle, starting on the west.

I froze when a figure floated into the side of the mirror. Given the combination of the green-tinted light amplification and perhaps a five-degree field of view through the mirror, it was difficult to estimate how far away it was. More than thirty meters, less than fifty.

However, I could clearly make out the silhouette of two rifles.

It was him.

He was standing absolutely still, but seemed to be looking away from me, so I resumed swiveling the mirror, slowly, 360 degrees to check the rest of the horizon. I could make out two more figures, one to the east and another farther to the west, but couldn't see a fourth, which was worrisome. But their tactical separation was at least fifty meters, so it was likely the remaining individual was simply be too far away to make out. They appeared to be staged in a staggered W, which would reduce their crossfire hazard should I have appeared in between them. Proper thinking.

I swiveled slowly back to the sniper. He was still looking away, so I raised the mirror a few inches to get better perspective. He had walked around the end of the shorter slot to the west, and was standing a few feet from the edge. Probably forty meters away from me, but only a few from the far edge of the other slot. I lowered the mirror again so it was barely above the rock, and settled in to see how often he altered his view.

In the meantime I had noticed something. The soft breeze that had been caressing the plateau from the north was rapidly gaining strength. It was now moaning through the slots as though someone was blowing on dozens of huge, empty bottles. I knew it would keep rising through the night, and that soon the seas would rise with it.

The sniper turned to check his six every few minutes, but mostly he remained looking west, away from me. I guessed the figure I'd spotted behind me was one of the principals, who he didn't entirely trust to maintain vigilance.

With zero preamble a plan announced itself in my head—confidently, boldly, conceding no apparent concern for my chances of a comfortable dotage. The audacity and stupidity of it had one side of my brain standing with arms akimbo looking at the other with an *Are you out of your mind?* expression. The other side shrugged and looked back with a *You got something better?* air of arch superiority.

I crouched and moved back down the slot until I got to the opening at the cliff. I leaned out and looked left and inspected the little shelves and pockets that formed the hand and footholds I'd noticed. Funny how much smaller they looked. The wind was now sliding up the face and curling over the top, eddying gusts into the clefts. The sound of the surf below had increased dramatically, to a constant dull roar. At least I wouldn't have to worry about noise, unless of course I peeled off the face and screamed all the way down to the rocks below.

I reached out and gripped one knob with my right hand, then moved my right foot out to an inch-wide shelf. Left hand to the same knob, right hand to a finger-width crack two feet beyond. Left foot to the inch-wide shelf, right foot to a lovely fist-sized protrusion. Repeat. Keep checking ahead and up in case the sniper decides to take a look at the surf. Make sure the ATNs don't whack into the rock. Ten feet, then ten more. Ten to go. I was just waiting for a foot to slip off and leave me hanging precariously—isn't that what always happens in action novels?—but no; I made steady progress and finally ducked into the next opening in the face.

Immediately I slipped out the Wrist Rocket, unfolded it and popped one of the ammunition balls into the firing pocket. I mounted the slingshot on my left hand with the brace over my wrist, grasped the firing pocket with my right thumb and forefinger, and crouched, motionless, watching the lip of the slot above me.

No one appeared.

The sniper had to be no more than twenty feet away. I crept along the floor of the little ravine, which got rapidly shallower until in just a few feet I found a ledge that would not only get my head above the surface, but from which I could easily climb out. At this point I needed to take a chance on which way the guy would be looking, so I rose slowly and looked.

He had moved.

Fortunately for me where he had moved to was closer to the edge of the escarpment. He appeared to be evaluating the rising wind and seas.

He was maintaining discipline. His pack was on, his carbine slung over one shoulder, the big sniper rifle cradled in his arms and hanging from a sling around his neck. The boonie hat was off, his monocular night-vision goggle secured in place on the head mount. That ruled out a forehead or eye shot.

Time to move. Ignoring the possibility that I'd be spotted by one of the others, I hoisted myself out of the slot while retaining the firing grip on the slingshot. I stood, raised the slingshot, and drew the elastic bands all the way back to the anchor point on my chin.

I stepped toward him. One step. Two. Another.

I was fifteen feet away when he turned and saw me.

The cyclopean eye of the night-vision lens, combined with the otherworldly green of my own view, lent an alien insectoid look to him as his head snapped up in alarm.

I released.

A black hole a little less than a half-inch in diameter appeared magically in the center of his suprasternal notch—the depression in the throat right between the clavicles.

The sniper dropped the rifle on its sling, clawed at his throat with both hands, staggered backwards, and disappeared over the edge of the cliff.

The wind and surf masked the clatter his equipment must have made when he hit the rocks 100 feet below.

So much for snagging his weaponry. Or radio headset. Also, as I mentioned, my original plan had not included leaving any corpses on land. But as I've mentioned: No plan survives contact with the enemy. I hoped the next tide would carry him off, and made a note to check. If I had the chance.

Still—two down, four to go. I wondered briefly if I should send a letter of endorsement to the Wrist Rocket people. But more pressing matters were at hand.

I looked right and left. Incredibly, the figures fifty or so meters on either side of me hadn't noticed anything amiss. Yet. Even with nothing but starlight to amplify, I could make them out pretty clearly. Their monocular units wouldn't be quite as crisp, but if they looked closely it would be obvious I wasn't their guy. It looked like the two principals were on either side of me; farther to the west I could barely make out the figure of the other pro. Good—the farther away he was, the better.

There was no sense hiding again—I needed to go for the hills to the south. I decided the best strategy would be the bold one.

There was an old, rather crooked limb from an ironwood nearby. I picked it up and cradled it in my arms, hoping it would roughly assume the silhouette of a rifle barrel. Then I walked straight south away from the cliff, attempting to look casual.

It didn't work for long. Undoubtedly someone tried to contact the oddly-behaving sniper through his headset and got no response. I made it about thirty meters when an obviously suspicious voice cut across the plateau, blowing their opsec.

"Gonzales! Qué pasa?"

I kept walking.

An LED weapon light flashed on and pinned me in its glare.

I dropped the stick and ran.

Vile cursing erupted behind me, and the weapon erupted as well, in a full-auto rip that was more danger to the island's bats foraging overhead than me. Another light came on and another magazine-emptying stream of bullets arced overhead—but then the pro at the other end switched on and started in with disciplined three-round bursts. I was probably over 150 meters from him by then and moving fast, but despite the shooting conditions I felt a round rip through the pack. Then I was over a ridge and safe for the moment.

As soon as the lights moved off I turned back to watch through the ATN lenses, peeking over a boulder. Discreet radio communication was binned as the remaining contractor and the principals screamed at each other and at the missing sniper while they reloaded. Weapon lights stabbed in every direction as they looked for their man, and congregated where he'd been stationed, illuminated by the reflections of the light on the rock. The remaining pro shouldered his rifle, pulled a flashlight from a holster on his side, and peered over the edge, pointing the light downward. He looked for several seconds, stepped back, and walked over to the pair. He jerked his head toward the edge and spoke. The principal whose voice I had recognized started screaming curses again that carried to me clearly on the wind, then stepped to one side, raised his rifle, and blew through a magazine spraying lead in my general direction.

I was beginning to wonder just how much ammo this group had brought with them to cap a single meddlesome biologist.

The contractor took two strides over to the principal. He grabbed him by the front of his shirt, shook him like a terrier shaking a rat, and gave him a lecture, nose to nose. Apparently he had had enough of amateur hour.

I smiled. This was awesome.

The principal backed off and raised a hand in acquiescence. He ejected the empty magazine, inserted yet another from a pocket, and racked the charging handle to chamber a round. Then he stepped to one side, raised the rifle, and fired a burst into the face of the contractor.

Oh my.

This was even awesomer. Third one down and I hadn't lifted a finger.

The dead mercenary thumped to the ground.

Eerily, the other principal seemed to take this development with complete calm. Clearly *no one* dissed either of them and got away with it. I was beginning to understand why poor Che had looked so spooked.

The two laid down their rifles to illuminate the scene with their weapon-lights, then unceremoniously plundered the contractor's pack and pockets for ammunition and water bottles, then rolled him over the edge to join his mate at the water's edge. They conferred for a couple of minutes, and took off their packs. It looked like they removed their night-vision headsets, and I was proven correct when bright white light blossomed from each forehead—they had switched to LED headlamps.

They re-shouldered the packs and headed my way.

CHAPTER 37

I faded back into the desert and pondered this development.

The headlamps made it obvious they weren't going to try to track me, at least not immediately. My bet was they were headed back to the camp where their sole remaining professional contractor waited in ignorance of the fact that he was their sole remaining professional contractor.

There were two possibilities.

They could have decided to cut their losses and leave me stranded, hoping for a lingering death by dehydration.

Unlikely.

Much more likely: They were massively humiliated, massively pissed, and going for reinforcements. They now realized what a mistake it had been to expect that a quartet of hired mercenaries and a recreational helicopter would be enough to take care of me.

Heh, heh.

I didn't think they'd send just one person and leave two to split twenty-four-hour guard duty. I expected they would all leave and come back with a shitload more mercenaries, and quite possibly another aircraft or two —for all I knew they could reach out to their contacts in the Sinaloa Cartel and show up with an Apache loaded with Hellfire missiles.

I was intensely curious that they didn't seem to be able to call all this up with a sat phone, which I assumed they had with them.

Finally it hit me, and I nearly laughed out loud at the absurdity of it.

Their tightly run, insular, and strategically isolated business framework had come back to bite them. I had completely destroyed their production infrastructure, and their quarterly earnings statements would be flat for the next year at least. No one was going to extend them credit. Anything they were buying and anyone they were hiring was undoubtedly on a strictly cash basis. And while they surely still had plenty of that, at this point they probably had to show up in person with stacks of hundreds in a suitcase to get anything accomplished.

In the overall hierarchy of the Mexican drug-trade economy, they had hit TitleMax-level rock bottom.

Furthermore, you could bet news of their botched attempts at retribution on a woman and an 80-year-old had made the rounds, and they would remain laughing-stocks as long as I was alive. So yeah—they'd be back with a whole bunch more hired help.

I considered their mercenaries.

Mercs in my limited experience could be divided into two basic types. There were those who had excelled honorably in the armed services of their country, but had been suited neither to a standard rank-climbing military career nor to what they saw as the searing banality of civilian life. So they went freelance, usually picking jobs or causes they saw as just. They worked security for government figures or celebrities, or joined corporate paramilitary organizations such as the infamous Executive Outcomes.

The other type had also done well in the military in terms of training and skills, but proved to be disciplinary nightmares, either barely making it through an enlistment or indeed collecting an early, dishonorable discharge. Frequently leaning toward the sociopathic, this type would take any job that came along, and the more shooting there was involved, the better.

The four they had brought here were clearly the latter species, despite their surficial tactical smoothness and the obvious skill of the sniper. First, they had been willing to sign on for what was obviously an extrajudicial hit. Second, with little effort I had been able to rile them into futile shows of firepower and temper, which betrayed poor discipline.

Still, if the principals flashed enough cash they could probably bring back four times as many of the same type, and that would be a problem. I didn't have that much slingshot ammo. And if they upped the airpower ante I'd be in serious trouble.

Obviously I couldn't let them make it off the island.

But I'd never had any intention of doing that anyway —at least, not very far off.

They had put themselves at a serious disadvantage by switching to the headlamps, as I could easily hang off their flank, well out of range of the lights but able to trail them at will. They were probably unused to using NV for long periods of time, and their monocular sets made traversing rough country more difficult. I figured they were simply trying to make it back to camp as quickly as possible.

I began shadowing them, which was easy enough to do so that I paused to hydrate and get some food down. At first I didn't understand why they kept changing direction, following first one valley, then a ridge vectoring off at 30 degrees, then back over a hill. Were they searching for me after all, or looking for something else? Another landing spot?

Eventually it became apparent that, overall, they were trending in a big circle south, then west, then back northwest, and I realized what was going on.

They were lost.

Many studies have tested the belief that humans tend to walk in a circle when disoriented. And it's absolutely true. When fitted with GPS trackers, turned loose in dark forests, and instructed to walk in a straight line, subjects invariably walked in circles, sometimes a hundred meters or less in diameter. The same thing happened in flat desert on overcast days. When the subjects were blindfolded, their circles shrank to shockingly small diameters, often only twenty or thirty meters across.

These two, by using their headlamps, were limiting themselves to a sight radius of only a few meters—near enough on a practical basis to being blindfolded, as they could not key in on a distant feature to use as a guide. Occasionally a much brighter weapon light flashed on and waved around for a few seconds, but not long enough to make any difference. Did they have no compass, no GPS? No concept of the North Star, for Christ's sake? Apparently they'd been too busy loading up on extra magazines to think about navigational aids. Or perhaps they'd been counting on the contractors for wayfinding? Oops. Maybe you shouldn't have shot that one in the face.

Obviously on an island not much more than four miles across they wouldn't stay lost for long. But the terrain was rough and they were moving slowly, and it was now past 1:00 in the morning.

This was all just fine with me.

The wind funneling down from that high-pressure system was now a fresh breeze here in the interior of the island, whistling eerily through the spines of the cardóns; on the sea it would be up to fifteen knots or so. Soon it would rise past twenty, and in a few hours the southward-driving waves it was raising would begin piling up against a surging northbound flood tide. I just needed to keep these two occupied for a few hours and then draw them to a particular coastal feature.

Time to raise their stress level a bit more.

I dug out the tape strip that held the rest of the ammunition for the slingshot, pulled free all the balls, and dropped them in a front shirt pocket. I closed up to about fifty meters—within range for the Wrist Rocket, but far enough away that its noise should be inaudible over the wind. The pair was about to reach the head of a minor drainage, so they were surrounded on three sides by loose, rocky slopes and dense vegetation.

I loaded one of the balls and aimed over their heads at the rocks. The little projectile arced invisibly above them and clattered nicely against some boulders.

They stopped, and weapon lights flashed on toward the noise—but to their credit neither of them fired.

I let loose another ball to the right. The lights flashed that way. They weren't panicking, but disembodied *something's-there* noises from multiple vectors had to have them flapping. They knew they were only up against one person. Or did they?

Another to the right, then one to the left. The weapon lights were rotating like a lighthouse on speed. Then I put one really close, and that did it. One of the weapons swiveled and opened up with a full-auto burst that bounced rounds whining off rocks in every direction, endangering the pair more than it would have the imaginary foe.

The lights kept swiveling. There was a heated, hissed discussion I could almost make out, and the two finally adopted a more tactically appropriate stance, back to back, with each light sweeping 180 degrees.

I laid off with the slingshot and let them sit.

They weren't stupid. I don't think it took them long to figure out I was somehow making all the noise. There was more consultation, then they climbed the head of the drainage and resumed their course toward the northwest coast—the wrong one. I followed with amusement.

Fifteen minutes later they descended into the upper reaches of Arroyo Limantour, through which I'd led them just the day before. But they either didn't recognize it or thought they were farther downstream after it had turned east. They crossed it without altering course and began climbing the slope on the far side. Halfway up, when they had some elevation on me, apparently on some quietly arranged signal they both spun and hit the switches on the weapon lights at the same time.

I had closed to within about 100 meters of them—stupidly within range of a concentrated full-auto burst from two rifles, even at night—but, by sheer dumb luck, I was directly behind a beautiful, massive cardón and completely in its shadow. Had they happened to fire at it a decent percentage of the rounds would have gone right through and hit me, but when they didn't see me they held off. Perhaps they were finally feeling short on ammo?

The lights switched off. I made a mental note to come back and give the cactus some water.

I resumed following at a more discreet distance, using all available cardóns.

Doggedly the pair continued climbing until, finally, they topped the last ridge before the coast. I knew that from where they stood a steep slope angled down to a short coastal cliff no more than twenty feet high. Nothing like the short but broad drainage that led to their camp.

The duo flashed the weapon lights down at the water and up on the ridge to each side. All they had to do was follow the coastline in the correct direction to find their base. But would they turn in the correct direction? I have often been surprised at the inability of many people to orient themselves in what I considered banally obvious situations. Then again, on a foray in downtown Manhattan once I got myself thoroughly, confoundingly lost.

They extinguished their headlamps and stood for minutes, looking back and forth and up at the sky, apparently discussing options. *C'mon, people, there are only two.* I had crept up again to within fifty meters—under suitable cover—and was actually on the point of shouting, "TURN LEFT!" when they turned left. Perhaps they had finally cued in on the stars. Or perhaps they had noticed the wind, which had been blowing from the NORTH for, like, the last three days. Whatever.

I now flanked them, as much to the side as in the rear. It soon became clear they had no intention of letting the water out of their sight. They clung to the tortured crest closest to the shore, which slowed their pace to a crawl due to numerous dead-end promontories and abrupt edges. Still, it was the first objectively smart thing they had done—except that it was also exactly what I wanted them to do. No further baiting needed.

After an hour and a half of this casting about they took a break and sat down. With the ATNs flipped up I used the binoculars to see what they were doing in the pools of light from their headlamps. Water and food, while edgily eyeing the surrounding darkness. Even from my distant viewpoint they looked properly rattled; losing three contractors probably bothered them less than not knowing where the hell they were. Not to mention being aware that I was out there laughing at them.

They buttoned up their packs but stayed put, and I realized after some time that they planned to wait for dawn to continue. We'd all been up for twenty-four hours now—I was feeling it despite the endorphin high of the pursuit—and one of them appeared to doze while the other stamped around to stay awake, sweeping the weapon light at frequent intervals.

Just before sunrise they were on their way again, moving with much more assurance. In thirty minutes they had covered more ground than they had in two hours earlier. A little more than half way down the west coast they crossed a ravine that took them almost down to sea level, then back up to a long, broad bluff.

At the end of which I stood, waiting for them.

They spotted me from a good 150 meters away— probably because I was waving cheerily at them and holding the snow disk, which flashed in the just-risen sun. Both instantly raised their rifles—another gamble on my part that they wouldn't immediately fire. Indeed, after a moment they dropped the weapons to low ready and stood looking at me and all around, wondering what kind of trap I could spring that would trump two assault rifles. But I was pretty sure their egos would win and they'd want to close within conversational distance.

They advanced slowly, checking every direction, keeping the rifles shouldered and a second or less from deployment.

I stood and waited, keeping both hands in sight and the snow disk out to the side so it couldn't be concealing anything. The wind on the bluff was strong enough to nearly twist it out of my grip. I had removed the rucksack and hidden it where the disk had been.

A hundred meters.

I glanced out at the water.

Chaos. The southward rolling whitecaps, few more than five or six feet high but steep and bunched together, were slamming into the incoming tide, creating confused—no, *bewildered*—seas that seemed to break in all directions. Streams of surface spume twisted in nonsensical patterns as though huge white serpents were swimming among the waves, blown in one curve by wind, then pushed another by current.

Fifty meters. I swung the snow disk around to get both hands in the handles.

They stopped twenty meters away.

Hinwood said over the wind, "What the fuck, Porter. A *shield*? Are you Captain Fucking America or something?"

I smiled and said, "How's that investigation coming along, Deputy Chief?"

Hinwood said, "As a matter of fact I'm just about to wrap it up."

He raised his rifle. His partner raised hers, too. And I turned and hurled myself over the edge of the bluff.

CHAPTER 38

I should back up and give you a little history. Remember that hardy band of Seris who lived on San Esteban? The men now and then indulged in a death-defying game. On the east coast of the island there is a bluff above a steep slope and a cliff almost identical to the one I had just thrown myself down—except at the base of that cliff, rather than water, there is a mass of boulders and rubble. Certain death if you went over the edge.

So the Seri men would up-end the shells of the giant leatherback turtles they caught for food, and slide down the slope. The winner would be the one who jumped off closest to the edge—and if one misjudged and did go over, whoever shouted first, "Hey, his wife is mine!" would indeed inherit the unfortunate's widow. True story.

Back home on Google Earth, I had calculated that doing the same thing here—except over water—would give me a 20 to 30-minute head start on any pursuers. But I had been pretty sure I wouldn't be able to find a leatherback turtle shell when I needed it, so I cheated.

Sorry, where was I? Oh yeah: *Shit.* As I dove over the edge I got the snow disk under me—barely. I landed with my butt in it but legs waving in the sky and the back of my head skimming the gravel as the disk rocketed off on gravity power. The steel against the rubble made a hideous rattling din as I heaved myself into a sitting position and watched the edge scream toward me. The question was whether I would be over it before the two arrived above me with automatic weapons.

Something or other caught the disk and spun it around so I was facing uphill. I saw faces appear, then muzzles, then muzzle flashes, and then I was over with a stomach-lurching rush.

As I fell I flung the disk away. I didn't want to land on it, and I didn't want it doing some freak Oddjob number and decapitating me. I was falling horizontally, face toward the sky—not the best way to hit water from thirty feet up. I twisted and jerked and had my feet mostly under me when I plunged through the surface no more than five feet from one of the car-sized boulders at the surf's edge. I knifed downward far enough for my ears to pop, then stroked up, broke the surface, and inhaled a gasp of breath. This section of the coast angled slightly eastward and was sheltered from the worst of the turmoil, but the waves were still directionless and impossible to anticipate, so I swallowed several mouthfuls of saltwater while I got my bearings and began stroking for the cleft about thirty meters north.

Waves were smacking either side of the opening and washing into it. I surfed in on one and slammed against the side of the slot, ripping open my shirt and taking a patch of skin off my shoulder. Then I was waist deep and half striding, half being hurled toward the shelf at the back.

The big duffel and the rest of the equipment I'd hidden were safe. It was still a few hours before high tide so I had a narrow rocky space about fifteen feet long in which to work that was only splashed now and then. Keeping an eye on the Sinn, I pulled aside the gear on top and zipped open the big duffel. I pulled out and unfolded a nylon and rubberized envelope about fifteen feet long, tapered at each end, a set of plastic frame pieces, and a pile of sectioned aluminum tubing about three-quarters of an inch in diameter. I snapped the tubing into sections as long as the envelope, then bent them around the frame pieces, where they snapped into recesses, creating two sub-assemblies. Finally the sub-assemblies went into each end of the envelope and snapped together, tensioning the structure. A rim clipped in to surround the opening in the center of the envelope, a foam seat snapped inside.

And I had a kayak.

It was a Feathercraft Kahuna, shorter than my late fiberglass boat but lighter and more maneuverable, and nearly as seaworthy. Its deck was, in contrast to the ocean-colored Cetus, bright red. My spare paddle was here, as was my PFD. I checked the latter to make sure everything I had stashed in the pockets was present and functional.

Twenty six minutes had passed since I hit the water. I donned the PFD and zipped it tight, slipped the Kahuna's spray skirt over my head, grabbed the paddle, and pushed the boat into the water. I stepped in when there was a lull in the waves, plopped down and secured the skirt, and pushed toward the entrance until I was rising and falling on the surge, fighting off the rock on either side. I waited for the next lull in the waves (they really do come in sets, although the number varies widely from the mythical seven), then shoved out and started paddling like crazy.

I detoured to the north first, under the shelter of the cliff, in case the two had waited to see what I was doing and were still standing above me with rifles. But I was pretty sure a second boat had not figured in their calculations. They would be guessing I was making for the wrecked one. Sure enough the skyline was clear once I turned west and looked back.

As soon as I was out from the minor protection of the coast the chaos engulfed me. There was no rhythm, no sense, no conformity except steepness and speed to the waves that came at me from every angle. My knees were locked under the cockpit and my boots jammed against the footrests to render me as much as possible a part of the kayak rather than its mere pilot. A high brace on one side would be followed instantly by a low brace on the other, then a lean and sweep to try to meet the next big wave head on, all the while getting offshore as quickly as possible.

When I could spare a second of inattention—which was not often—I twisted my head around quickly to check the southwest corner of the island, where the long gravel spit was. I could see waves sending spray over it, but no sign of a boat. I kept paddling, kept bracing, kept leaning and sweeping. I battled out to where I was half a kilometer offshore, then paused, riding the waves and being blown southward over the northward tide. I didn't want to go any farther offshore for fear they would miss me altogether—even a fifteen-foot red boat disappears with shocking ease in a rough sea, as any Coast Guard rescue crew will tell you.

And there they were—a glint of sun off the hull as the panga rounded the spit and forged northward along the coast. I predicted they'd be paying more attention to the shore than offshore, so I rode with the boat broadside to them, and flashed the paddle as obviously as possible—which wasn't hard as I was thrashing around trying to keep from capsizing. I hadn't practiced my Eskimo roll in ages and did not want to get a remedial lesson just now.

On they came. The big panga was made to handle rough seas but even it would be laboring in the directionless waves, and shipping water regularly. Despite the roar of wind and water, which completely masked the sound of the motor from this distance, I could hear the deep boom as the hull smacked down after dropping off each crest.

As the boat neared a point directly opposite me and the coast I was struck with the fear that they might not see me at all. Soon I would only be apparent if they looked behind them. I could see the last surviving contractor at the helm, doing a damn good job of making forward progress while keeping the boat bow-on to as many whitecaps as possible. The other two were on either side of the bow, hanging on grimly. Even from this distance I could tell none of them was wearing a PFD—life jackets were far from common equipment for subsistence fishermen even now, so that had not been an option with their gift boat from me.

I spun the Feathercraft on the crest of a wave and began fighting northward to stay abreast of the panga. I didn't know how long that outboard would run, but I wanted them well offshore when—and if—it quit.

At last someone looked the right way, for when I checked three faces were turned my way, quickly followed by the bow.

I turned west and paddled like the Devil was on my stern.

Farther away from shore the nature of the conditions changed. There were fewer of the directionless waves; they came more steadily from the north now. But they were also bigger and steeper, and breaking regularly. Progress was paddle like mad in the trough, sweep and turn north into the wave, then turn back and paddle like mad down the back of the wave and into the next trough. The Feathercraft was riding superbly—its construction meant it actually flexed slightly over waves—but these were marginal conditions for any sea kayak and I was soaked to my pores above the spray skirt.

I looked back. They were gaining, of course. The question now was that outboard. So far the damn thing seemed to be running just fine.

I paddled onward, then looked back. They were within 200 meters. In another sixty seconds they'd gained another hundred. And I could now hear the motor howling healthily at full throttle.

Gunfire. Wild and wide, but there was always the lucky shot, and there was nothing I could do to make myself a more difficult target than to be bouncing wildly on a mad ocean.

I turned to look again. They were fifty meters away, and the two in the bow had stopped firing. It occurred that they were going to come on and simply run me down, or drive in circles around me just for fun before finishing me off.

The panga started to curve around upwind of me.

And then the tone of the motor changed. The combustion roar stayed the same, but an underlying whine rose in volume until it became a screech and then became a scream and then the motor cut out with an almighty bang as something vital in the rod or main bearings seized solid.

The instant the panga lost power the helmsman lost control. The boat slowed and plowed, and the next wave slapped it broadside to the seas. The contractor staggered to the motor but there was nothing he could do; it was now a 230-pound lump of slag. The boat started rolling with the waves—twenty degrees, then thirty. A breaking wave dumped a couple hundred gallons of seawater inside.

The two in front had stopped firing and dropped the rifles; it was all they could do to hang on now. The contractor started to make his way forward for some reason I couldn't guess at, but a big wave hit as he was amidships. He was flung to the downwind side of the boat, as was Hinwood from the opposite side.

The panga capsized.

The contractor tried to fling himself free, but as he jumped, the opposite gunwale, arcing over with the force of the wave and a ton of fiberglass behind it, slammed into the back of his skull with a crack that carried over all the other noises. He went under and didn't come up.

I was now no more than thirty feet from the upturned hull, directly downwind and down-wave. The boat rolled drunkenly halfway back up, then back down again as I looked for the rest of the crew. The wind was blowing me south but the half-submerged boat was stalled between wind and tide, so I stroked to keep close enough to watch as the seas rolled over the boat and under me.

A head and arms appeared out of the face of a wave curling toward me, and the figure was surfed down directly onto my bow. Hands came up and grabbed the perimeter rescue lines. The hands pulled the head and shoulders out of the water, then grabbed the opposite side of the bow, pulling, jerking furiously, trying to capsize me. Dark, shoulder-length hair was plastered over the head, revealing an ear minus the top third. The face was turned toward me, a rictus of hate.

It was time.

I braced the paddle across the cockpit with my left hand. With my right, I unzipped the main pocket on the front of the PFD. I reached in, pulled out agent Jim Miller's Glock .400 Cor-Bon, and shot his wife between the eyes. In the micro-second as the pistol's striker snapped forward to detonate the primer that ignited the powder that sent the 150-grain bullet down the barrel, across the intervening atmosphere, and through her brain, the expression on Rachel Miller's face remained frozen in hate. Then it went blank, her hands slipped off the deck, and she slid beneath the waves.

I stuffed the pistol back in the PFD and got the kayak stabilized upwind. The panga was still wallowing; the flotation under the seats would keep it awash until, hopefully, it was discovered by some lucky fisherman. There was no sign of Hinwood, so I paddled around to the upwind side of the hull. Nothing.

Then I spotted him.

He was, admirably, breast-stroking toward the coast of San Esteban. I spun the kayak and paddled after him. In five minutes I was even with him downwind, then past, and I curved back north to get between him and the island. As soon as he saw me he stopped stroking and treaded water. I paddled up until I was next to him, the two of us rising up and down with each passing wave. He reached out and grabbed a bow line, but, unlike his partner, his faced was defeated and terrified.

"Look," he said, but then a wave slapped him and he coughed water.

"Look," he gasped again, "I can pay y . . ."

That was as far as he got.

I dropped the Glock in the sea. It would sink a thousand feet to the bottom, remain there for several eons until earth's oceans retreated again, and then probably be found in perfect operating condition.

Rachel Miller and Hinwood would be different. Bloating would bring their corpses back to the surface quickly. Then, decomposition and various scavengers both finned and winged would get to work on them, until one by one their bones would sink again, for good.

I turned the kayak and battled my way back toward the island and the spit, with nasty quartering seas slamming me around unpredictably. One nearly flipped me over and I barely managed to right myself with a desperate sweep of the paddle. But at last I turned the corner south of the gravel point, and instantly it was like paddling in a pond. With several quick strokes I powered the kayak onto the beach. I stepped out, shaking with fatigue and the aftereffects of the adrenalin dump, and heaved the kayak above the high tide line.

The camp was before me, rustling in the wind but at the same time eerily quiet. Beyond it the helicopter's main rotor blades bobbed gently up and down like a seesaw.

I walked by the tents and stacked provisions and instead hiked up the drainage and climbed to my bivouac. I pulled apart the rocks that hid my stashed equipment and food.

And made myself a cup of coffee.

CHAPTER 39

I came to at sunset, stretched out on my back under an ironwood tree, fingers still curled through the handle of an empty titanium coffee mug. I stood up in time to see the last warm orange sliver of sun disappear behind Isla San Jorge, chased by a fingernail of moon. I was still exhausted, but famished, so I heated and devoured two packets of beef stew, scalding the roof of my mouth. I didn't care. My fleece bedroll was still in the rucksack hidden where the snow disk had been, so I rolled myself in the ground sheet and conked out again.

Ten solid hours more sleep pretty well got me back to normal. I was awakened by the good-morning chattering of an ash-throated flycatcher in the tree above me, which was still swaying in the strong breeze. I wouldn't be leaving the island today, I suspected. That was fine, as I had some equipment to retrieve.

After two luxuriously protracted mugs of Ethiopia's finest I went back down to the spit and carried the Feathercraft farther back up the valley where it wouldn't be seen by any fishermen idly stopping by to gawk at a helicopter and an abandoned camp in the middle of the Sea of Cortez. I detoured and picked up the dry bag in which I'd carried the rattlesnake—I was unavoidably going to leave a lot of crap on the island, at least temporarily, but I drew the line at mere litter.

Then I hiked up and retrieved the pack, unloaded it at the bivouac, and headed out to pick up the caches of food and water I'd left scattered around. I took the time to check the cliff over which the two contractors had, respectively, backed and been shoved. There was a spray of dried blood where the second had had his face blown off, but looking over the edge I could see no trace of either of them on the rocks or in the surf below. I knew the coast dropped off quickly here, so my hope was their corpses had been washed well out to sea by the tide and were already on the way to decomposition.

I collected the stash of gear I had hidden remotely—the hacksaw, grappling hook, paracord, etc.—and brought it back to the bivouac, so by late afternoon I had all my equipment together again.

I had just one task left: to get home.

Barring any trouble my Land Cruiser should have been back at Alberto's by now. I had no intention of involving either him or Jorge further at the moment. I also had no intention of trying to cross the border at a port of entry. I had destroyed the operation and cut off its head, but there was a five-sigma certainty border guards had been bought at every gate to make sure I didn't drive back into the U.S. Once they "detained" me somewhere unofficial, then discovered there was no one left to pay them the ransom they'd been promised, then what?

I could buy an old truck for cash and possibly make it past a busy Mexican border checkpoint without being recognized, but then I'd be immediately faced with the

U.S. Customs people—in a Mexico-registered vehicle with no title in my name. Awkward at best.

No matter. I'd thought through all this before I left. I had a folding kayak, a hacksaw, 500 feet of paracord, a grappling hook—and a plan. All I had to do was paddle 200 miles to the north end of the Sea of Cortez, cross a forty-mile stretch of the driest desert in North America, and break into my own country over a thirty-foot-tall border wall.

I took stock of the water supply. There was about ten gallons left. I was sure there was plenty more in the camp on the beach, so that wasn't a problem. The problem was that I needed to cover that 200 miles of paddling as rapidly as possible, and the little Feathercraft wasn't designed for handling a big touring load. Weighing it down would increase stability but reduce speed.

I mentally tallied all the equipment I'd absolutely need to take, and balanced it against eight pounds per gallon of water. Finally I decided to take two of the Ortlieb ten-liter bags, plus a two-liter and one-liter bottle for the cockpit—just over six gallons. That should get me to the head of the gulf, when I could deploy the Katadyn desalinator to (laboriously) top up for the cross-country push to the border.

It should work.

I made a stash of all the gear I wasn't taking in the hope that I could either come back for it or send Jorge to retrieve it. I was planning to have him pick up the shattered remains of the Cetus anyway. I took only one dry bag, just to save a few ounces, reserving it for the fleece bag—the only piece of gear I had that wasn't immune to damp.

There was nothing left to do but wait out the weather, so out of curiosity I strolled down to the beach and—being careful not to leave any fingerprints (just because)—inspected the bwana camp. Cots with mattresses, folding chairs, bedside tables, even mirrors. Nice. I'd been wondering if Hinwood and Rachel Miller had perhaps been romantically involved, but this appeared to be a strict his and hers setup. The contractors had smaller cots set up outside, and there was a comprehensive field kitchen set up between two massive ice chests.

Curiosity got the better of me, and I opened the lids on the ice chests. One was stocked with fresh vegetables, tortillas, eggs, and, *lordy*, a pile of individually wrapped steaks. The other was full of beer and wine.

It looked like they had been planning a blowout party once they got rid of me.

I considered my touch-nothing approach for a moment.

Screw that. I grabbed a steak, a stack of tortillas, and two ice-cold Pacificos, hiked back to my camp, and had a party of my own, first enjoying a fire, then lying back and watching meteors streak across the pollution-free, star-spangled sky.

CHAPTER 40

I awoke at 3:00 the next the morning to the awareness that something had changed.

I lay perfectly still, listening.

Nothing.

Exactly—nothing. The wind had died. Time to go.

I packed up using the ATNs, which preserve night vision better than using an LED headlamp. It took me three trips to get all the water and the rest of the gear down to the beach. I carried the kayak down to where the sea barely whispered at the sand, and packed it as evenly as possible. Spray skirt, PFD, paddle. I turned to look at San Esteban once more, with curiously different emotions than the previous times I'd left it. I stashed the ATNs, launched, and stroked eastward along the coast, with Orion—yes, he was a hunter again—rising ahead.

At the southeast corner of the island I turned straight north toward the westernmost spur of Tiburón, about ten miles away. The air was calm but the sea was still rolling southward—even, non-breaking waves that were instinctive to manage head-on. As pre-dawn light painted a lavender Belt of Venus around the horizon above the steel-gray sea, I paddled past the Seris' turtle-shell slide and its lethal base of rocks, then angled out into the open water.

The waves diminished as I progressed, and the incoming tide pushed me north along with my steady paddling, so I was off Tiburón by 8:00. Fortunately there were no road extensions on this coast, so all I had to watch out for were Mexican Marine patrols. I paddled around the rocky point and on another ten miles before stopping on a broad alluvial beach to rest and eat. I hadn't yet regained my taste for Tanka Bars, so I broke out the stove and heated a pouch meal of pasta to get some carbohydrates down for the afternoon's traveling, and followed with some fruit for quick energy. I wanted to get as far from San Esteban as possible as quickly as possible, and planned to push on late into the evening. I'd been hydrating regularly, and noted the water supply already diminishing quickly. Maintaining four or five knots in a short, not particularly hydrodynamic sea kayak takes some effort.

The northwest coast of Tiburón gets progressively rockier and steeper, with fewer safe landing spots. Through the afternoon I paddled beneath a full-spectrum rainbow of geology, from volcanic tuff to Cretaceous granodiorite to shale to sedimentary rock—the gaping wounds of the tectonic forces that had split the Baja Peninsula from the mainland.

At dusk I reached the northwest corner of the island. Just around to the east there was a lovely, mile-wide beach—but also the terminus of one of the military's roads. I couldn't risk that, so I turned straight north again, toward an isolated square mile of salt-bush-covered sand and rock called Isla Patos, about five miles away.

Before I moved on I turned to gaze back at Tiburón. I'd spent many inspiring months on the island working on a variety of research projects, and I wasn't at all sure I'd ever be able to return. As I looked, I noticed movement by the shore, and saw a family quartet of coyotes—a subspecies unique to Tiburón—watching me with curiosity. I didn't know if it was a good omen or bad, but it made me smile. As I turned the kayak the group broke into the usual coyote chorus of *howdy-let's-go-hunting* yaps and yowls. The music followed me until it was subsumed by the swish of the water.

I landed on Isla Patos well after dark, with a total of forty-five miles of paddling under my hull. I had just enough energy to eat and collapse, but I'd put some significant distance between me and that abandoned camp.

In three more days I'd covered another 130 miles of the mainland coast, dodging well offshore past the villages and ports of Libertad, Puerto Lobos, and Desemboque Norte, stealth-camping on wilderness shorelines. Late one afternoon I pulled the kayak up on a gravel beach on Isla San Jorge—actually a narrow, mile-long chain of islands about twenty miles southwest of the big fishing and tourism town of Puerto Peñasco, in the northern end of the Sea of Cortez.

San Jorge was another bit of déjà vu, as it had been the site of one of my first studies, a survey of nesting brown boobies. It was now a rubicon—from here I faced a 60-mile offshore dogleg to circumvent the busy port at Puerto Peñasco and then head north to my final landing spot in Bahia Adair. I was losing a little more stamina each day, and drinking more water than I had hoped, partly thanks to a persistent, freshening headwind and a rising, inopportune fall heat wave.

After unloading the kayak and pulling it out of sight over an embankment, I tallied my remaining supply. One full and one empty Ortlieb bag, an empty one-liter and a full two-liter Nalgene. Plenty for the final ocean leg.

I launched from the island the next morning to try to get around the port activity of Peñasco during the daytime, as the majority of the commercial fishing boats would be moving during the night, and I didn't want to be guessing which direction and at what speed the port and starboard running lights of 80-foot vessels were heading. A colony of sea lions saw me off with much curious barking and zooming around the boat.

I paddled directly west at first—perpendicular to the wind and waves, a course that required constant focus. But the day was glorious, and the sea had what Alan Moorehead once described in the Mediterranean as "the multihued blue of a butterfly's wings." Only a few fishing boats transited in the distance, nothing close. The double-gradient Bausch & Lomb sunglasses cut the glare, but I still had to squint into the millions of wave-reflected shards of sunlight.

I'd been checking my position on the Motorola sat phone. By the time I turned north at 113.8° west longitude it was afternoon, I had already covered thirty-five miles, and I was twenty miles from the nearest shore, much of which was now below the horizon. I'd been farther offshore in sea kayaks before, but never in a 15-foot-long folding craft. I now headed straight into the waves and wind, which meant no energy-wasting bracing merely to stay upright; nevertheless it was an uphill slog. My goal in Bahia Adair was still thirty miles away and I was already exhausted. Suddenly Tanka Bars sounded astonishingly appealing again, and I mowed through three of them, which helped revived me.

Five hours later the sun was setting over limitless water to the west. I still could see no land in front of me, although I knew the volcanic peaks of the Pinacates should be showing to the northeast; they were probably hidden by dust blown off the Pinta Sands. The wind had died, as had the waves, and despite my situation it was extraordinarily peaceful. A pod of common dolphins passed by a hundred meters off without noticing me. I was now in what had been the territory of the *vaquita*, the world's smallest dolphin at only four or five feet in length, and which had been driven to what was now assumed was functional extinction by illegal gill-netting in what was supposed to be a protected zone in the upper gulf.

I turned and watched through raw eyes as the burnt-orange globe of the sun touched the water and sank smoothly beneath the surface. At the instant the last sliver disappeared, I gasped as an electric, emerald-green spark strobed in its place for a fraction of a second. Then there was just the warm orange afterglow over the deepening blue of the sea.

I had only seen the rare atmospheric phenomenon of the green flash once before, and despite my exhaustion it cheered me immensely.

There was a waxing crescent moon now, which provided plenty of light for paddling for a couple hours after the sunset's glow was gone. Soon the kayak and my paddle blades were leaving ghostly green trails of bioluminescence. The fatigue was hammering at me again, and several times the luminescence mesmerized me so that I found myself off course, the North Star off to my left or right. In another two hours I was stroking dully, mechanically, on complete instinct, and the water was so flat that my paddles dug into sand below me before I realized I had neared the shore, which sloped so gradually here that the actual beach was a full fifty meters farther on.

I climbed leadenly out of the kayak when it grounded in four inches of water, unhooked the bow line, and splashed onward, towing the craft, until I hit dry sand. Vaguely I realized I needed to get farther away from the water, so I dragged the boat another fifty meters before collapsing next to it. I pulled out the empty Ortlieb bag and set it on the sand, then retrieved the remaining full one. I opened it, guzzled a liter or more, and set the bag down on the empty one, then lay back, shattered, to rest for a couple minutes before continuing.

And woke up half submerged.

The blood-warm water had made no impression on me until it was lapping at my ear canals. I bolted upright. The moon was gone and the night was velvet black, water and sky merging so seamlessly that only where the stars began gave away the horizon. I reached to the side —the kayak was gone. I stood, cursing myself vilely for my stupidity, oriented the North Star, and splashed that direction, searching frantically. A darker oblong coalesced out of the darkness surrounding it, and with a near-sob I grasped the kayak, floating calmly in on the tide. I reached into behind the seat, pulled out a flashlight, and clicked it to its highest, 800-lumen setting.

As far as the powerful light would reach was only flat, black water. I was in the upper reaches of the gulf's enormous tidal range, on a nearly billiard-table-level expanse of sand where the high tide line might be a mile inland from low tide.

The Ortlieb water bags were nowhere to be seen.

I unhooked the bow line and started splashing northward, towing the boat behind me, and continuing to sweep with the light for the Ortliebs. There was no sense of scale, no perspective. I could have been on a planet completely covered by a six-inch-deep ocean.

I waded for a half hour before the light revealed a pale strip ahead, then a rise covered in saltbush that indicated actual land. I dragged the kayak up it and some way farther on found—miracle—a scrubby, waist-high mesquite tree, a guarantor of above-tideline elevation. I collapsed again and didn't stir until the sun rose.

CHAPTER 41

Three liters.

That was the sum total of capacity in my remaining two Nalgene bottles—both of which, incidentally, were empty—to sustain me for a 40-mile hike across the *Gran Desierto*.

The tide had gone out while I slept. It was now on its way in again but still out of sight. However there were several pools left, so I deployed the Katadyn desalinator and started refilling my supply. At a liter per hour it was a two-steps-forward, one-step-back operation as I had to drink half a liter for every one I produced. I'd scoured the high tide line for flotsam that might serve as an emergency container, but all was UV-rotted plastic that disintegrated in my hands. I dug into my cook kit and got out the one-liter MSR Titan that serves as both pot and kettle, and the titanium coffee mug, which held perhaps 12 ounces. Slowly I made progress until by early afternoon I'd filled everything.

Then I got to work.

I pulled all the gear out and disassembled the kayak. Using the hacksaw, I began cutting up the tubular frame pieces into six-inch-long sections, until I had two dozen of them. I cut short strips of the Gorilla tape and wrapped a layer around each end of each tube. I ran out of tape a few tubes from the end, but figured it would be sufficient.

I unspooled about eighty feet of the 750-paracord and folded it in half. About a foot down from the apex I folded each side of the cord into an overhand loop, then pulled a section of cord below the loop through it, in a pattern called a marlinspike hitch. I inserted one of the aluminum tube into each hitch's loop about an inch, and pulled it tight. I moved down a foot and repeated the process. In a half hour I had made a very stylish ladder just about twenty-five feet long. The Gorilla tape was intended to compensate for the slickness of the aluminum and the slight natural slipperiness of the nylon paracord, so the knots wouldn't shift.

That all took me a liter of water to accomplish, so I pumped another hour. I was still racking my brain to come up with another way to carry water when I spied it right in front of me—the dry bag in which I'd stashed the fleece sleeping envelope. It would hold at least a couple of gallons. Problem solved. I pulled out the fleece and dumped one of the Nalgenes into the dry bag to test for leaks—and was rewarded with a shower of fresh water disappearing into the sand.

Shit! I upended the bag back into the bottle, losing half the water in the process.

Like an idiot, when packing up on San Esteban I had unwittingly grabbed the same dry bag in which I'd stashed the rattlesnake—the one in which I had sliced a bunch of holes.

And I was out of Gorilla tape.

Another thought occurred. I looked at the flaccid hull of the kayak—the waterproof hull.

I pulled out the Helle knife, gritted my teeth, and sawed off the front 18 inches of the bow. I'd already hacked up the frame; what difference did it make? Gingerly I poured in some water. It held. I poured some more—no problem. Finally I got in everything that had been in both Nalgenes, giving me a blessed extra three liters for the trek. I rolled the ragged, cut opening and secured the lopsided container with paracord, then gently leaned it against a shrub—it would only hold water if kept upright.

I went back to pumping with the Katadyn, and by sunset I had two Nalgenes, the bow pouch, and the MSR pot and coffee mug filled—give it seven and a half liters or two gallons. Not great but better than I'd feared after the loss of the Ortliebs. One last top-up before leaving: I forced down an entire liter from the MSR pot, then spent an hour pumping it full again.

At last I was ready to go in bright quarter moonlight. I arranged the bow pouch in the bottom of the Mystery Ranch pack, wedging it upright with the binoculars, the ATNs, and the fleece bag. The Nalgenes went in the side pockets. I shouldered the pack and, finally, picked up the full MSR pot in one hand and the full coffee mug in the other, and headed comically north into the desert with mincing steps to avoid sloshing any more than necessary out of the open containers. I looked rather like a barista who had seriously lost his way trying to serve a *café au lait* and pot of tea.

As deserted as this stretch of tidal flat seemed, just three miles north Highway 3 and a railroad track curved around the north end of Bahia Adair. I crossed them shortly after 10:00 once I ensured there were no headlights visible for miles. By then I'd drunk what was in the coffee mug and enough from the pot to minimize the sloshing.

A few miles farther on, the real challenge began— the massive sand dunes of the *Gran Desierto de Altar*— the only active region of erg dunes in North America, and at 2,200 square miles the largest wilderness in the Sonoran Desert.

The fourteen cubic miles of sand blanketing this region all originated in the Colorado River during the Pleistocene, and it all lay ahead of me, sucking at each step. From atop each dune the moonlit desert looked like nothing so much as the sea I had just escaped, frozen in place and turned dun-colored. The dune crests are oriented east-west with slip faces on the north, so my progress was a repeated effort of a slow climb up a windward slope followed by a schuss down the face, infiltrating the Israeli boots with sand. Fortunately I'd drunk the last water in the MSR pot and it was now in the pack, but I still had to be careful to keep the pack upright so the kayak storage pouch didn't empty itself.

The moon set at midnight, but starlight on the dunes was enough to navigate by; no need for a flashlight or the ATNs. Still, despite the cooler temperatures it was strenuous going. According to the Motorola's GPS I was making barely three miles per hour, and sweating freely. I stopped and got out the improvised bota bag, untied it, and carefully tipped it up to my mouth. The water tasted like, well, like the inside of a kayak, but it was wet.

I drank until I was sated.

As I think I mentioned earlier, one of the persistent myths of desert travel is that one can train oneself to get by on less water, and armies have tried forcing the theory on their troops for centuries. But even if you are perfectly fit you're going to use a certain amount of water for metabolism, and you're going to sweat a certain mount more to keep your core temperature down. Trying to cheat the system *never* works.

I now faced a dilemma. I wouldn't be more than halfway to the border by dawn, and continuing on all day would drastically increase my water use. On the other hand, resting for the day in the shadeless dunes would still require hydration, and in the meantime I'd make no progress.

In the end I decided to detour about two miles east, to the outer edge of the Pinacate lava flow, where there would be vegetation and shade. I just had to hope the shade would compensate for the two-mile deficit in water. I turned northeast and continued diagonally across the dunes until I was skirting the small dead-end arroyos that rare rains cut out of the lava hills and washed partway into the dunes before they evaporated. As dawn lightened the horizon I turned right and followed one "upstream" as its scrub turned into shrubs and then small trees. Finally I found an ancient, gnarled ironwood tree shouldering its way out of what seemed like an unbroken lava flow, with a good-sized organ-pipe cactus growing within its branches. Between the two the shade would be thick and cool if I moved every hour or so to stay inside it.

Gratefully but carefully I removed the pack and set it upright against the tree's trunk. As I was doing so I heard a slight noise, and looked up to see a kit fox—a canid the size of a small house cat, with ears as big as a German shepherd's—watching me from the shade beneath a knee-high volcanic ledge. The perseverance of life in this habitat never failed to astonish. The fox was probably just back from a night of hunting kangaroo rats with those radar-like ears. The fox could get all the liquid it needed from eating the kangaroo rats, which in turn metabolized all their own water from the dry seeds they eat.

I pulled out the kayak bow, which had ridden nicely, untied it, and drank. Afterwards there was still about a liter and a half inside—I was encouraged. I set the pouch against the tree trunk where I could get to it again, and lay down with my head on the pack.

I dreamed. I dreamed of splashing water— understandable in the circumstances but still vaguely amusing to my unconscious self. It was one of those dreams that persists into wakefulness, so that when I opened my eyes and looked to the side I could still hear the splashing.

The kit fox looked up at me calmly, its furry little chin dripping.

It had tipped over the nose of the kayak and was contentedly enjoying a treat from the water that had collected in a pocket in the rock.

I bellowed wordlessly and flailed upright, sending the poor little thing bolting for its crevice. Without hesitating I plunged my face into the little pool and sucked water in as the porous lava drained it. I got a cup or so out before it was gone.

And then . . . I laughed. In fact I laughed hysterically —not irrationally but with genuine mirth at the absurdity of the situation. I would have traded off one of my liberated packets of $100 bills to have had a video of the entire event. Every time I caught my breath I'd picture the fox creeping up, sticking its nose in the bag and delicately tipping it over, and I'd start giggling again. I was really not doing well on securing my water supply.

However.

I now had three liters of water to last me through the rest of the day and all night and twenty miles through the sand dunes to a thirty-foot-tall steel wall. And over it.

There was nothing to do for now but stay as cool as possible and get as much rest as possible. I was starving, but contented myself with the last of my fruit pouches. It would help hydrate and give me energy. The pemmican bars with their hit of protein would actually require additional fluid to metabolize, so I left them.

I dozed the rest of the day, keeping the rucksack safely under my head and rotating clockwise under the tree to remain in shade. At sunset I emptied the pack and examined the contents. It was time to jettison unnecessary stuff. That meant leaving behind about $12,000 worth of night-vision goggles and Zeiss binoculars, plus the pot and mug and several other bits.

I removed the strap from the binoculars, and took the head harness off the ATNs, in case some residual salts might attract some animal which might then drag off the whole thing. I hid the equipment under the other end of the fox's ledge and piled boulders in front. The odds were infinitesimal that a human would stumble across the cache out here. I fired up the sat phone and noted the coordinates, just in case I could come back or send someone else to retrieve them.

An hour after dark I started out again. The lighter load was immediately noticeable and welcome, except that part of it was significantly less water. Under the moon I made slow but steady progress, steering back slightly northwest to hit the stretch of border I wanted.

In an hour and a half I needed a drink, and emptied the one-liter Nalgene. Five miles gone. In another hour I had passed through the deepest dunes and was finding firmer ground in the alluvial plain of the volcanic hills ahead, which straddled the border. Six more miles, and another liter.

By the time I neared Mexico 2, the major highway that connects Sonora with Baja, I was desperately thirsty, subconsciously and stupidly putting off drinking that last liter. I actually dully contemplated stopping a car or truck and asking for water. But some still-functioning tactically aware part of my brain realized that I couldn't risk anyone making a call to any Mexican officials about a gringo wandering across the desert. So I waited until a lone semi blasted past, then staggered across the tarmac and into the desert again.

At daybreak I was out of water and still four miles from the border. The last liter had only revived me fractionally; I should have had another two liters in me by then. I cursed the kit fox for a brazen opportunistic flea-ridden thief and wished mange on him. I trudged onward—I wouldn't make it through another day of rest and metabolic consumption. I had to finish, despite the rapidly rising sun and heat.

In a couple hours of, basically, shuffling—I don't really know how long because I'd long since stopped looking at the watch—I glanced up, and there it was.

From horizon to horizon stretched a slotted, rust-colored barrier, a surreal, hostile chimera in an otherwise exquisite desert landscape. Its size was illusory; it looked like I was a few hundred feet away but it took me another debilitating hour to reach. I collapsed at the foot of the thing, knowing full well I hadn't the strength left to complete this last task, this last point zero one percent of the whole bloody mess to get beyond something just inches wide that might as well have been a billion miles of outer space.

I touched one of the steel posts, knocked on it. It clunked densely, filled with concrete. I looked up. The square posts were set diagonally, making them appear diamond-shaped. Across the top five feet of the wall was a blank steel plate to prevent anyone simply shimmying up it.

I pulled the equipment out of the pack. There was the collapsing grappling hook, a swivel and stainless-steel pulley clipped in at the bottom. The ladder and its loop of paracord at the top. And the rest of the spool of cord.

From a side pocket I pulled the Motorola satellite phone. Once it spooled up and indicated connectivity, I hit a saved phone number.

Magdalena answered before the first ring had ended.

"Clayton! My God, is it really you?"

I croaked, "Hi Mags." Strangely, the sound of her voice made me sit up straighter, look around with more awareness.

"Where are you?"

I looked at the screen. It was a blur. What to do?

I said, "Um, I could use a lift." Like, maybe from a helicopter?

She took over. Her voice firmed. "Clayton, listen to me. Call up your coordinates on the screen. You can text them to me."

I knew that, on a theoretical level. It was putting it into practice that seemed confusing. Magdalena ran me through the procedure again. Finally I managed to hit the correct buttons.

There was a long pause, then:

"Clayton. What side of the wall are you on?"

I thought that through, then said, "The wrong side. I'm working on it."

She said, "I'm on my way."

I rang off and looked up at the wall again. Somehow hearing Magdalena's voice had energized me.

I unspooled seventy or eighty feet of paracord and cut it off. I threaded one end through the Ronstan pulley and pulled it back so I had a doubled leash on the grappling hook longer than the wall was high. Clumsily I tied the ends of the leash to my belt, so I wouldn't lose the whole damned contraption if I over-threw—unlikely in my present condition.

I stood up and grabbed the leash a couple of feet from the grappling hook, which felt much heavier than its twenty-six ounces. I began twirling it in a vertical circle, looking up and gauging the distance to the top panel of the wall. When I thought I had enough centrifugal force on it I hurled it toward the top.

It soared upward about fifteen feet and plunged back straight at my head. I fell over dodging it.

I tried again. This time it went higher, but clanged off the steel posts and bounced outward and down.

Again.

Again.

Finally, incredibly, I managed a perfect throw that brought the grappling hook just over the top panel— but two feet out from it.

Shattered, I gave up and collapsed again. Each throw had drained a considerable amount of the scant energy and will I had remaining.

I sat in the sun and muttered curses, then self-pitying whines. That got me pissed off at myself, and *that* got me wondering what Magdalena would think if she showed up and found me whining self-pityingly on the Mexico side of the barrier. So I got up and tried again.

And again.

Then something went wrong and the stupid grappling hook didn't come down after I threw it.

Shit. I looked.

It was hooked over the lip of the wall.

I found myself staring at it, thinking *now what?* I couldn't climb a doubled length of paracord.

Oh. Right. The ladder.

With exaggerated precision, I untied the paracord at my belt. If I lost an end of it now it would zip through the pulley and I'd be well and truly screwed. I looped one end of the line around the apex of the ladder's cord and tried to dredge from my tired brain the procedure for a bowline—a knot I'd tied a thousand times. Dumbly I looped the cord one way and the other. It fell apart. I tried again. *Does the fucking rabbit come out of the hole and around the tree, or . . . ?*

At last it held. I pulled on the other end of the leash, and the ladder rose until the apex hit the pulley, and the rungs dangled—beautifully—to within two feet of the ground.

Laboriously I tied two clove hitches with the free end of the cord around the base of a post. I stuck the sat phone through a gap in the posts and set it down. I left the pack where it was. Cautiously I put one foot on a rung and tested my weight on it.

It held. The knots held, the aluminum tube didn't collapse. The 750-paracord had minimal stretch. I raised the other leg to the next rung. It held too.

One step at a time I climbed, my head spinning with fatigue. I didn't dare look down. I could see my goal—my own country— through the gap in the posts, and it kept me going until my vision went dark, and after a moment of confusion I realized I had reached the steel panel. The ladder was pressed hard against it, which made it difficult to get my fingers around each rung. But then I was at the top. I reached over the edge and drew myself up and had an unobstructed view over the Cabeza Prieta Wildlife Refuge where this lunacy had all begun.

I draped myself gingerly across the top of the wall and slowly drew up the ladder, rung by rung, and lowered it over the other side. When the cord had gone taut and the ladder was over as far as it could go, I eased over the edge, gripped the rungs and, fighting a nauseating wave of vertigo, got my feet in and began backing down. My vision was constricting, and I had stopped sweating again. Didn't this happen not long ago?

Down to twenty feet, then fifteen, then ten. At seven one boot landed wrong and slipped out of a rung. I lost grip with my hands, upended completely, and fell to the ground on my extended left arm, which snapped crisply as I hit.

I lay with my face in the dirt, strangely in acute pain and yet acutely exhilarated and relieved. Finally I rolled over and sat up, letting the arm drag, with an extra joint in it now below the elbow. I backed up and leaned against the wall and fell deeply unconscious.

Noise. No, pain. No, noise. No, *pain*, dammit! Finally I realized two such things could co-exist—my arm hurt like hell and I heard the noise of an engine. I looked up and saw a slightly dusty but brand-new Nissan pickup roaring down the wall's access road toward me. It felt undignified and ungrateful to be sitting, so with immense effort I got my legs under me and stood as the truck slid to a halt in front of me and Magdalena got out.

I stepped forward; she ran toward me, and then— didn't this happen some time ago, too?—she tilted 90 degrees and the Sonoran Desert came up and hit me in the side of my face.

I awoke once in the passenger's seat of the truck—how she got me in there I'll never know. I rolled my head toward her; she glanced at me and smiled.

I mumbled, "Listen, just because I faint every time I see you it doesn't mean I like you or anything."

Magdalena looked back at me, smiled again, and rolled her eyes.

She said, "Well, I'll try to rein in my ego then."

And that was the last thing I remembered.

CHAPTER 42

I threw the book across the hospital room, rattling the IV tube against the bracket from which dangled my second liter of lactated ringers. Since there was no gunshot trauma this time they had altered the protocol for treating the dehydration.

And what was it with the book this time?

This time yet another "troubled ex-Navy SEAL," after emptying his .45 Colt at some bad guys and reloading with "a fresh clip of bullets," remarked on "the stench of cordite" in the room.

Ignore the incorrect "clip" and "bullets" for the moment. Cordite hasn't been used as a propellant in firearm cartridges for at least 60 years. It's gunpowder. Just plain old gunpowder. Trash fiction writers please take note.

Sorry. Where was I?

The nurse came in, carrying my breakfast on a tray.

A confession: I love hospital food. The neat compartments, the little *haute cuisine* covers over everything, even if they are plastic. And after my diet of the last week and a half, even rubbery scrambled eggs, white toast, and flaccid bacon would have been an exquisite repast. And this was a cut above that.

"Doing okay this morning?" the nurse asked as he set down the tray. His name was Scott; he'd been a paramedic for 15 years before becoming a nurse, and he'd seen everything. So he wasn't about to let me feel sorry for myself for having a sore arm and being thirsty. Which was just fine with me. At least he didn't smell like cigarette smoke; in fact it turned out he competed in Iron Man triathlons for "fun."

He left, and I contemplated turning on the television. No. Not that desperate. I'd have Magdalena bring me a non-fiction book, something in history. Another Alan Moorehead or Michael Korda perhaps.

Speaking of Magdalena, here she came—thankfully not trailing any government agency representatives this time. She gave me a lovely quick kiss on the lips and pulled up a chair. First she told me she had called Jed to give him a brief update, assuring him I was okay and would be discharged within a day or two.

To which he had replied, "Well tell him I'm getting tired of watering his damn plants and feeding his damn . . . " etc. etc.

I had filled her in on the basics of the events in Mexico the previous afternoon, after being partially rehydrated and having my arm set and put in a cast. We had been debating what, if anything, to do regarding the disappearance of a U.S. Border Patrol sector chief when questions were asked. But as far as we knew there was no reason for anyone to ask me anything. Officially I had simply had a stupid accident while doing research on the refuge. Most certainly as far as his bosses knew Hinwood had asked for some leave and then simply vanished. I was sure he'd had ways of crossing the border without leaving a paper trail.

Magdalena still had questions for me.

"So, what made you take Miller's pistol with you? If you'd been searched at the border they could have done away with you right then and saved a lot of trouble.

"Not to mention saving themselves," she added as an afterthought.

I said, "I took the risk of bringing Miller's Glock because I suspected his wife was the principal—or one of them—and to be honest I wanted to apply a little poetic justice if it proved true."

"Wait. You knew it was her? *How?*" Magdalena looked dubious.

"Correction: I *suspected* it was her. Several things. First, she knew what a burner phone was. That's not so unusual, but she managed to get hold of one between 9:00 PM, when she first called me, and 6:00 the next morning. Like perhaps she already had one, or a collection. Then, when she texted me, she didn't ask if I was up yet or when I could be in town. She asked where I was. I'm still not sure how, but I think she *knew* I was already in town. The thought even occurred that the 4Runner Hinwood arranged might have had a tracker on it."

"Hmm . . . okay. And then?"

"Then, when we met, she had the timid, frightened, abused widow act down brilliantly. I mean like Meryl Streep-level acting. But she was carrying the same purse you have." I gestured.

Mag glanced down, then said, "You mean a *concealed carry* purse?"

"The exact same model. And when I hefted it and checked the contents in the main compartment under the pretense of looking for another phone, it was obvious there was a full-sized pistol in the hidden compartment, not some .32-caliber lady's gun. That didn't fit with the act. Then, in the coffee shop, she did a great job of acting terrified when she looked around at the vehicle I saw pull in across the street. But when I knocked a coffee mug off the table . . ."

"On purpose," Mag said. Not a question.

"Yep. She should have jumped out of her chair. She tried to act startled but it really didn't faze her a bit. Under the Meryl Streep she was cool as a cucumber. As I said, I couldn't be sure. And her disappearance was perfectly staged. It took some guts to add a piece of an ear to the blood."

Magdalena said, "So . . . *why*? Why did she contact you and give you the whole act?"

"Three reasons, I think. First, she was curious. I'd managed to get the better of her husband—with whom, I'm willing to bet, she was more annoyed than anything else—and she wanted to see what I was like. And to have a cohort get a photo of me. Second, I think she got a thrill out of toying with me. And third, of course, she was fishing for information about people important to me."

Magdalena said, "So, then . . . who was the poor woman in the pit back at the facility in Sonora?"

I shook my head sadly. "Who knows? Probably just someone who spilled one too many drinks."

She nodded, and was silent for a moment.

"And what about Hinwood?"

"That was much more of a vague unease. At first the only thing that caught my attention was how much he played up the fact that I'd ruined the investigation into Miller. When I called him on it I think he realized he might have been over-acting. But he also mentioned the two Mexican nationals who had blown through the border in the Hilux with the whole story, and then said they'd been deported within a day. That was really odd. The system is so glacial such things usually take weeks or months. I wondered if he handled that particular deportation personally, and alerted someone on the other side. Finally, when we saw him in Ajo and he fished around, said he'd tried to call me to see how I was doing, that seemed weird. And it would have been right about the time Che was trying to find out where I was. Even so, it just seemed too facile a theory to be real. It wasn't until he climbed out of the helicopter that I was sure."

I had finished the eggs and bacon and coffee. I started to butter toast, somewhat awkwardly with the cast. Magdalena offered to help but I needed to get used to it.

Scott, carrying a clipboard, stuck his head in the door. "Dude, what's your middle name?"

Magdalena laughed out loud.

I said, "It's just 'T.'"

He shrugged, said, "Whatever, Mr. *T*," and ducked out.

Magdalena said, "Okay. Give."

I said, "No way."

She said, "Do you know what would have happened to me if I'd been caught using that access road to help someone bypass a port of entry?"

Damn it. Difficult to argue with that.

I sighed resignedly.

"Okay, look: My mother was, let's just say, an *enthusiastic* Edgar Rice Burroughs fan. My middle name is Tarzan."

I knew Magdalena would accept this with the solemnity that would reassure me I was justified in trusting her.

She collapsed in hysterics.

I glared at her in open-mouthed rage, which only deepened and lengthened the hysterics, until tears were streaming down her face and she was hiccuping and gasping for breath.

I looked at the door—pointedly—and tapped my fingers on one knee.

At last she got control of herself, caught her breath —but then her eyes widened.

"Wait a minute. *Clayton?* As in John Clayton, Lord Greystoke?"

Good grief. She had actually *read* those books?

Sigh . . . "Yep."

"Oh my God. And *Porter?* As in Professor Archimedes Q. Porter, Jane's father?"

I rolled my eyes. "Well the Porter was just an accident of marriage, although sometimes I suspect it wasn't at all and she picked my father strictly to appropriate his surname. When he died I'm surprised I didn't wind up with a stepfather named Burroughs, or at least Edgar. I can only be grateful she didn't saddle me with something like 'Korak' as a first name."

I pointed the butter knife at her.

"And if you ever tell anyone I will feed you to a jaguar."

ACKNOWLEDGMENTS

Trail of the Jaguar is a work of fiction. Yet aside from plot and characters, I strived to maintain geographical[1] and biological accuracy in the settings and portrayals of animals, as well as authenticity regarding weapons and tactics, vehicles, the Seri Indians and the Maasai, sea kayaking, astronomy, and a hundred other obscure references. To do this I began compiling data at age seven.

No kidding—that's when my family moved to a rural neighborhood northeast of Tucson and I began exploring the Sonoran Desert and Catalina Mountains with my best friend, Bruce Douglas, who would go on to help me absorb much of the random information you might shake out of this book. Together we tried roasted rattlesnake and earned NRA sharpshooter badges, caught invasive (but tasty) sunfish in Sabino creek, and, later, hunted deer and

---

[1] One notable exception to the geographical accuracy is the concept of the seep and nearby water-filled mineshaft in the Cabeza Prieta. That was generous fictional license—although a mineshaft near our remote desert cottage southwest of Tucson routinely retains water in the bottom—so, hey, who knows?

elk and competed in combat handgun matches. (One of the few parallels between me and Clayton Porter is that in those early days I was also staying as far away as possible from a stepfather who would have been happy had I never made it back. This, happily, only deepened my immersion in the wild.)

Later, after meeting my life's companion, Roseann, and while studying Ecology and Evolutionary Biology together, she and I were blessed to benefit from the vast experience of the University of Arizona's last generation of pioneering field scientists—Charles Lowe, Steve Russell, Lendell Cockrum, John Hendrickson, Charles Mason, and others. It was during those impecunious student years that I took up sea kayaking, gaining a brief flash of scholarly glory when, for the ten-species plant collection I had to procure for Mason's undergrad botany course, I sourced the lot from Isla San Esteban in the middle of the Gulf of California during a storm-aborted attempt to paddle from the mainland to Baja. My massive plant press took up room that *should* have been devoted to extra drinking water.

My sea kayaking mentor and dear friend, Tommy Thompson, accompanied me on that ill-fated crossing attempt, when we wound up stranded by weather on San Esteban for several days, and eventually had to retreat. Tommy is the most accomplished paddler I've known—he tackled the Bering Strait solo—but I found his *bête noire* when I proudly showed up in camp carrying a San Esteban chuckwalla I'd caught. When presented with the 20-inch-long lizard Tommy started backpedalling toward the raging surf. "*What the hell is that?!*" he demanded. When I explained it was an endemic species known only to that island, he replied in horror, "You mean there are *more* of them?" I had to talk him down from launching his kayak then and there. (Tommy later overcame his phobia by buying his young son a pet snake.)

In the 1990s, when I ran a business leading sea kayak tours in the Gulf, I counted as friends several Seris, including Jorge and Marta Ybarra, and Ernesto Molina. I did make several abortive attempts to learn Seri—which could have served as a backup code language to Navajo in WWII. Once I was standing chatting with three women, and tried to repeat a phrase I was memorizing. I'm not sure if I screwed up vocabulary or accent or both, but all three women threw their long overskirt-aprons over their heads and fled, shrieking with laughter. It was several visits before any of them could look at me without snickering, and they steadfastly refused to tell me what I'd actually said.

A couple of details, not less vital for their brevity: For insight about the early—and vastly under-appreciated, aside from a short-lived pop song—history of the U.S. Special Forces (Green Beret) groups in Vietnam, I'm indebted to Nicolas Panarella and Doug Livermore, both veterans of that service. Any mistakes I made in that regard are mine alone.

For the (astonishingly easy) technique for disabling a Robinson R44 helicopter, thank you Geoff Foster, and to Michelle Lamphere for connecting us.

While I'm lucky enough to own a 70-Series Land Cruiser, it is a Troop Carrier rather than a pickup. For the photo of the spot-on example graphic designer Oliver Bennett used to design the front cover, I'm indebted to Andy and Clara Shaffer, as well as Jeff Lupien and other members of the IH8MUD forum who stepped up with offers.

Real people were the inspiration for several characters in *Trail of the Jaguar*, although I changed many details. Dexter Oliver—biologist, writer, trapper, op-ed gadfly, and the second reader of this manuscript—could easily play Wyatt Earp, and he's probably a better shot. Tony Davis actually is the Wikipedia entry under "Grizzled Reporter"—a bulldog who can be counted on to chew through any wall of corporate or political obfuscation to find the real story, especially on critical environmental issues. As far as I know he does not drive a crappy Volvo, nor as far as I know is he in the habit of downing a half bottle of Jack Daniels at a time. But I wouldn't be surprised if he still uses a Vic Commodore. Or an Underwood. My friend Bill Lee is an actual Toyota Master Mechanic, actually does live in remotest New Mexico, and actually did rebuild the engine in my FJ40 (although not because of anything as stylish as gunfire).

Speaking of real people—*not* mentioned in the book— Diana Hadley and the late Peter Warshall were the founders of the Northern Jaguar Project, which has worked diligently since 2003 to preserve habitat for the world's northernmost breeding population of jaguars, in the state of Sonora, Mexico. Through patient diplomacy (and sometimes financial incentives) they have changed the attitudes of many ranchers in the Sierra Madre, who no longer shoot predators on sight but instead help monitor their status. I'm proud to donate a portion of each sale of this book to support their efforts.

A major non-human "character" in this book is the border wall that was hammered across so much pristine landscape in 2019 and 2020—including exquisite, fragile habitat far, far from any potential smuggling or immigrant routes. Unlike other political whims, the ramifications of this one will echo for years, if not decades. Its effects on the Sonorn pronghorn, as well as the jaguars and ocelots that we are occasionally lucky enough to document north of the border, remain to be seen—but can hardly be expected to be positive.

Finally, thank you Roseann, my companion in exploration of both the planet and life. Her work in conservation led to our close association with the Maasai of the Rift Valley. Our work as caretakers in Brown Canyon on the Buenos Aires National Wildlife Refuge in southern Arizona led to us standing outside the isolated canyon residence one afternoon in 1996, listening to an unearthly noise neither of us recognized initially—until we discovered it had been the call of a male jaguar, later caught on video not two miles from there and named Macho B, one of a handful of jaguars documented north of Mexico. And it was Roseann's awesome grasp of the English language that molded this book into its final shape, as she wielded a scalpel on esoteric grammar questions and perceptively ferreted out continuity mistakes. Without her support I never would have found the courage to tackle a 108,500-word flight of imagination.

ABOUT THE AUTHOR

Jonathan Hanson grew up northeast of Tucson, Arizona, with Sabino and Bear Canyons as his backyard, providing him with years of desert expeditions, hunting like the Apaches and building wickiups (which failed spectacularly). He has since written for a score of outdoor and adventure magazines including *Outside, National Geographic Adventure, Nature Conservancy*, and *Global Adventure*, and has authored a dozen books on subjects including natural history, sea kayaking, wildlife tracking, and expedition travel. Jonathan's exploration experience encompasses land- and sea-scapes on six continents, from the Atacama Desert to the Beaufort Sea, from the Rift Valley to the Australian Outback, and modes of transportation from sea kayaks to sailboats to bicycles to Land Cruisers. He has traveled among and worked with cultures as diverse as the Seri Indians and the Himba, the Inuit and the Maasai. Jonathan has taught tracking, natural history writing, four-wheel-driving techniques, and other subjects for many conservation and government organizations. He is an elected fellow of the Explorers Club and the Royal Geographical Society, and a charter member of Backcountry Hunters and Anglers.

You can follow Jonathan's blog and order books at *ExploringOverland.com* or learn more about Clayton at *ClaytonT.Porter.com*

Author photo by Gary Haynes

Made in the USA
Columbia, SC
20 March 2021